AS
LEVEL

BIOLOGY
FOR CCEA AS LEVEL

COLOURPOINT
EDUCATIONAL

Rewarding Learning

Dr James Napier

© James Napier and Colourpoint Creative Ltd 2012

ISBN: 978 1 78073 009 7

First Edition
Fourth Impression 2015

Layout and design: April Sky Design
Printed by: W&G Baird Ltd, Antrim

COLOURPOINT EDUCATIONAL

Colourpoint Educational
An imprint of Colourpoint Creative Ltd
Colourpoint House
Jubilee Business Park
21 Jubilee Road
Newtownards
County Down
Northern Ireland
BT23 4YH

Tel: 028 9182 6339
Fax: 028 9182 1900
E-mail: info@colourpoint.co.uk
Web site: www.colourpoint.co.uk

The Author

James Napier is a former Vice-Principal in a large Northern Ireland Grammar School and is now a full time author. Dr Napier has written and co-written, a number of GCSE Biology and Science textbooks supporting the work of teachers and students in Northern Ireland. He has also published a range of popular science books throughout the areas of genetics and evolution.

The author would like to thank Rachel Irwin (Editor) and her colleagues at Colourpoint for their expertise and support, and in the development of this book. Thanks also to Dr Terence Henry for his invaluable feedback and advice throughout the process.

Rewarding Learning

Approved/endorsed by CCEA on 16 August 2012. If in any doubt about the continuing currency of CCEA endorsement, please contact Heather Clarke at CCEA, 29 Clarendon Road, Belfast, BT1 3BG.

Whilst the publisher has taken all reasonable care in the preparation of this book CCEA makes no representation, express or implied, with regard to the accuracy of the information contained in this book. CCEA does not accept any legal responsibility or liability for any errors or omissions from the book or the consequences thereof.

Publisher's Note: This book has been written to help students preparing for the AS Level Biology specification from CCEA. While Colourpoint Educational and the authors have taken every care in its production, we are not able to guarantee that the book is completely error-free. Additionally, while the book has been written to closely match the CCEA specification, it is the responsibility of each candidate to satisfy themselves that they have fully met the requirements of the CCEA specification prior to sitting an exam set by that body. For this reason, and because specifications change with time, we strongly advise every candidate to avail of a qualified teacher and to check the contents of the most recent specification for themselves prior to the exam. Colourpoint Creative Ltd therefore cannot be held responsible for any errors or omissions in this book or any consequences thereof.

Health and Safety: This book describes practical tasks or experiments that are either useful or required for the course. These must only be carried out in a school setting under the supervision of a qualified teacher. It is the responsibility of the school to ensure that students are provided with a safe environment in which to carry out the work.

CONTENTS

AS1 Molecules and Cells

AS2 Organisms and Biodiversity

Unit AS 1: Molecules and Cells

Chapter 1 – Molecules

Students should be able to:

1.1.1	Understand the importance of water.
1.1.2	Outline the role of inorganic ions – potassium, calcium, magnesium, iron, hydrogen carbonate, nitrate and phosphate.
1.1.3	Recognise the occurrence, structure and function of carbohydrates.
1.1.4	Recognise the occurrence, structure and function of lipids.
1.1.5	Recognise the occurrence, structure and function of proteins.
1.1.8	Practical work to include biochemical tests to detect the presence of carbohydrates and proteins and the paper chromatography of amino acids.

Molecules and living organisms

Although there are many naturally occurring elements, only a small proportion are found in living organisms. The elements present in the largest proportions in living organisms are carbon, hydrogen, oxygen, nitrogen, phosphorus and sulphur, with the first three being by far the most abundant. Atoms of the elements found in living organisms combine to form biologically important molecules linked by strong covalent bonds.

Water

Most of the oxygen and hydrogen in living organisms exists as water. In a water molecule (H_2O), each hydrogen atom shares a pair of electrons with the oxygen atom, forming a covalent bond. In a water molecule the hydrogen has a slight positive charge and the oxygen a slight negative charge. Therefore the molecule is described as being **polar**, a term used to describe molecules with an uneven distribution of charge.

The polar nature of water results in the formation of hydrogen bonds between adjacent water molecules. The hydrogen bonds extend between the oxygen on one water molecule and a hydrogen atom on another. Hydrogen bonds are important in many biological molecules, but although common they are not strong and relatively easily broken.

Hydrogen bonds in water

Water is an excellent **solvent**, capable of dissolving a wide range of inorganic and organic substances. Molecules with charged groups, such as glucose and amino acids, and ions dissolve in water with the polar water molecules readily forming clusters around them.

Water forms between 50% to over 90% of the cells in living organisms. Its value as a solvent includes:

- the fact that most of a cell's reactions take place in an aqueous solution.
- its ability to act as a transport medium in living organisms.

- the different effects it has on hydrophilic ('water loving') and hydrophobic ('water hating') molecules. For example, lipids are hydrophobic and do not dissolve in water. The importance of lipids being insoluble in water is discussed later (on pages 47–48) in terms of its role in the cell-surface membrane.

Buffers and pH

Proteins are crucially important biological molecules, largely due to their ability to be formed in very specific three-dimensional (3-D) shapes. However, protein shape, and consequently function, is affected by changes in pH. While most proteins operate most effectively in the normal cellular pH of around 7 (neutral), some have a very different optimum pH. For example, the stomach enzyme pepsin has an optimum pH of around 2.

Buffers are chemicals or substances that resist changes to pH and ensure that a particular environment maintains a particular pH. Examples include hydrogen carbonate ions and blood proteins such as albumin. Buffers are often used in practical investigations involving enzymes. The buffers help regulate the pH of solutions to ensure that the enzymes involved are operating at their optimum pH.

Ions

Ions are atoms or a group of atoms that have an electrical charge due to the number of protons and electrons not balancing. Atoms of metals tend to lose electrons and therefore become positively charged ions. Atoms of non-metals tend to be able to gain electrons, thus becoming negatively charged.

Biologically important ions include:

- **calcium** (Ca^{2+}) – In plants calcium pectate is an essential component of the middle lamella of plant cell walls. Calcium is an essential component of bones and teeth in animals, and is essential in blood clotting and muscle contraction.
- **iron** (Fe^{2+}) – is part of the haem group in haemoglobin and an important constituent of electron carriers in respiration.
- **magnesium** (Mg^{2+}) – is essential in giving chlorophyll its light-absorbing properties.
- **potassium** (K^+) – is important in maintaining electrical gradients across neurones.
- **nitrate** (NO_3^-) – is a component of amino acids, nucleic acids and chlorophyll.
- **phosphate** (PO_4^{3-}) – As phospholipids, phosphate is the main component of cell membranes. It is also a major component of other important biological molecules including adenosine triphosphate (ATP) and nucleic acids.
- **hydrogen carbonate** (HCO_3^-) – is important as a natural buffer.

Organic molecules

Organic molecules are complex carbon-containing molecules. **Carbohydrates**, **proteins** and **lipids** are all examples of organic molecules. Organic molecules form the basis of all life on Earth and it is essential that you have a good understanding of the key organic molecules in 'A' level Biology. Many organic molecules are formed of sub-units called **monomers**, which join together to form larger **polymers** through the process of **polymerisation**.

Carbohydrates

Carbohydrates contain carbon, hydrogen and oxygen only. The ratio of hydrogen atoms to oxygen atoms is 2:1.

Carbohydrates are divided into three main types:

- **Monosaccharides** – are the basic carbohydrate monomers, ie single sugars. There are different categories of monosaccharide depending on the number of carbon atoms present. Biologically important monosaccharides contain three (**trioses**), five (**pentoses**) or six (**hexoses**) carbon atoms.
- **Disaccharides** – are double sugars formed from two monosaccharide monomers.
- **Polysaccharides** – are complex molecules usually consisting of many monosaccharide monomers.

Monosaccharides

Glucose is a hexose monosaccharide with the formula $C_6H_{12}O_6$. The diagram below shows how the atoms of α-glucose are arranged. **α-glucose** is the basic sub-unit of complex polysaccharides such as starch and glycogen.

The simplified diagram is often used. Although simplified, it still shows detail at carbon positions 1, 4 and 6 – the positions important in bonding different monosaccharide molecules together.

α-glucose

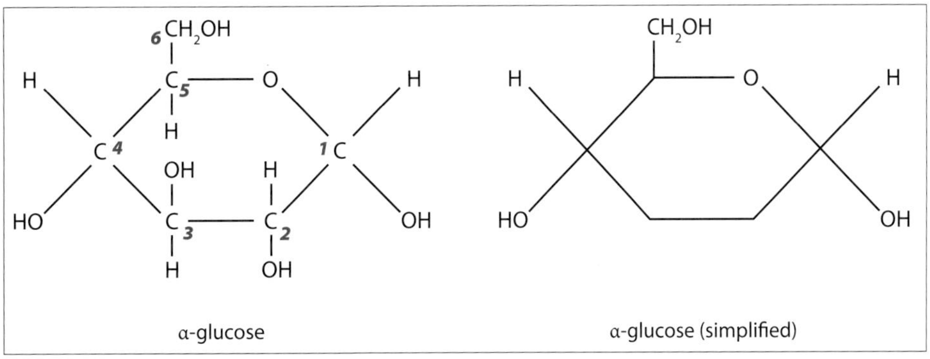

α-glucose   α-glucose (simplified)

A slight change in the arrangement of the atoms gives **β-glucose**. In β-glucose the hydrogen and hydroxyl (-OH) groups at carbon (position) 1 are reversed. β-glucose has different properties to α-glucose and it is the constituent monomer of cellulose. Further small changes give the hexose sugar **fructose**.

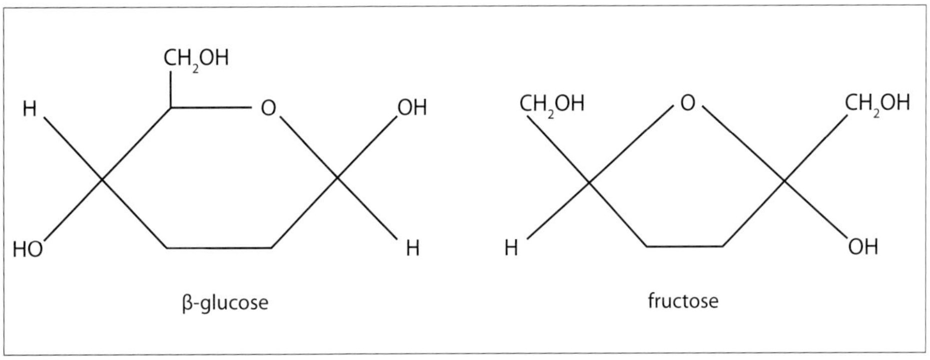

β-glucose and fructose

β-glucose   fructose

Hexose monosaccharides, such as glucose, are very important as energy sources in living organisms.

Substances such as the monosaccharides just discussed, which have the same **molecular formula**, but different **structural formulae**, are described as being **isomers** of each other.

Disaccharides

Disaccharides are formed when two monosaccharides, usually hexoses, react together in a chemical reaction known as a **condensation** reaction. This is a reversible reaction, as a disaccharide molecule can be broken down into its constituent monosaccharide monomers in a **hydrolysis** reaction. Hydrolysis reactions are important in the digestion of food.

Note: during condensation one molecule of water is lost – during hydrolysis one molecule of water is gained.

The bond that is formed between two hexose sugars in the formation of a disaccharide is called a **glycosidic bond**. If you study the diagram opposite closely, you will see that the bond is between the carbons 1 and 4 on the respective monomers (α-glucose); therefore the bond is described as being an **α-1,4 glycosidic bond**. Note in the diagram that the orientation of the bond means that the two glucose residues lie at an angle when the disaccharide is formed.

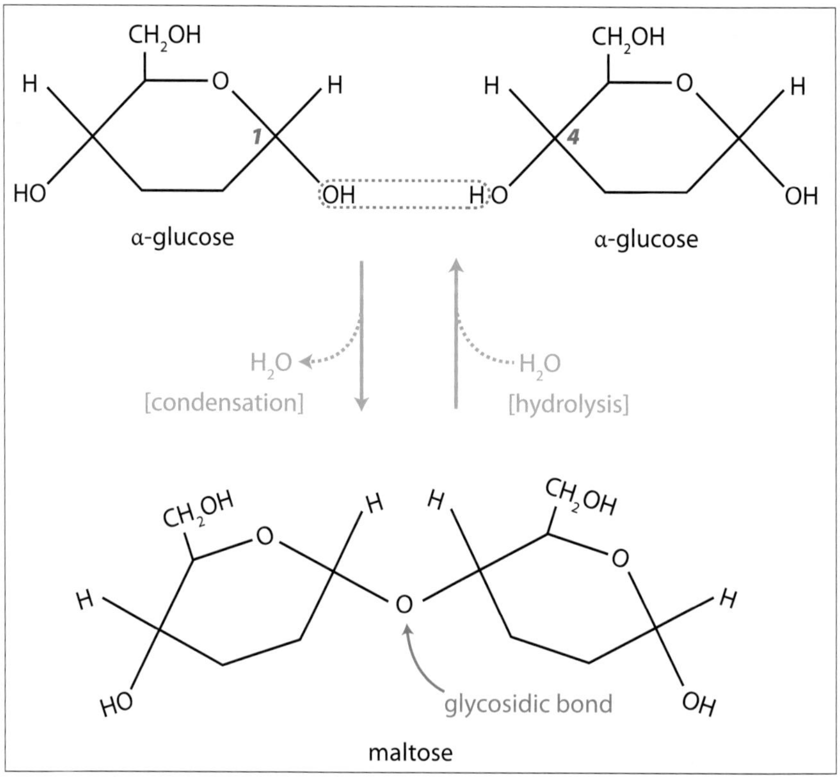

Note: many candidates in examination questions mix up the type of **reaction** with the name of the **bond**!

All disaccharides have the general formula $C_{12}H_{22}O_{11}$. They dissolve in water to produce sweet tasting solutions, as they are all 'sugars'.

The formation and breakdown of the disaccharide maltose

Important disaccharides include:

- **maltose** – formed when two α-glucose molecules are linked through a condensation reaction.

- **sucrose** – formed when an α-glucose molecule condenses with a fructose molecule.

Maltose is formed when starch is digested – the maltose requires further digestion to form the monomer glucose. Sucrose is the form in which carbohydrates are transported through phloem in plants.

Polysaccharides

These are complex carbohydrates which often form very long chains. They are formed through condensation reactions joining a large number of monomers together to make complex polymers.

The general formula for a polysaccharide is $(C_6H_{10}O_5)_n$ where n is a large number that can vary. Polysaccharides are not 'sugar'; they are not sweet and they are insoluble in water. Very important polysaccharides are **starch**, **glycogen** and **cellulose**.

Starch

Starch is a polymer of α-glucose. However, starch consists of a mixture of two types of chains. Although each type of chain consists of only α-glucose, the α-glucose has different bonding arrangements in each type of chain.

1. **Amylose** – in amylose, α-glucose molecules are linked by **α-1,4 glycosidic bonds**. These chains are coiled to form a spiral, with the spirals held in place by hydrogen bonds. As only 1,4 bonds are involved, amylose forms long **unbranched chains**. Approximately 20% of starch is formed from amylose. Due to the presence of the bulky side groups that cause the α-glucose molecules to lie at different angles, amylose chains form a coiled configuration.

Amylose

2. **Amylopectin** – amylopectin also links its constituent α-glucose monomers together by **α-1,4 glycosidic bonds**. In addition, **α-1,6 glycosidic bonds** form side branches to produce a **branched** molecule. The branches may occur as often as one branch every ten α-glucose monomers. About 80% of starch is normally in amylopectin form.

Amylopectin

Why is starch such a good storage molecule?

Starch is an excellent storage carbohydrate and is the storage compound of many plants. It is commonly stored as solid grains and can often be seen in electron micrographs of plant chloroplasts. Its benefits include:

*   the molecules of both amylose and amylopectin are very **compact** (aided by the coiled configuration), therefore they contain a rich store of glucose in a small space.
*   as it is **insoluble** it will not affect the water relations of the cell – if significant quantities of carbohydrate were stored as glucose this would cause a lot of water to enter by osmosis.
*   being a **large molecule** it can be retained in the cell and will not easily pass through the cell membrane.
*   the **branching** nature of amylopectin creates **many terminal ends** that are **easily hydrolysed**. This aids in the rapid enzymatic breakdown of starch into its constituent glucose at times of high respiratory demand.

Glycogen

This is the storage carbohydrate found in animal and fungal cells. It is stored in the form of small granules. Structurally, glycogen is very similar to amylopectin, being formed of chains of α-glucose monomers. Glycogen, also has α-1,4 glycosidic and α-1,6 glycosidic bonds but the chains are **more branched** and shorter than the amylopectin chains.

Glycogen is stored in **liver** and **muscle** cells in mammals. Its properties are very similar to starch. It is compact and insoluble, therefore not affecting cell water relations. However, as it has no unbranched chains and shorter chains than in amylopectin, it has proportionally **more terminal ends**, enabling **faster hydrolysis** when conditions demand.

Cellulose

Cellulose is not a storage polysaccharide – its role is **structural**. Consequently, it has a very different structure to the relatively similar starch and glycogen.

Cellulose is made of monomers of **β-glucose**. In cellulose, when the two β-glucose molecules join together and form β-1,4 glycosidic bonds, alternate molecules are rotated through 180°. This rotation is a necessary consequence due to the different structure of β-glucose compared to α-glucose.

This 'flipping' of adjacent glucose monomers has two effects:

- the unbranched chains are **straighter**, as the bulky -CH$_2$OH side groups alternate between being above and below the chain.

- **hydrogen bonds** can form cross-linkages between adjacent chains (due to the oxygen and the side groups being available on both sides of the chain following the inversion of alternative β-glucose molecules).

The cellulose chains (molecules) are grouped together in **microfibrils**, with each microfibril consisting of many cellulose molecules. Plant cell walls are formed of the cellulose microfibrils orientated into many planes in a lattice structure to further increase its **tensile strength**.

The formation of cellulose

β-1,4 glycosidic bond

Chains of β-glucose (further simplified), and oriented in the opposite direction, form hydrogen bonds between adjacent chains as shown.

Cellulose

Lipids

Lipids contain carbon, hydrogen and oxygen but the proportion of hydrogen relative to oxygen is much greater than the 2:1 ratio associated with carbohydrates.

Although lipids form large molecules (macromolecules), they are not polymers. They are not soluble in water (**hydrophobic**) but they are soluble in organic solvents such as ether or ethanol.

The main types of lipids are **triglycerides** (fats and oils); **phospholipids** (a major component of membranes), waxes and steroids.

Triglycerides

Triglycerides are formed through the combination of **glycerol** and **fatty acid** molecules.

Fatty acids are organic acids that form long hydrocarbon tails linked to a carboxyl group (-COOH) at one end of the chain. Different fatty acids have different lengths of hydrocarbon tail.

Glycerol and fatty acid

In each triglyceride, one glycerol molecule is joined with three fatty acid molecules by (three) **condensation reactions**. There are over 70 types of fatty acid and in each triglyceride the three fatty acids can be the same or a range of different types. The condensation reactions are formed between the -OH groups of the glycerol and the carboxyl group of each fatty acid. For each condensation reaction, an **ester bond** is formed.

The reverse reaction can also occur. Hydrolysis of a triglyceride (as happens during lipid digestion) uses three molecules of water and produces three fatty acids and one molecule of glycerol.

The formation and hydrolysis of a triglyceride

Unsaturated and saturated fatty acids

Saturated fatty acids contain the maximum number of hydrogen atoms, ie along the length of the hydrocarbon chain each carbon atom is linked with two hydrogen atoms (the carbons are saturated!). Also, the carbon atoms are linked by C-C single bonds.

Unsaturated fatty acids have at least one C=C double bond in the chain. If there is one double bond it is **monounsaturated** and if there is more than one double bond, it is **polyunsaturated**.

Oleic acid, the lower fatty acid in the diagram opposite, has only one double bond within the chain and is therefore a monounsaturated fatty acid. Other fatty acids, such as linoleic acid, have more than one double bond and are polyunsaturated fatty acids.

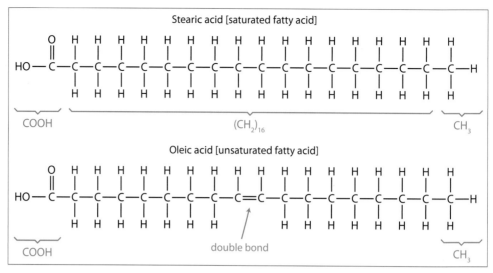

Saturated and unsaturated fatty acids

Fats and **oils** are both triglycerides and chemically very similar. Fats are solid at room temperature and oils are liquid at room temperature. In general, though not exclusively, fats are animal products and oils are made by plants, for example, energy stores in seeds.

Fats tend to be formed from saturated fatty acids, whereas oils are usually formed from triglycerides with unsaturated hydrocarbon chains (or shorter chains).

Triglycerides are an excellent **energy store** as they release more energy per unit mass than carbohydrate. Fats are also important for **insulation** and are stored in a layer below the body surface in many animals. Many body organs are **protected** by a layer of fat.

Phospholipids

Phospholipids are similar to triglycerides, except that one of the fatty acid molecules is replaced by a phosphate group.

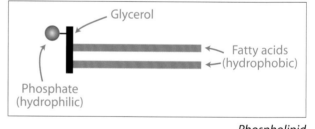

Phospholipid

The fatty acid molecules repel water and are insoluble in water, forming **hydrophobic** 'tails', whereas the phosphate gives the glycerol part ('head') of the molecule **hydrophilic** properties and it is soluble in water. Phospholipids are **polar** molecules and this property is important in determining their orientation and function in cell membranes.

Cell membranes also contain the steroid **cholesterol**. Cholesterol is hydrophobic and located among the hydrocarbon chains of the phospholipid bilayer – the phospholipid bilayer will be covered in detail in Chapter 3.

Proteins

Proteins contain the elements carbon, hydrogen, oxygen, nitrogen and usually sulfur. They are large polymers formed from **amino acid** sub-units. As there are 20 different types of amino acid, there are an infinite number of amino acid arrangements in a protein.

The function of most proteins is very closely related to its shape. In turn, the shape of the protein is determined by the **sequence** of the amino acids in the protein. The diagram opposite shows the generalised structure of an amino acid.

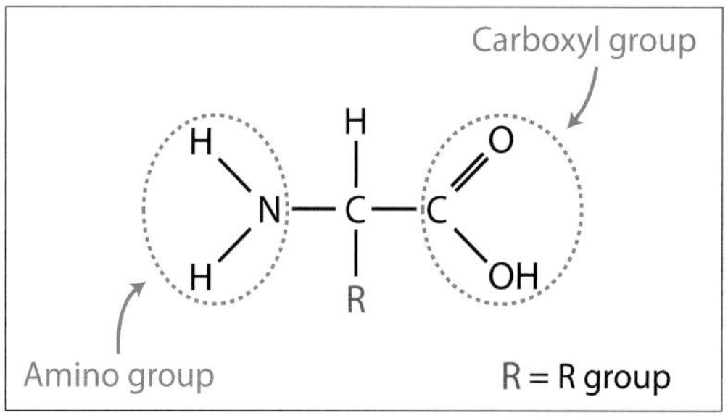

Amino acids differ through having different **R-groups**. In the amino acid glycine the R-group is a single H atom and in alanine it is a methyl (-CH$_3$) group. If sulfur is present in an amino acid, for example, cysteine, the sulfur atom will be contained in the R-group.

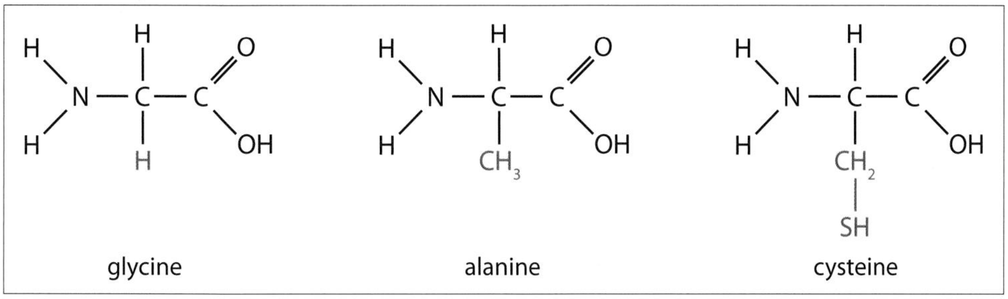

A generalised amino acid

Some amino acids

Amino acids are linked together by **peptide bonds**. These involve **condensation reactions** with the loss of water. The condensation reaction takes place between the amino group of one of the amino acids and the carboxyl group of another linking the nitrogen and carbon atoms involved. Two amino acids joined together form a **dipeptide**. As with the other organic molecules studied in this chapter, hydrolysis can take place as well as condensation: a peptide bond can be broken with the release of the two constituent amino acids with the addition of water.

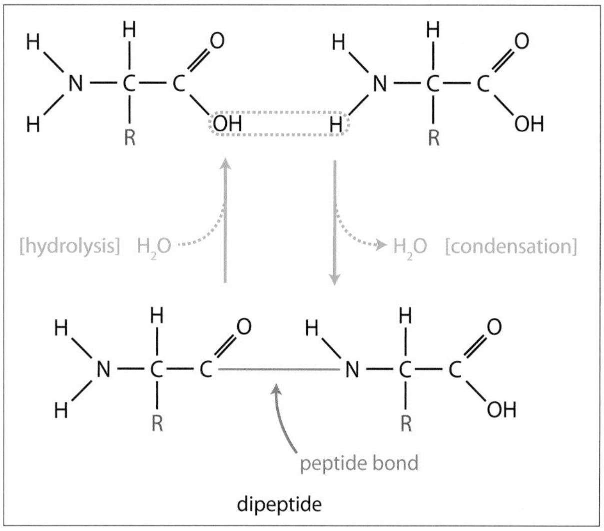

Many amino acids can be joined together in a chain through peptide bonding to form a **polypeptide**.

The formation and hydrolysis of a dipeptide

Protein structure

Primary structure – the primary structure of a polypeptide (protein) is the **sequence** of the amino acids in the polypeptide chain. Polypeptides are usually formed from hundreds of amino acids linked together by peptide bonds.

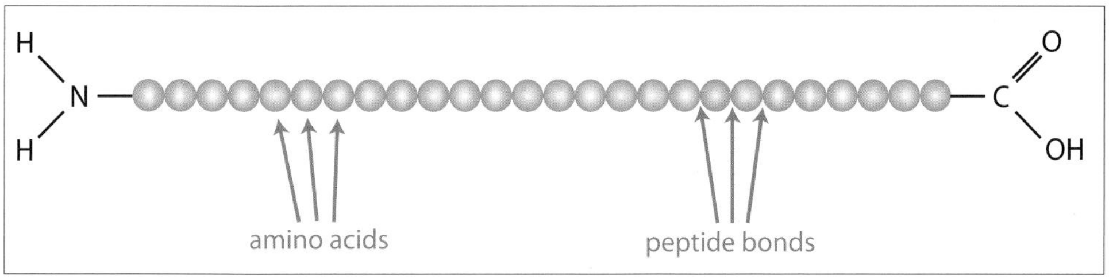

The primary structure of a polypeptide (protein)

13

Secondary structure – the amino acids in a polypeptide contain –NH and –C=O groups on either side of each peptide bond. The O of the –C=O group has a negative charge, whereas the H of the –NH group has a positive charge. This enables the formation of **hydrogen bonds**, which in turn cause generalised secondary structures to be formed. The two most common types of secondary structure are:

- **α-helix** – In the α-helix the hydrogen bonds are formed between amino acids occurring at regular intervals in the sequence. The bonds twist the chain of amino acids into a spiral or helical shape. Small sections (or the entire polypeptide) can be held in an α-helix shape by the hydrogen bonds involved.

The α-helix and β-pleated sheet

- **beta-pleated sheets** – These are more rigid and less flexible configurations than the α-helix. They are formed by sections of the polypeptide chain, orientated in opposite (anti-parallel) directions, lying adjacent to each other. Hydrogen bonds form between the C=O and NH groups.

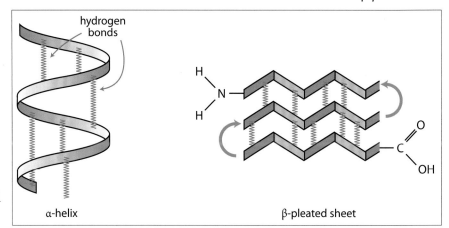

Tertiary structure – This involves the **further folding** of the secondary structure. This additional folding gives each protein its unique 3-D shape and is a consequence of the range of bonds formed between the **R-groups** of amino acids in the chain.

The bonds involved include:

- **hydrogen bonds** – are numerous but relatively weak and easily broken.
- **ionic bonds** – are formed between amino and carboxyl groups in some of the amino acid R-groups. They are stronger than hydrogen bonds but are damaged by changes in pH.
- **disulfide bonds (bridges)** – are covalent bonds formed between R-groups of sulfur-containing amino acids, for example, cysteine. They are very strong bonds and are very important in giving strength to structural (fibrous) proteins such as collagen.

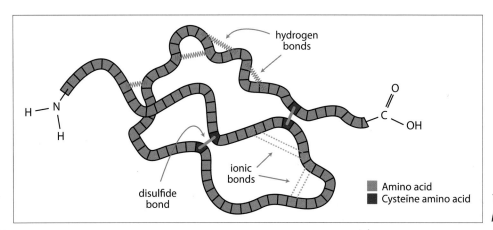

The tertiary structure of a polypeptide (protein)

Hydrophobic interactions involving amino acids with hydrophobic R-groups, which tend to take up positions within the molecule surrounded by other parts of the polypeptide (as opposed to water), further influence the tertiary structure.

Quaternary structure – some proteins consist of two or more polypeptides bonded together (largely by disulfide bonds). This is the quaternary structure. Some quaternary proteins contain non-protein components (**prosthetic groups**) that are integral in their function. These **conjugated proteins** include **glycoprotein**, which is important in membrane structure. **Haemoglobin** is a conjugated protein that consists of four polypeptide chains (two each of two different polypeptides). Each chain is attached to an iron-rich haem group, which is an essential part of the molecule in the transport of oxygen.

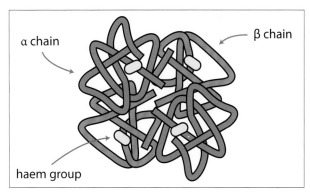

Haemoglobin

Proteins can be broadly grouped as being fibrous or globular.

- **Fibrous proteins** – consist of polypeptides arranged in chains that form fibres or sheets. The parallel chains are linked by cross-bridges to form very strong and stable molecules. Fibrous proteins are invariably **structural** in function. **Collagen** is an example of a fibrous protein. Each collagen molecule consists of three identical polypeptides wound round each other and held together by hydrogen bonds. Collagen is found in tendons that link muscle to bone. Obviously, it is very important that it is a very strong molecule and one that does not stretch when tension is applied.

- **Globular proteins** – have a **metabolic** role and include **enzymes** and **antibodies**. The ability of protein to form very specific 3-D shapes is crucial to their roles as enzymes and antibodies. **Haemoglobin** is also a globular protein.

Practical work

Biochemical tests to detect the presence of carbohydrate and protein

Carbohydrate

1. **Benedict's test** – is used to detect **reducing sugars**. A reducing sugar is a sugar that can donate electrons to (or reduce) Benedict's reagent. When a reducing sugar is mixed with Benedict's reagent and **heated**, the blue reagent will turn through the sequence **blue** – green – yellow – orange to form a **brick red precipitate**. To some extent, the Benedict's test allows you to estimate the quantity of sugar in the solution being tested. If there is only a small amount of sugar present, the reaction will stop at the green or yellow stage. However, it is only semi-quantitative as it can only approximate quantities.

   All monosaccharide sugars and some disaccharide sugars, such as maltose, are reducing sugars. Some disaccharide sugars, such as sucrose, are non-reducing sugars.

Non-reducing sugars can be identified through giving a negative Benedict's test result initially, but if hydrolysed into its constituent monosaccharides with dilute hydrochloric acid (and subsequently neutralised), it gives a positive result.

2. **Clinistix** – is used to detect glucose. Clinistix strips are strips impregnated with chemicals that change colour in the presence of glucose. Unlike the Benedict's test, which cannot distinguish among different monosaccharides, the Clinistix test is **specific**. The strips are dipped in the test solution and if **glucose** is present, they will turn **purple/blue**.

   Clinistix tests are a quick and easy way for doctors to test for the presence of glucose in urine, a symptom of diabetes.

3. **The iodine test** – is used to detect starch. Starch changes the colour of iodine, dissolved in potassium iodide solution, from **yellow-brown** to **blue-black**.

Protein

1. **The Biuret test** – this is the standard test for protein. It detects the presence of peptide links. If peptide links are present, protein must be present.

   The test is carried out by adding equal volumes of **potassium** (or sodium) **hydroxide** solution to a test sample, followed by a few drops of dilute **copper sulfate** solution (Biuret reagent) and shaking gently. If no protein is present the solution will remain **blue** but a positive result will give a **lilac/purple** colour.

2. **Identifying amino acids through the use of paper chromatography**

   The principle of paper chromatography is that some solutes are more soluble than others in the same solution. The more soluble substances will 'travel' further in a solvent that is moving through chromatography paper. Due to the separation of the different solutes by this process, the different solutes present can be identified. The method is particularly useful in identifying which amino acids are present in a mixture of amino acids.

   Paper chromatography involves several distinct stages:
   - preparing the chromatogram.
   - running the chromatogram.
   - developing the chromatogram.
   - calculating R_f values.

   Preparing the chromatogram – The chromatography paper is cut to fit the tank/vessel used to hold it in a vertical position. The paper (chromatogram) should be long enough to allow attachment to the lid of the apparatus and to drop to just above the base of the tank. In due course solvent will be placed into the bottom of the tank. It is important that the chromatogram is long enough to extend into the volume of solvent being used.

   A horizontal line should be drawn in pencil a few centimetres above the base of the chromatogram. It is important that the line should be drawn in a position that will lie above the solvent when the chromatogram is placed in the solvent.

   The solution containing amino acids to be tested (and/or a solution of individual reference amino acids) needs to be 'spotted' on the pencil line. Each solution is added to a pre-determined position by a micro-pipette. After adding a drop of the solution it is then dried before the process is repeated. This allows the solution to be concentrated. At this stage, the chromatogram has been prepared and it is ready to 'run'.

It is important to ensure that the concentrated spot forms as small an area as possible. This can be aided by ensuring that the spot is dry before adding additional drops of solution. In addition, it is important to avoid contamination of the chromatogram. Only hold the chromatogram at the edges and avoid setting it on laboratory benches that could be contaminated with a range of chemicals. Before placing the prepared chromatogram in the tank, the solvent should be added and the lid placed on top to allow the atmosphere to become saturated.

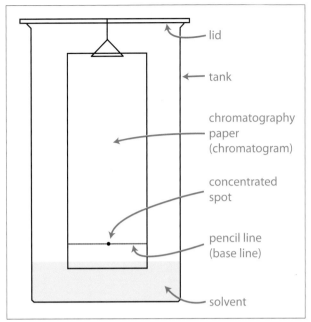

Preparing the chromatogram

Running the chromatogram – The chromatogram is carefully suspended into the solvent and attached to the lid of the tank. This is an important and risky stage. It is important to ensure that:

- the line (and concentrated spot(s)) do not make contact with the solvent.
- the chromatogram is securely attached.
- the chromatogram is not suspended at an angle – if at an angle the solvent cannot 'run' the length of the chromatogram.

As the solvent 'runs' up the chromatogram, it carries the amino acids, although they will not be visible at this stage. The 'run' of the solvent should be stopped when it is well up the chromatogram but **before** it reaches the top.

Developing the chromatogram – The chromatogram should then be dried. Before the solvent is dry, it is important to mark the 'solvent front' on the chromatogram with a pencil. As amino acids are colourless on the chromatogram, it should be sprayed with ninhydrin in a fume cupboard (this is necessary as ninhydrin can be harmful if breathed in).

Following staining, the chromatogram should be re-dried (with a hairdryer or in an oven) and the amino acids will appear as purple spots (proline is an exception as it appears yellow). The spots should be encircled with a pencil as they subsequently fade.

Calculating R_f values – An R_f value is the distance moved by a solute (in this case an amino acid), divided by the distance moved by the solvent front.

It is calculated by measuring the distance from the origin (initial position of concentrated spot) to the position of the solvent front and measuring the distance from the origin to the position of the amino acid being investigated. As each amino acid (purple spot) will extend over an area of the chromatogram, it is essential that a consistent approach is taken to measuring the length from the origin. Either the distance from the origin to the leading edge of the spot is measured or from the origin to the centre of the spot.

The R_f value is then calculated (X/Y in diagram).

R_f values are always approximately the same for the same amino acids separated by chromatography in the same solvent. Consequently, the amino acids in an unknown solution can be identified by comparing them with known amino acids run in the same chromatogram or identified from a table of amino acid R_f values.

Note: an R_f value is always less than 1, so if you calculate a value greater than 1 you have probably got your two values the wrong way round.

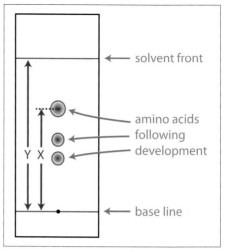

Working out R_f values

Worked example

Identify the amino acid in the chromatogram.

R_f value = 61/100 = 0.61

Amino acid must be valine (0.61 in table).

Amino Acid	R_f Value
arginine	0.20
glutamic acid	0.30
valine	0.61
leucine	0.73

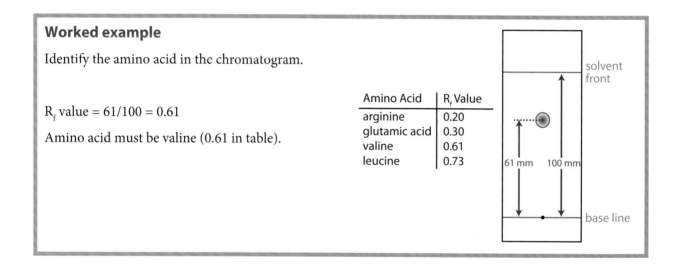

Note: calculated R_f values are not always exactly the same as tabulated values. Small differences can be due to many factors, including the degree of saturation of the atmosphere in the chromatography tank.

Exam questions

1. α-glucose molecules can be linked together to form the helical and branched polysaccharide, amylopectin.

   (a) State what type of reaction occurs when one glucose molecule bonds with another glucose molecule. [1]

   (b) State which carbon atoms in adjacent glucose molecules are linked to produce a branch in amylopectin. [1]

   (c) Describe an advantage of amylopectin having many branches. [1]

   (d) Name another branched polysaccharide. [1]

(e) (i) Name a biochemical test that could be used to distinguish glucose from polysaccharide molecules. [1]

(ii) Describe the biochemical test you have named. [1]

(iii) Describe the result of the above test that would allow you to distinguish glucose from polysaccharides. [1]

Question taken from CCEA's Biology Assessment Unit AS 1, Module 1: Cell Biology, June 2009, © CCEA 2012

2. The diagram below shows a continuous flow reactor containing an immobilised enzyme. Substrate is poured into the reactor and product emerges at the other end.

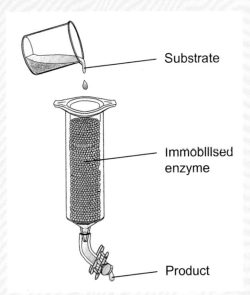

(a) State what must be added with the substrate to control the pH during the process. [1]

(b) The product is checked for contamination by protein. Describe a biochemical test for the presence of protein. Your method must include a description of a positive result. [3]

(c) The product is a reducing sugar. State what reagent you would use to confirm a sugar has been produced. [1]

Question taken from CCEA's Biology Assessment Unit AS 1, Module 1: Cell Biology, January 2010, © CCEA 2012

3. (a) Write out the following passage which describes the primary structure of a protein and write the most appropriate word(s) in the blank spaces to complete the account.

Proteins are polymers, consisting of long chains of _____ joined together by _____ reactions to form numerous _____ bonds. The sequence of monomers in a protein is known as its primary structure and is encoded in the _____ of an organism. [4]

(b) Proteins are complex molecules with a level of organisation beyond the primary structure. Describe how a final overall shape is produced in a protein. [4]

(c) Describe the colour change which indicates the presence of protein in a food sample when it is tested with Biuret reagent. [1]

Question taken from CCEA's Biology Assessment – Unit AS 1, Molecules and Cells, January 2011, © CCEA 2012

4. Using a series of tests, a key was produced to identify the following carbohydrates:

cellulose, glucose, maltose, starch and sucrose

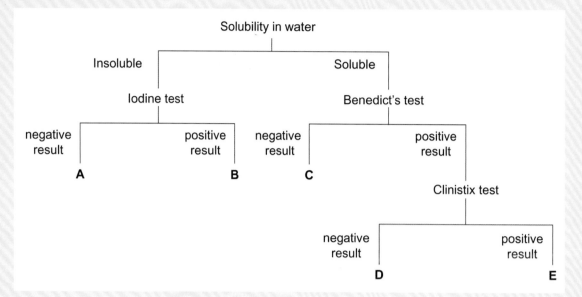

Using the key identify each of the carbohydrates **A** to **E**.

A _____   **D** _____

B _____   **E** _____

C _____

[5]

Question taken from CCEA's Biology Assessment Unit AS 1, Molecules and Cells, June 2011, © CCEA 2012

5. Paper chromatography can be used to separate a mixture of amino acids.

When trypsin, a protease enzyme, was incubated with a protein, a mixture of amino acids was produced. The diagram shows the separation of the amino acids in a chromatogram. Three known amino acids were spotted on the paper as part of the procedure.

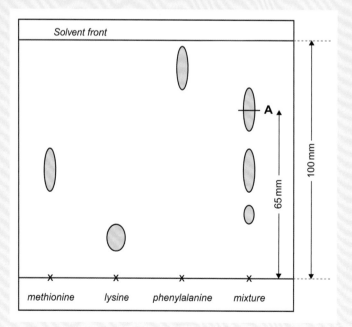

(a) Using the information in the chromatogram answer the following:

(i) State how many different types of amino acid were present in the protein. [1]

(ii) State the identity of any of the amino acids in the mixture. [1]

(iii) Calculate the R_f value for the amino acid **A**, using the measurements shown on the chromatogram. (Show your working). [1]

(b) Describe the procedure used to develop the chromatogram, during which the spots are stained. [3]

The first biological detergent contained a protease enzyme, which removed protein-based stains, such as egg and blood.

(c) (i) State the type of reaction catalysed by the protease enzyme. [1]

In later years amylase and lipase were added to biological detergents to remove a wider variety of stains.

(ii) Triglycerides are removed by lipase. State the products of this reaction. [1]

(iii) Explain why it is difficult to produce a detergent containing a mixture of enzymes which includes protease. [2]

Cellulase has been added to biological detergents as a means of restoring the fabric in clothes which contains cotton. Cellulase digests any loose and damaged cellulose microfibrils from cotton fibres restoring the original smooth surface.

(d) Using your knowledge of starch and cellulose structure, explain why a starch stain can be completely removed by amylase whereas only the loose cellulose microfibrils are removed from the surface of the cotton fibres. [3]

Question taken from CCEA's Biology Assessment Unit AS 1, Molecules and Cells, January 2010, © CCEA 2012

Chapter 2 – Enzymes

1.2.1   Understand the structure of enzymes.

1.2.2   Understand the relationship between enzyme structure and function.

1.2.3   Understand the application of immobilised enzymes in biotechnology.

1.2.4   Practical work to include investigating the factors affecting enzyme activity, enzyme immobilisation and using a colorimeter to follow the course of an enzyme-catalysed reaction.

The structure and function of enzymes

Enzymes are biological **catalysts** that speed up metabolic reactions. The enzymes themselves are not changed by the reaction and can be reused. Some enzymes can make reactions happen many million times more quickly than they otherwise would.

Enzymes are **globular proteins**; we will see later the advantages in them being protein.

Activation energy

In a chemical reaction, there is an energy barrier that must be overcome before a reaction can take place. In many chemical reactions, this barrier is overcome by heating the reactants. In living organisms, the temperatures required make this unfeasible.

Enzymes lower the energy required (**activation energy**) to overcome the energy barrier. This reduction in activation energy enables reactions to take place at the rapid rate necessary to sustain life.

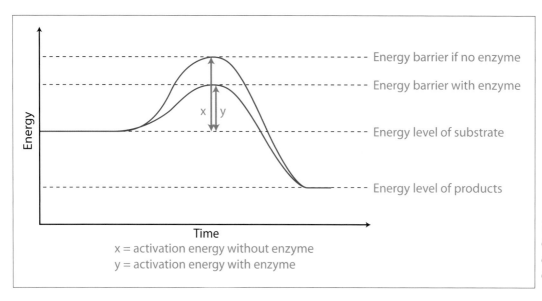

x = activation energy without enzyme
y = activation energy with enzyme

The effect of an enzyme on the activation energy of a reaction

Enzyme action

Enzymes act on substrates. The substrate fits into a special site (groove) on the enzyme, the **active site**, and this forms the **enzyme-substrate complex** (ES). The enzyme and substrate interact with bonds forming between some of the amino acids of the enzyme and parts of the substrate molecule. The reaction changes the substrate, it becomes an **enzyme-product complex** (EP), so that the **product(s)** no longer fit the active site and are released.

Enzyme action

Enzymes can both build up and break down molecules. There are many obvious examples: carbohydrates, proteins and lipids are broken down by digestive enzymes, and starch and glycogen are built

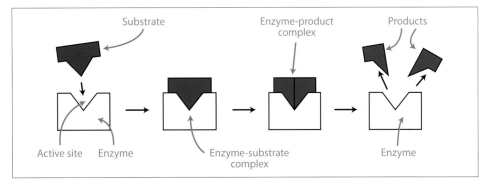

up from simpler sub-units for storage. **Catabolism** is the breakdown of molecules and **anabolism** is the building up of molecules.

The active site of an enzyme usually involves only a few amino acids and it is a very small part of the overall enzyme structure. **Enzyme specificity** is the term used to describe the fact that each enzyme is **specific** to a particular substrate. Enzyme specificity is due to only one substrate (or a very small number) being an exact complementary shape to the active site. Being globular proteins, enzymes are able to form the wide range of 3-D shapes necessary to facilitate enzyme specificity.

Lock and Key and Induced Fit models of enzyme action

The Lock and Key model

The Lock and Key model of enzyme action proposes that the enzyme active site is an exact match to the shape of the substrate, ie the two are **complementary shapes**. The earlier enzyme diagram above demonstrates the Lock and Key model. Note that the enzyme's active site and the substrate are an exact fit.

The Induced Fit model

The Induced Fit model proposes that rather than being an *exact* fit, the active site of the enzyme *very closely* matches the shape of the substrate.

The Induced Fit model of enzyme action

The Induced Fit model proposes that the active site can **mould** itself around the substrate, forming a precise fit. The active site is therefore **flexible** and as it changes shape to fit the substrate, the enzyme is able to put

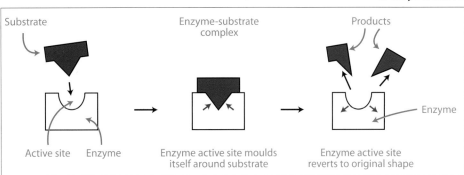

pressure on the substrate, breaking particular bonds and therefore lowering the activation energy required for the reaction to take place. The products will be released, as they are a different shape to the active site when it returns to its 'pre-reaction' shape.

Cofactors

Cofactors are non-protein substances that enzymes require in order to function. Examples include metal ions (such as Mg^{2+}, Ca^{2+} and Fe^{3+}) that form attachments to the enzyme and change the shape of the active site, enabling the reaction to take place. For example, chloride ions act as cofactors for salivary amylase, binding with the amylase, slightly changing its shape and making it easier for enzyme-substrate complexes to form.

Prosthetic groups

Prosthetic groups are another type of cofactor. We have already come across the prosthetic group haem when investigating the haemoglobin molecule – haem is also present as a prosthetic group in the enzyme catalase.

Coenzymes

Coenzymes are a particular type of cofactor. They are non-protein, organic molecules necessary for enzyme action. Unlike some other cofactors, they are not permanently attached. Coenzymes are very important in the biochemistry of respiration and photosynthesis. The coenzymes NAD and FAD act as hydrogen acceptors in respiration.

An Enzyme with a cofactor (prosthetic group)

Factors that affect enzyme activity

There are many factors that affect the rate of enzyme activity. In living organisms conditions are normally controlled to the extent that maximum activity is achieved.

Substrate and enzyme concentration

Not surprisingly, the availability of substrate and enzyme concentration will affect the rate of reaction. If the number of enzymes is kept at a fixed rate and the level of substrate is increased, enzyme activity will also increase. This can be explained by there being more substrates to fill the available active sites. Eventually the rate levels off as the number of enzyme active sites becomes limiting, ie all the available enzymes are working at maximum rate. After this level, the addition of more substrate will have no increased effect.

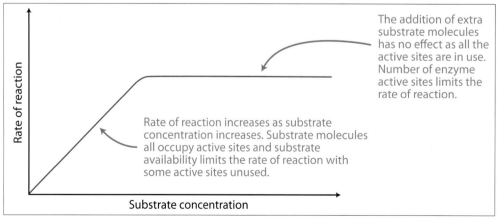

The effect of substrate concentration on the rate of reaction

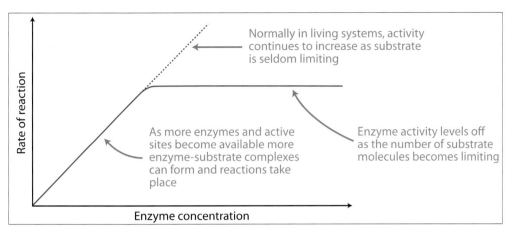

The effect of enzyme concentration on the rate of reaction

If substrate availability is kept at a fixed rate and the number of enzymes increased, a similar shaped graph is produced. As more enzymes are available, the rate increases up to a limit, by which time the number of substrate molecules becomes limiting. However, for most enzyme-catalysed reactions there will usually be sufficient substrate to allow the rate to increase up to the maximum imposed by the enzyme concentration.

As it is often the number of enzymes, and not substrate, that limits reactions in living organisms, there are many adaptations to increase enzyme number. The extensive infolding of mitochondrial cristae to increase the surface area of the inner membrane, and consequently the number of respiratory enzymes located on the membrane, is an excellent example (see Chapter 3 Cells, pages 42–43).

Temperature

Increasing temperature gives both the substrate and the enzyme molecules more **kinetic energy**. This increased kinetic energy means that the molecules are able to move around faster, increasing the possibility of collisions between enzyme and substrate, and the formation of enzyme-substrate complexes. Typically, the rate of enzyme activity doubles for every 10°C rise below the **optimum** temperature. In mammals the optimum for enzyme activity is around 40°C.

Above the optimum, the increasing temperature causes some of the bonds (especially the weak hydrogen bonds) to break. As the temperature rises, more and more bonds break and the shape of the enzyme and, in particular, its active site changes. Around 60°C the change is so great that the enzyme ceases to function; it has become **denatured**. This is a permanent and irreversible change.

The effect of temperature on enzyme activity

The optimum rate for different enzymes varies considerably. The optimum temperature for plants is well below that for mammals. Enzymes in the bacteria that inhabit hot springs can have an optimum temperature in excess of 80°C. For species that cannot control their internal temperature (all except birds and mammals), the optimum temperature for their enzymes often closely mirrors the temperature of their typical environment.

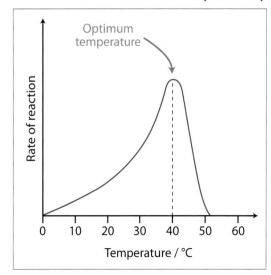

pH

Each enzyme also has an optimum pH. At either side of this optimum, changes in pH will reduce activity. This is caused by changes in pH disrupting the bonds that are important in determining protein shape (especially the enzyme active site). **Ionic bonds**, in particular, are subject to disruption when in a non-optimal pH. The further the pH is away from the optimum, the greater the degree of disruption to the bonding, until eventually denaturation results.

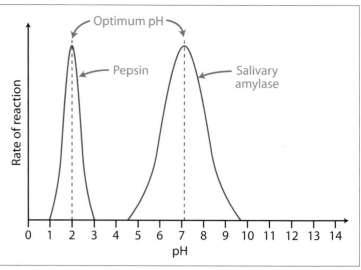

The effect of pH on enzyme activity

Enzyme inhibition

Enzyme inhibitors are substances that interfere with enzyme action. They reduce enzyme activity by either directly or indirectly affecting the functioning of the active site.

Competitive inhibition

Competitive inhibition is when the inhibitor substance **competes** with the usual substrate for the active site. Competitive inhibitors are very similar in shape to the usual substrate. The effect of the inhibitor depends on the relative concentrations of the substrate and the inhibitor – if the quantity of inhibitor substance is low compared to the substrate, it will have little or no effect; if it is relatively high it can significantly affect enzyme activity.

An example of competitive inhibition can be seen through the effect of the inhibitor malonic acid (malonate) on the respiratory enzyme succinate dehydrogenase. Malonate has a very similar molecular shape to succinate (the normal substrate). If malonate is present in high enough quantities, it can reduce the activity of succinate dehydrogenase and therefore the respiratory process itself.

Non-competitive inhibition

Non-competitive inhibition is when the inhibitor attaches itself to a part of the enzyme other than the active site. The presence of the non-competitive inhibitor leads to the active site changing shape so that it is no longer complementary to the substrate molecule. In non-competitive inhibition, an increase in substrate concentration does not reduce the effect of the inhibitor, as the two molecules are not in direct competition, but in effect, the number of functioning enzymes has been reduced.

Enzymes that have a second site where (non-substrate) molecules can attach are described as **allosteric enzymes**. Although used here as an example of non-competitive inhibition, they are often important in the regulation of enzyme activity through negative feedback. When enough products have been produced for the cells' needs, the product (or another substance linked to product amount) is present in sufficient quantity to join the allosteric site of the enzyme and effectively act as a

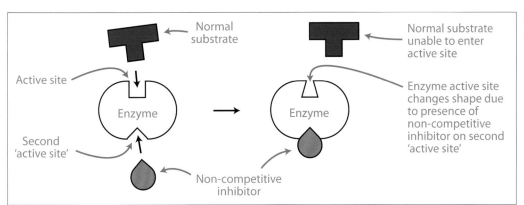

Non-competitive inhibition

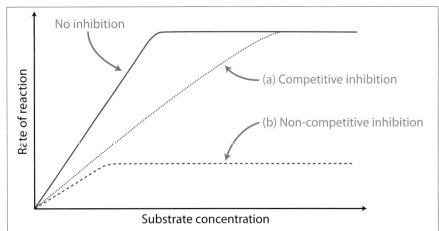

The effect of substrate concentration on rate of reaction in the presence of (a) competitive inhibition and (b) non-competitive inhibition

non-competitive inhibitor. In this situation, enzyme activity above and beyond the cells' needs ceases.

Many competitive and non-competitive inhibitors are **reversible**, ie when they are removed the enzyme can operate as normal. Some inhibitors are **irreversible**, ie their effects cannot be reversed and the enzyme is permanently damaged. This usually occurs through weakening or breaking the bonds in determining the 3-D shape of the enzyme (and in particular the active site). Cyanide is a non-reversible inhibitor of the respiratory enzyme, cytochrome oxidase.

Immobilised enzymes

Enzymes are vitally important molecules in regulating metabolism in living organisms. They have become increasingly important in biotechnology. To maximise efficiency many enzymes are **immobilised**. Immobilised enzymes are trapped within or attached to appropriate inorganic or organic materials.

There are four principal methods of immobilisation:

- **adsorption** – The enzyme is attached by weak forces to an inert substance such as glass or a matrix.
- **entrapment** – The enzymes are trapped within polymers such as alginate beads or microspheres.
- **encapsulation** (enmeshment) – The enzymes are trapped inside a selectively permeable membrane such as nylon.
- **cross-linkage** – The enzymes are bonded covalently to a matrix, such as cellulose, as a consequence of chemical reactions (or even to each other using linking chemicals).

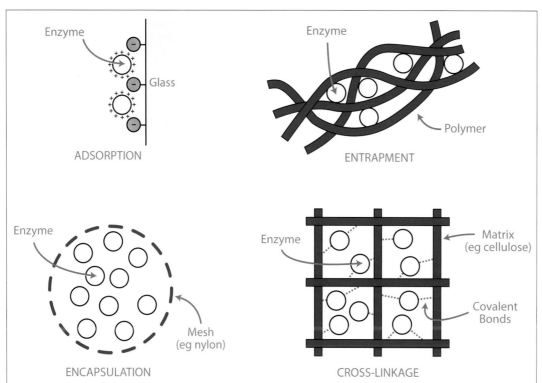

Methods of enzyme immobilisation

The gels or materials involved in some types of immobilisation may reduce the speed of diffusion between substrate and enzyme. The immobilisation process may also hold some enzymes in physical positions that make some of the enzyme active sites inaccessible.

Different methods are preferred in different industrial settings, taking account of effectiveness, efficiency and commercial considerations. Adsorption is a relatively straightforward and inexpensive method. However, it is not always reliable, as the enzymes can be easily washed from the adsorptive material. A further disadvantage is that some of the enzyme active sites may be inaccessible, as part of the enzyme is attached to the glass. However, adsorption does have advantages, as the substrate and products do not have to diffuse through a gel barrier to reach (or leave) the enzyme, as has to happen with entrapment.

In general, enzyme immobilisation has the following advantages:

- the enzymes are **thermostable**. They remain stable and are more effective over a wider range of temperatures than enzymes that are not immobilised.
- the enzymes are more resistant to changes in **pH**.
- the enzymes can be retained and reused.
- commercial processes can be continuous, which is faster and produces less wastage.
- there is no contamination of the end product with enzyme, simplifying the downstreaming process, reducing purification costs and avoiding possible allergic reactions in consumers.

Immobilised enzymes are often used in continuous flow column reactors that ensure maximum production. Rates of flow, method of immobilisation and environmental conditions can be controlled to ensure maximum efficiency.

Diagnostic reagent strips as biosensors

Enzymes are very effective biosensors. They are very **specific** in that they can be used to identify individual molecules, for example, glucose, and they are **quantitative**.

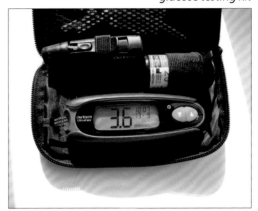

A digital blood glucose testing kit

The general principle is that the molecule being monitored reacts with immobilised enzymes and the reaction produced causes a colour change, such as Clinistix, or is converted into an electrical signal (digital blood glucose monitors).

The blood testing kit opposite shows the blood testing meter, a box of diagnostic test strips and a lancing device for obtaining a small blood sample.

Biosensors have a wide range of applications in, for example, industry, medicine and environmental monitoring. Chemical pollution of water can be quickly identified using biosensors.

Practical work

Enzyme investigations

As part of your course you will be expected to have investigated the effect of temperature, pH, substrate and enzyme concentration on enzyme activity. When carrying out enzyme experiments, it is important to ensure that all appropriate variables are controlled. For example, if you are investigating the effect of pH on catalase activity, through using buffers to produce a range of solutions with different pH values, it is important that other factors that can affect catalase activity are controlled. These include enzyme and substrate concentrations and volume, and also the temperature that the reactions take place at. In examination questions you are often required to describe how you control particular variables (instead of just listing the variables), for example, temperature can be controlled using a water bath.

Illustration of enzyme immobilisation

Many 'A' level candidates are familiar with the immobilisation of lactase in alginate beads. In this experiment the activity of the lactase can be demonstrated by its effect on milk. Milk initially has no effect on a Clinistix strip but after passing through a column of alginate beads (with immobilised lactase), the Clinistix test becomes positive. This can be explained by the lactose being broken down to its monosaccharide constituents, glucose and galactose. It is the presence of glucose, not the galactose, that causes the colour change in the Clinistix.

This investigation (or other similar ones) is a useful way of examining how factors such as flow rate, number of beads in the column, and bead size affect enzyme activity and the rate of reaction.

The effect of immobilised lactase on milk

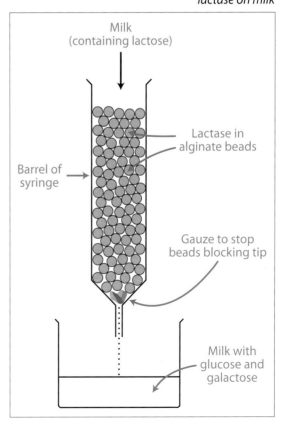

Milk (containing lactose)

Barrel of syringe

Lactase in alginate beads

Gauze to stop beads blocking tip

Milk with glucose and galactose

Using a colorimeter

A colorimeter is a piece of apparatus that measures the change in intensity of light as it passes through a solution.

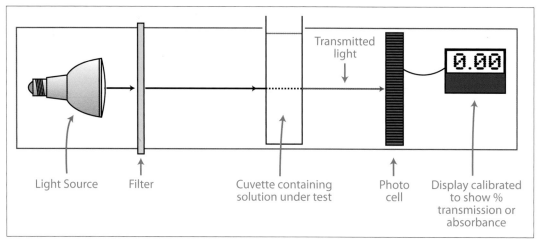

The colorimeter

Colorimeters can record the amount of light that is absorbed (**absorbance**) by the solution *or* the amount of light that passes through (**transmission**). The light that is not absorbed by the sample passes on to the photo-sensitive cell and the electrical current produced is converted into a digital readout.

As an enzyme reaction progresses, the solution can either become more or less turbid (more or less cloudy) depending on the reaction that is taking place.

It is important to calibrate the colorimeter. For example, if the colorimeter is going to follow the course of amylase breaking down starch to maltose, a weak solution of iodine could be calibrated as the end point or 'blank', ie 100% transmission.

An appropriate filter is used that will maximise the **change** in transmission/absorbance as the investigation progresses (provides the biggest range of colorimeter readings). For example, when following the course of a starch-amylase catalysed reaction, a red filter is usually used. Red is at the opposite end of the spectrum to the colour change observed (degree of blue/black colouring produced when the test solution is tested with iodine), therefore maximising the percentage absorbance/transmission change.

As with all practical investigations, it is important to maximise validity and reliability. For example, it is essential that the cuvettes are clean, as any marks on the surface of the cuvette will affect light transmission and produce invalid results.

Whether using absorbance or transmission, the values of the percentage of initial starch remaining against time in a starch-amylase reaction should follow the pattern shown in the graph opposite.

The shape of the curve can be explained by the rate of reaction being very rapid at the start, when the concentration of starch is high and therefore the likelihood of collision between the amylase and starch is also high (and consequently the formation of enzyme-substrate complexes). As the reaction

The course of a starch-amylase reaction

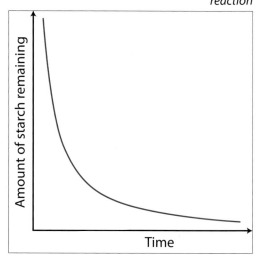

progresses, the number of starch molecules decreases and therefore fewer enzyme-substrate complexes will form per unit time, as collisions between enzyme and substrate will be less frequent. This will be due to there being fewer starch molecules and also the presence of product molecules (maltose) that 'block' the movement of the enzyme and the substrate.

A colorimeter calibration graph

Note: a graph of products produced against time would be a different shape but the same principles would apply. Maltose would be rapidly produced at the start of the reaction but the rate of reaction would decrease over time.

In colorimeter experiments it is often necessary to produce **calibration graphs (curves)** if the investigation will involve calculating specific quantities of a substance. In effect, this involves measuring transmission or absorbance values for known concentrations of the substance being investigated. A calibration graph can then be drawn that will allow unknown substance concentrations to be measured from the curve.

Note: colorimeters are typically used to monitor enzyme reactions but can be used to monitor any process that involves change in turbidity, for example, change in bacterial numbers over time.

Some general points about graphs

It is very important that you are able to draw graphs accurately and interpret them. Graphs involving enzyme reactions are commonly used in examination papers (see the exam questions section at the end of this chapter).

Drawing graphs is an important skill in biology and you should stick to the following rules:

- The graph should have a title (caption) which identifies the relationship shown. This must include the independent variable, the dependent variable and the biological material being investigated.
- The independent variable is placed on the x-axis, with the dependent variable being on the y-axis.
- Suitable scales should be used, making effective use of the graph paper available. The axes should be labelled with the name of the variable, followed by a solidus or forward slash (/) and the unit of measurement, for example, percentage starch remaining /%.

Generally in Biology it is best to use straight lines to join the points.

However, in some circumstances a line of best fit should be used (this could be a straight line or a smooth curve). A line of best fit can be used if there are a sufficient number of points to be confident that intermediate points fall on the line or an understanding of the theory involved suggests that a best fit line is appropriate. However, when drawing a line of best fit, be careful that you do not extend your line beyond the range of the points available (extrapolation) unless there is good reason to do so. Also do not always assume that it is appropriate to start at the origin (0,0 coordinates).

When drawing a line of best fit, there should be approximately the same number of data points on each side of the line. Your line of best fit may or may not go through any of the plotted points.

Lines of best fit are used in constructing graphs for enzyme reactions over time using colorimeter readings, as there is good reason to assume that the process follows the curvilinear pattern discussed earlier (see diagram on page 30). Lines of best fit are also used in determining the water potential of plant tissues, either through using the percentage change of mass of plant tissue or incipient plasmolysis investigations (see Chapter 4).

You should also be aware of the range of graph types that can be used in 'A' level Biology.

Line graphs – are used when both the independent (IV) and dependent variables (DV) are continuous, and there is probably a causal link between the two variables, ie it is the change in the IV that causes the change in the DV.

Bar charts – are used when the IV is discontinuous or categoric (for example, the type of plant or type of solution tested in an investigation). There should be a space between the bars of a bar chart.

Scattergrams (scatter diagrams) – are also used when both the IV and DV are continuous but there is not necessarily a causal link between them. An example could be number of species in a quadrat and the pH of the soil.

Other types of graph you need to be familiar with include **histograms**, **pie charts** and **kite diagrams** (although it is less likely that you will be asked to draw one in an exam).

Exam questions

1. An experiment was undertaken to investigate the effect of pH on two proteolytic enzymes, enzyme 1 and enzyme 2. Cubes of protein, each of 200 mg mass, were placed in solutions of each enzyme at different pHs, and the time taken for the protein to be digested was measured. The results are shown in the table below.

pH of reaction mixture	Time for protein to be digested/minutes	
	Enzyme 1	Enzyme 2
1	80	–
2	50	–
3	7	–
4	55	80
5	72	65
6	80	52
7	–	32
8	–	20
9	–	42
10	–	71
11	–	80

(a) Plot the data in the table, using the most appropriate graphical technique (use graph paper). [6]

(b) (i) Suggest how the pH in each reaction mixture would have been maintained. [1]

    (ii) State **one** factor that should have been controlled in the experiment and explain the influence of that factor on enzyme activity. [2]

(c) Using the information in your graph, calculate the rate of reaction for enzyme 1 at pH 2 in units of mg hour^{-1} (show your working). [2]

(d) Which of the two enzymes would normally be found in the mammalian stomach? Explain your answer. [1]

(e) State the pH range over which both enzymes are active. [1]

Question taken from CCEA's Biology Assessment Unit AS 1, Module 1: Cell Biology, June 2009, © CCEA 2012

2. The diagrams below represent the structure of an enzyme with its associated substrates and the same enzyme after the addition of both a competitive and a non-competitive inhibitor.

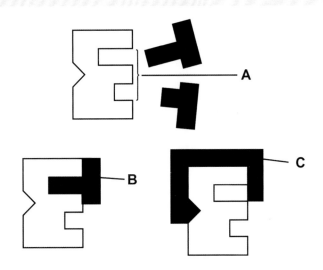

(a) Identify the part of the enzyme labelled **A**. [1]

(b) (i) Which of the two inhibitors, **B** or **C**, is a competitive inhibitor? [1]

    (ii) Explain your reasoning for your answer in part (i). [2]

The graph below illustrates the effect of substrate concentration on the rate of an enzyme-controlled reaction with no inhibitor present. The effects of the addition of a competitive inhibitor and of a non-competitive inhibitor are also shown.

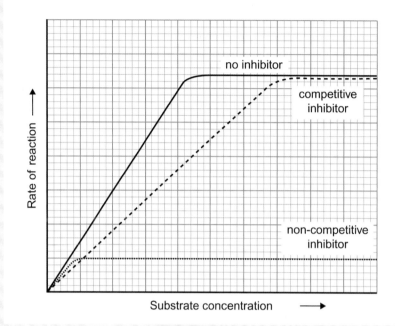

(c) Describe and explain the effect of substrate concentration on the rate of reaction for the enzyme with no inhibitor added. [3]

(d) (i) Describe the effects of each of the two inhibitors below:

- Competitive inhibitor
- Non-competitive inhibitor [2]

(ii) Explain how an increase in substrate concentration influences the effect of the competitive inhibitor. [2]

Question taken from CCEA's Biology Assessment Unit AS 1, Module 1: Molecules and Cells, January 2010, © CCEA 2012

3. In an investigation into the effect of temperature on the movement of pigment through cell membranes, small cylinders were cut from fresh beetroot. In beetroot cells the red anthocyanin pigment occurs within the vacuoles. Each vacuole is surrounded by a tonoplast membrane and, outside this membrane, the cytoplasm is surrounded by the cell-surface (plasma) membrane.

After cutting and rinsing six beetroot cylinders, each small cylinder was placed in a test tube containing water. Each of the six test tubes had been maintained at a particular temperature. Each cylinder was left for one minute during which some pigment leaked out.

After cooling, samples from each test tube were placed in cuvettes and the percentage transmission of light through each sample was measured using a colorimeter.

(a) (i) Explain why a blue filter was selected for use in the colorimeter. [2]

(ii) State **one** precaution required, when using a colorimeter, to ensure that an accurate meter reading is obtained. [1]

(iii) Explain precisely how the colorimeter is used to measure the amount of red pigment in each sample. [2]

The results of the investigation are shown in the table below.

Temperature/°C	Percentage transmission/%
40	90
50	90
55	80
58	25
60	20
70	15

(b) Plot the above results, using an appropriate graphical technique (use graph paper). [5]

(c) (i) Identify the trends evident in the results. [2]

(ii) Suggest explanations for the trends identified in (i) above. [2]

Question taken from CCEA's Biology Assessment Unit AS 1, Molecules and Cells, June 2010, © CCEA 2012

4. This question is about the digestion of jelly by protein-digesting enzymes.

(a) Jelly contains the protein gelatine, which is broken down to amino acids by protein-digesting enzymes. State the type of reaction which takes place during digestion. [1]

(b) The procedure used for an investigation of the effect of pH on the activity of two protein-digesting enzymes is outlined below.

1. Five buffer solutions were prepared at pH 4, 6.4, 7.4, 8, and 9.
2. 10 strips of jelly were cut from a jelly block. Each strip was approximately 1 to 2 mm in thickness.
3. Each strip was trimmed to a rectangle of 10 by 20 mm and the surplus jelly discarded. Trimmed strips were placed in separate Petri dishes.
4. 10 cm³ of each of the five buffer solutions was added to two of the Petri dishes, so that two Petri dishes had pH 4, two had pH 6.4, etc. The Petri dishes were divided into two sets, each set having one dish at each pH.
5. 10 cm³ of enzyme A was added to one set of the Petri dishes and 10 cm³ of enzyme B was added to the second set of Petri dishes.
6. All Petri dishes were left at room temperature for 90 minutes.
7. The area of the jelly remaining was measured and the results are shown in the table overleaf.

pH	Area of jelly remaining/mm^2	
	Enzyme A	Enzyme B
4	0	200
6.4	100	190
7.4	171	98
8	190	48
9	200	0

(i) Plot the table's results, using an appropriate graphical technique (use graph paper). [5]

(ii) Describe the trends evident in the graph. [3]

(c) Explain why pH influences the activity of an enzyme. [2]

(d) There are several potential problems with the design of this experiment. Suggest four possible problems in the procedure used. [4]

Question taken from CCEA's Biology Assessment Unit AS 1, Molecules and Cells, January 2011, © CCEA 2012

5. The enzyme amylase catalyses the following reaction.

Starch ⟶ maltose

(a) Starch and maltose are both carbohydrates.

(i) Describe how they are similar in their molecular structure. [1]

(ii) Describe how they are different in their molecular structure. [2]

In an investigation of the above reaction, 0.1% amylase was added to a 1% solution of starch. The amount of starch remaining in solution was determined over time.

(b) (i) Describe a method that you would use to determine 'the amount of starch in solution over time'. [3]

(ii) Suggest one possible limitation in your method. [1]

The results are shown in the table below.

Time/minutes	Amount of starch remaining in solution/%
0	1.0
0.5	0.5
1.0	0.25
2.0	0.07
3.0	0.02
4.0	0.01

(c) (i) Describe the pattern of change in the amount of starch remaining in solution over time. [2]

   (ii) Explain the changes in the amount of starch remaining in solution over time. [2]

   Question taken from CCEA's Biology Assessment Unit AS 1, Module 1: Cell Biology, January 2009, © CCEA 2012

6. Quality of written communication is awarded a maximum of two marks in this question. [2]

   Enzymes are sensitive to a number of factors. The three graphs in this question illustrate the influence of three independent variables on the activity of an enzyme. For each of the three graphs:

   - identify the independent variable
   - describe trends evident in the graph
   - explain the trends described [13]

(a)

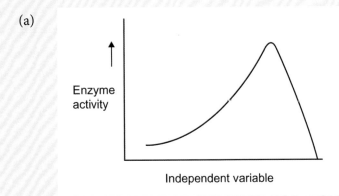

(b)

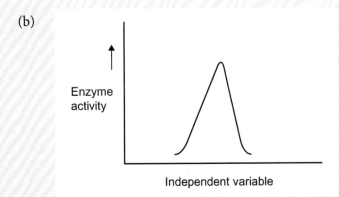

(c)

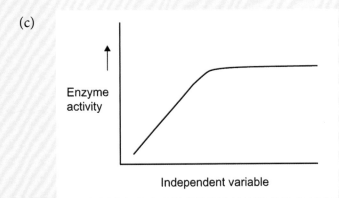

Question taken from CCEA's Biology Assessment Unit AS 1, Molecules and Cells, June 2010, © CCEA 2012

Chapter 3 – Cells

1.5.1   Describe the ultrastructure of eukaryotic and prokaryotic cells.

1.5.2   Understand the structure and function of membranes.

1.5.3   Understand the structure and function of eukaryotic cell components.

1.5.4   Compare eukaryotic cell structure (plant, fungal and animal cells).

1.5.5   Understand the use of microscopy in examining cell structure.

1.5.6   Practical work to include recognising cell structures from photomicrographs and electron micrographs (TEM/SEM), and the calculation of true size (in μm) and magnification, including the use of scale bars.

The cell is the basic unit of living organisms. Most living organisms are formed of a single cell but most of us are not aware of this, as they are too small to see with the naked eye. A common cell structure evolved very early in the development of life on Earth; consequently most cells are a variation of themes superimposed on a basic plan.

The use of microscopy in examining cell structure

Cells under the light (optical) microscope

It is relatively easy to tell the difference between animal and plant cells when viewed by the light microscope. There are several easy ways to recognise differences between them.

Animal cells are often irregular in shape and appear very homogenous, with a granular cytoplasm being bounded by a cell-surface (plasma) membrane. A prominent nucleus is invariably present. Plant cells appear more complex (most students will be familiar with onion epidermal cells). In addition to the cell-surface membrane, cytoplasm and nucleus, they contain a peripheral cell wall and a large central vacuole (which is very difficult to see unless the contrast is very good). Palisade cells, found in the palisade layer immediately under the upper epidermis in leaves, are also rich in chloroplasts.

Note: the positions of the cell-surface, nuclear and tonoplast membranes are labelled but not the membranes themselves. This is because the detail of membrane structure cannot be seen using the light microscope.

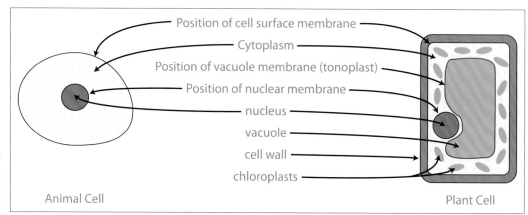

Position of cell surface membrane

Cytoplasm

Position of vacuole membrane (tonoplast)

Position of nuclear membrane

nucleus

vacuole

cell wall

chloroplasts

Animal and plant cells as seen under the light microscope

Animal Cell

Plant Cell

Units of measurement

When working with cells and cell components it is important to be able to appreciate cell and component sizes. It is also important to be able to calculate the magnification used or to calculate/estimate the size of cells and cell structures. To do this you need to be familiar with the units relevant in cell microscopy.

The standard unit for the measurement of most cells, and most cell structures, is the **μm** (**micrometre** or **micron**). There are 1000 μm in every millimetre; therefore one million μm in each metre. Some very small cell structures are measured in **nanometres** (**nm**). There are 1000 nm in each μm.

Unit	Symbol	Size in metres
1 millimetre	1 mm	10^{-3} m
1 micrometre	1 μm	10^{-6} m
1 nanometre	1 nm	10^{-9} m

The electron microscope (EM)

The electron microscope, as its name implies, uses electrons rather that light to produce images. The key term in using high powered microscopes is **resolution**, not magnification. Anyone using a photocopier or printer will appreciate that it is possible to keep enlarging an image, but eventually this gets to the stage where magnification is at the cost of clarity and no further detail can be gained.

Resolution is the ability to see two adjacent (but separate) points as distinct entities following magnification. Electron microscopes can resolve points down to 0.1 nm (10^{-10} m), whereas light microscopes can only achieve 0.2 μm (200 nm). This means that the electron microscope can achieve meaningful magnifications in excess of 1 million. In contrast, the light microscope can only magnify meaningfully up to a few thousand. The difference is due to the fact that **electrons** have a **shorter wavelength** than light.

The development of the electron microscope has shown that cell structure is much more complex than suggested by the light microscope. Nonetheless, the light microscope has its advantages. Living specimens and biological processes can be viewed under the light microscope, whereas the electron microscope can only be used on dead material (there must be a vacuum inside an electron microscope as air molecules would deflect the electron beam). In addition, **artefacts** (distortion due to preparation techniques) are often a feature of electron micrograph images. Electron micrograph images require a lot of preparation work. The specimen must be cut very thin using specialised cutting

The electron microscope

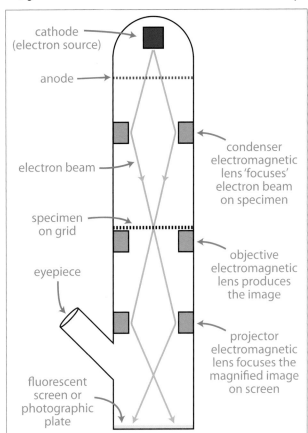

cathode (electron source)

anode

electron beam

specimen on grid

eyepiece

fluorescent screen or photographic plate

condenser electromagnetic lens 'focuses' electron beam on specimen

objective electromagnetic lens produces the image

projector electromagnetic lens focuses the magnified image on screen instruments and stained to provide appropriate contrast between the structures being viewed or photographed. The degree of preparation involved can sometimes produce 'artefacts' or changes in the image.

There are two types of electron microscope, the transmission electron microscope and the scanning electron microscope.

The transmission electron microscope (TEM) involves electrons passing through a very thin specimen. It produces images with a very high resolution and consequently can be used for very high magnifications (see pages 51 and 52 for examples).

The scanning electron microscope (SEM) involves electrons reflecting off the surface of the image as opposed to going through it. Resolution and magnification are not as high but it is useful for giving a 3-D image of surface features as can be seen in the SEM electron micrograph of pollen grains opposite.

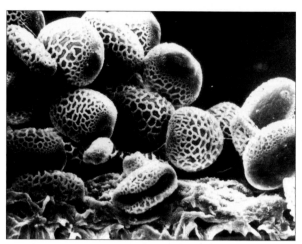

SEM image of pollen grains
Image courtesy of Dr Gerard Brennan, School of Biological Sciences, Queen's University, Belfast

Cell ultrastructure

Understanding the eukaryotic cell

The typical eukaryotic cell (a cell with a nucleus) consists of a cell-surface membrane (we will revisit the cell-surface membrane later) and cytoplasm, within which a nucleus and a host of membrane systems and organelles are embedded.

The detail of a cell when viewed through an electron microscope is known as its **ultrastructure**.

Eukaryotic cells are found in **animals**, **plants** and **fungi**. The organelles and membrane systems covered in the next section are not all found in animals, plants and fungi; some are specific to certain group(s) only.

Membrane systems and organelles of animal cells

The nucleus

The nucleus is the largest and most obvious organelle in most cells. It is usually between about 10–25 μm in diameter. The nucleus contains DNA in chromosomes. When cells are not dividing the chromosomes are not visible but are more diffusely organised in a form called **chromatin**. In parts of the nucleus, the chromatin is more densely packed (**heterochromatin**), appearing dark when viewed by the electron microscope. In other parts it is less densely packed (**euchromatin**), and therefore appears lighter when viewed.

The nucleus often contains one or more **nucleoli** (1–3 μm). When viewed under the electron microscope, a nucleolus appears even darker than the densely packed heterochromatin and is a more discrete structure than the more diffuse heterochromatin, which is often concentrated close to the nuclear membrane. A nucleolus synthesises ribosomal RNA (rRNA) makes ribosomes, which are components essential in the process of protein synthesis.

In general, the nucleus is the control centre of the cell, as the DNA in the chromosomes codes for the synthesis of proteins in the cytoplasm. By isolating the chromosomes (and DNA) from the rest of the cytoplasm and the reactions that take place there, the DNA is protected from damage. However, the 'DNA code' for protein synthesis needs to be taken from the safety of the nucleus to the cytoplasm, where protein synthesis takes place and other molecules (for example, enzymes involved in making DNA) need to enter the nucleus from the cytoplasm. This is achieved by the presence of **nuclear pores** in the **nuclear envelope** (membrane). The nuclear envelope is in fact a double membrane, with a very narrow space between each membrane.

Endoplasmic reticulum (ER)

The ER is a membrane system that extends throughout the cytoplasm – it is very common and will be evident in virtually all electron micrographs of cytoplasm. Its three-dimensional membrane system encloses sacs called **cisternae**. Some of the ER has ribosome organelles dotted along the outside (cytoplasmic side) of the membranes. This is **rough endoplasmic reticulum (RER)**. Other parts of the ER do not have ribosomes attached. This is **smooth endoplasmic reticulum (SER).**

The RER provides the 'scaffolding' for the ribosomes to make protein and the ER then operates as a distribution network for the proteins. The ER is joined with the nuclear envelope, facilitating the transport of the RNA (which carries the DNA code) from the nucleus to the ribosomes (the sites of protein synthesis). Not surprisingly, RER is particularly common in cells whose function is to secrete protein.

The SER has many roles involving the metabolism of lipids, including the synthesis of cholesterol.

Ribosomes

These very small organelles (up to about 30 nm in diameter) are visible as small black dots in EM micrographs. They are found either free in the cytoplasm or attached to the outer surface of the ER as described above.

Each ribosome is formed of a large and a small sub-unit, and is made of protein and ribosomal RNA (rRNA). They frequently occur in groups called **polyribosomes**, creating 'hot spots' of protein synthesis.

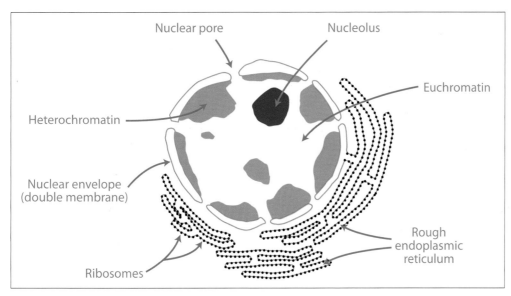

The nucleus and surrounding rough endoplasmic reticulum (RER) containing ribosomes

Golgi apparatus

The Golgi apparatus (body) can be described as a series of curved flattened sacs (**cisternae**). They characteristically have a number of small **vesicles** both entering and leaving the system. Vesicles containing newly synthesised protein pinch off from the RER and coalesce with the 'forming' (convex) edge of the system (usually the edge closest to the nucleus). Within the main body of the Golgi, the proteins are modified, for example, they may have carbohydrate added to form glycoprotein. Once the protein is modified, vesicles containing the 'finished' protein are pinched off from the 'maturing' (concave) face (usually the side furthest away from the nucleus). These vesicles transport the protein either within the cell or fuse with the cell-surface membrane to release their contents outside the cell.

The organelles and membrane systems discussed so far (nucleus, ER, ribosomes and Golgi apparatus) are all intricately linked in function – they play important roles in protein synthesis and the subsequent modification and transport of the protein produced.

Lysosomes

Lysosomes are tiny vesicles usually about 0.5 μm in size. They are formed by the Golgi apparatus and they contain **hydrolytic enzymes** for internal use. They fuse with other vesicles in the cell that contain something that has to be destroyed or digested (for example, worn out cell organelles or other cell debris). When they fuse they form secondary lysosomes. They have an important role in **phagocytes**, where they digest engulfed bacteria enclosed in a phagosome (membrane bound vesicle in the phagocyte). Lysosomes have relatively thick membranes (compared with other internal organelles), as obviously it is important that the hydrolytic enzymes are not accidentally released inside the cell.

Note: vesicles are not restricted to association with the Golgi apparatus – they can be used for the storage and transport of substances throughout the cell.

Mitochondria

Mitochondria are present in almost all types of animal cell. They are relatively large

Golgi apparatus producing (A) secretory vesicles and (B) lysosomes

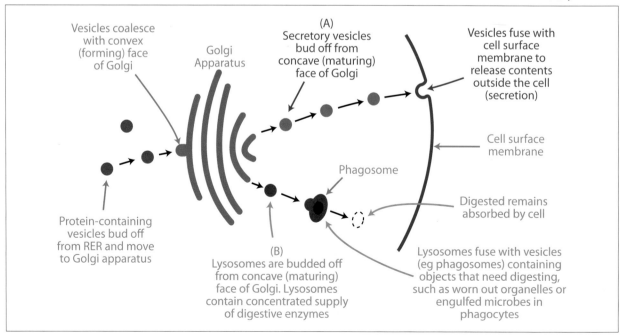

organelles (up to 10 μm in length). They are typically 'sausage shaped' but can be very variable in shape. Mitochondria are enclosed within a **double membrane**, separated by an inter-membrane space. The inner membrane is folded to form **cristae** that extend into the **matrix** of the mitochondria. This infolding gives the inner mitochondrial membrane a greater surface area, therefore increasing the number of enzymes that can be embedded within the membrane.

The mitochondrion is the 'powerhouse' of the cell. It is the site of **ATP synthesis** during **aerobic respiration**. Mitochondria are particularly common in cells that have high energy requirements, such as muscle cells. Additionally, as many of the enzymes involved in ATP synthesis are located within the inner mitochondrial membrane, the cristae tend to be more numerous and more deeply infolded in highly active cells.

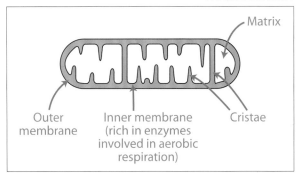

A mitochondrion

Microtubules

Microtubules are hollow cylinders formed from the protein tubulin. They are about 25 nm in diameter and up to 10 μm in length.

Ultrastructure of a generalised animal cell

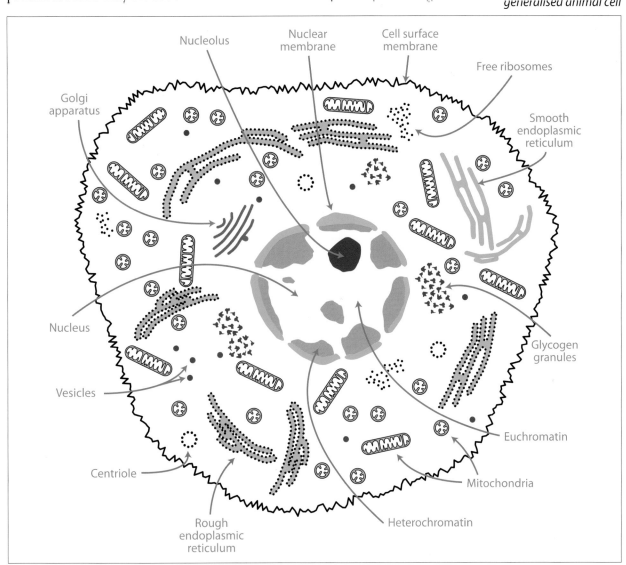

Although found throughout the cytoplasm they tend to be concentrated in specific areas and for specific functions. They occur within the centrioles that form the spindle fibres essential in nuclear division. In the centriole they form nine triplets of microtubules arranged in a circular formation. They also are found in cilia and flagella. As part of the cytoskeleton of the cell they help direct the movement of cell organelles.

Membrane systems and organelles of plant cells

Similar to animal cells, plant cells have a nucleus, ER, ribosomes and Golgi apparatus. They differ from animal cells in **not** having **lysosomes** or **centrioles**. However, the major difference is that they possess some organelles and membrane systems that are not present in animal cells.

These include:

Plant cell wall – All plant cells are surrounded by a cell wall that lies immediately outside the cell-surface membrane. Cell walls are around 1 μm thick. The main component in plant cell walls is the polysaccharide **cellulose**. The cellulose is laid down as **microfibrils**. Each microfibril consists of many cellulose molecules cross-linked to each other. The **primary cell wall** is made up of many microfibrils orientated in different and random directions. The relatively loose arrangement of microfibrils allows the cell wall to expand as the cell grows.

Secondary cell wall – When the cell reaches full size, additional layers of cellulose can be deposited to form the secondary cell wall. In the secondary cell wall, each layer of cellulose has the microfibrils orientated in the same direction. However, additional layers are orientated in different directions to other layers. This lattice type arrangement gives the great strength necessary in cell wall function.

Middle lamella – Cell walls of adjacent cells are linked by the middle lamella. The middle lamella is largely made of polysaccharides called **pectin**. **Calcium pectate** forms a gel or 'cement' that acts as an adhesive and holds neighbouring cells together.

The function of plant cell walls is to provide support. As they form fairly rigid structures they can support the cells directly, but are also very important in turgor. They restrict the outward expansion of the cell contents (**protoplast**) as the cell takes in water, thus providing the supporting force associated with turgor pressure. Unlike the cell-surface membrane, which is selectively or differentially permeable, the cell wall is fully permeable and plays no part in determining which substances can enter and leave cells.

Plasmodesmata

Plasmodesmata are strands of cytoplasm that extend between neighbouring plant cells. Plasmodesmata provide 'gaps' in the cell walls of adjacent cells that enable different kinds of molecules to pass through. As the cell membranes of the adjacent cells pass through the pores, the neighbouring cells are joined, physically and metabolically.

Plant cell wall with plasmodesmata

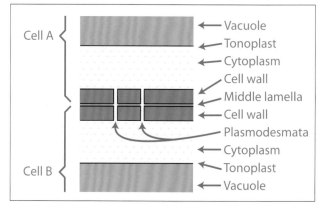

Cell A
— Vacuole
— Tonoplast
— Cytoplasm
— Cell wall
— Middle lamella
— Cell wall
— Plasmodesmata
— Cytoplasm
— Tonoplast
Cell B
— Vacuole

Chloroplasts

Chloroplasts are large organelles and are usually intermediate in size between the nucleus and mitochondria. They are bounded by a **double membrane** or **envelope**, which encloses the **stroma**. Within the stroma is a system of membranes, called thylakoids. At intervals, the **thylakoids** are arranged in stacks called **grana**. Between grana the membranes are less concentrated and are referred to as **inter-grana**.

The thylakoids contain chlorophyll, which is most densely concentrated in the grana.

Chloroplasts usually have one or more **starch grains** and smaller **lipid** droplets produced through photosynthesis.

Chloroplasts are the sites of **photosynthesis** and are located in photosynthesising cells, in particular cells in the palisade layer of leaves. Not surprisingly, most actively photosynthesising cells tend to have many chloroplasts that have many-layered grana, with many grana being present in each chloroplast.

A chloroplast

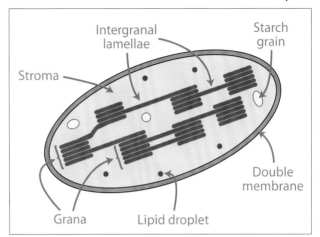

Large vacuole

Plant cells have a large vacuole within the cytoplasm. The vacuole is important in the storage of ions and water, and plays an important part in the development of turgor for support.

Ultrastructure of a generalised plant cell

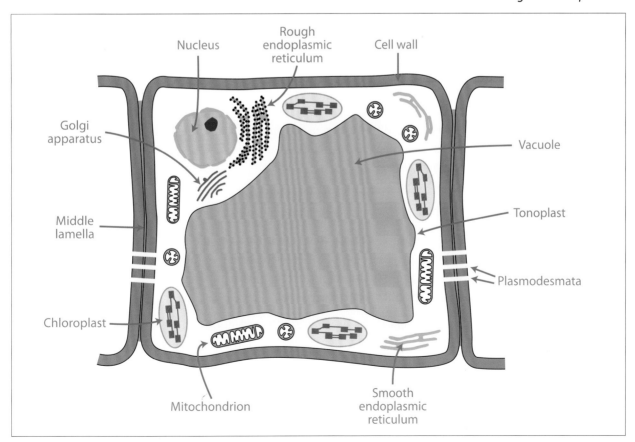

Fungal cells

Fungi (like animals and plants) are eukaryotic organisms and therefore they have eukaryotic cells.

Fungal cells have cell walls, but unlike plants their cell walls are made of the glycoprotein **chitin**, not cellulose. They have other plant-like features such as the presence of a **vacuole**.

They are significantly different to plants in that they do not photosynthesise, and therefore do not have chloroplasts. They are more similar to animal cells in having **glycogen** as the carbohydrate store and also through the presence of **lysosomes.**

Fungi do possess nuclei but the cells of many species are **multinucleate**.

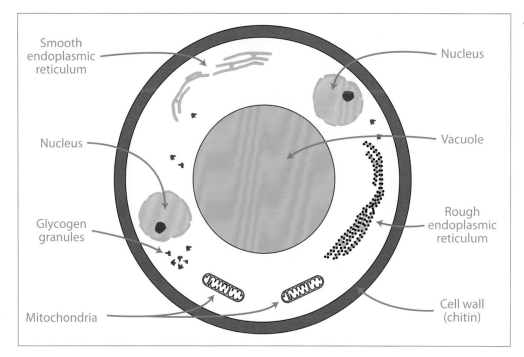

A typical fungal cell

The diagram above shows a transverse section through a fungal cell. Many fungi are in the form of long, elongated threads of hyphae that spread through the substrate. The cells are often elongated and multinucleate.

Prokaryotes and Eukaryotes

There are two distinct categories of cell in the living world, **prokaryotic** and **eukaryotic** cells. Prokaryotic cells are generally simpler. They do not have a nucleus and the membrane-bound organelles more typical of more complex cells. Bacteria have prokaryotic cells and they are described as **prokaryotes**.

We have already looked at eukaryotic cells in detail. They are the cells found in animals, plants and fungi. They have a membrane-bound nucleus, chromosomes and a range of complex organelles that have specific roles within the cell.

The table opposite summarises the main differences between eukaryotic and prokaryotic cells.

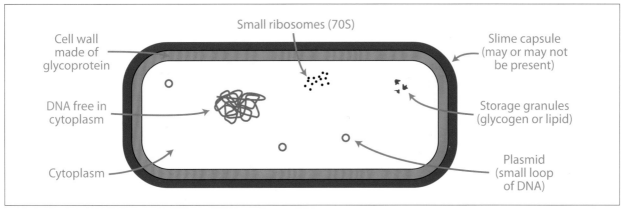

A generalised prokaryote cell

	Prokaryotic cell	**Eukaryotic cell**
Size	Usually < 5 μm	10–200 μm
Site of DNA	DNA free in cytoplasm	DNA inside membrane-bound nucleus
DNA organisation	Circular and without associated protein	DNA linear and in chromosomes. Chromosomes contain both helically arranged DNA and packaging protein (histones)
Ribosomes	Small – 20 nm (70S)	Large – 25 nm (80S)
Internal structure	No complex organelles	Complex membrane-bound organelles including nucleus, mitochondria and Golgi apparatus
Cell walls	Complex – made of peptidoglycan (glycoprotein)	Cellulose cell walls in plants Chitin cell walls in fungi
Plasmids	Usually present	Not present
Microtubules	Not present	Present as centrioles in animal and some fungal groups

The cell-surface membrane

The cell-surface (plasma) membrane is a critical component of cells. It is the boundary or interface with the outside world, whether that is the environment (in unicellular organisms), other cells or internal cavities, such as the gut, in multicellular organisms.

The cell-surface membrane consists of two basic components, a **phospholipid bilayer** and **protein**. It is the phospholipid bilayer that forms the 'skeleton' of the membrane and this is largely due to the properties of the phospholipid molecules.

As noted in Chapter 1 on molecules, phospholipids consist of **hydrophilic** (water loving) 'heads' that can mix with water but not lipid and two **hydrophobic** (water hating) 'tails' that will mix with lipid but not water.

Note: the terms 'water loving' and 'water hating' have been used here for explanatory purposes. In examinations you should use the scientific terms hydrophilic and hydrophobic.

Due to these properties the two layers (**bilayer**) of phospholipid molecules arrange themselves as shown in the diagram opposite. The hydrophobic tails turn away from the solution and join with other hydrophobic tails, whereas the hydrophilic heads readily mix with the surrounding aqueous medium.

In the cell-surface membrane the hydrophilic heads are always on the outside and the tails are in the inside (centre) of the membrane.

Protein molecules are scattered throughout the membrane. They can be attached peripherally to the bilayer (**extrinsic**) or integrally embedded into one of the two layers (**intrinsic**). Some intrinsic proteins (**transmembrane**) extend across the bilayer.

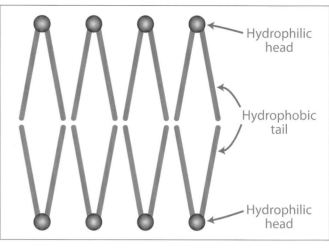

A bilayer of phospholipid molecules

> **Note:** the terms extrinsic and intrinsic refer to protein position – the protein molecules are given other names that relate to their role.

Animal cell membranes also contain **cholesterol** molecules that lie between the phospholipid tails.

The structure of the cell-surface membrane is described as the **fluid-mosaic** model. In essence, the phospholipid molecules can 'flow' sideways, although always keeping the bilayer arrangement, with the protein molecules 'floating' between the phospholipid molecules.

Extending from the **outer** phospholipid layer of the membrane is the **glycocalyx**. The glycocalyx contains **polysaccharides** that are bound to membrane proteins (**glycoproteins**) or to the phospholipids (**glycolipids**). The carbohydrate component is always on the outside, peripheral to the phospholipid bilayer.

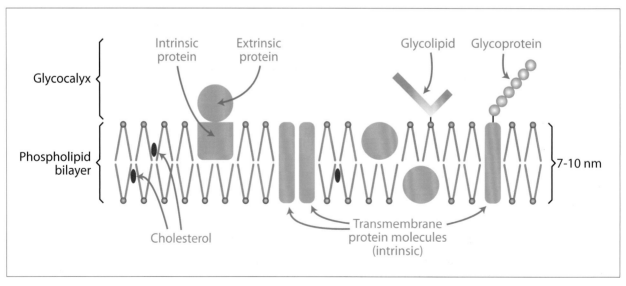

The fluid mosaic model of cell-surface membrane structure

Functions of the membrane components

1. **The phospholipid bilayer** – as well as being the backbone of the cell-surface membrane, gives the membrane much of its **selectively** or **differentially permeable** properties.

2. **Cholesterol** – increases membrane stability by restricting the sideways movement of phospholipid molecules at high temperatures. At low temperatures the cholesterol helps to maintain membrane fluidity by acting as a wedge between adjacent phospholipid molecules and stopping adjacent molecules sticking together. In effect, the cholesterol makes the membrane less fluid at high temperatures and more fluid at low temperatures.

3. **Proteins** – are very important molecules in the membrane. They help provide **stability** and support as they help to 'anchor' the phospholipid molecules. They also act as **enzymes**. There are many advantages to having enzymes in the membrane – they are kept in the ideal place in terms of substrate availability and pH, and need replaced less often than other enzymes, such as gut enzymes, which can pass through and out of the alimentary canal. Examples of enzymes in the membrane include those in the membrane of the small intestine, which are very important in the digestion of disaccharides. Some membrane proteins act as **adhesion sites** – areas where adjacent cells are held together. Proteins are also involved in **cell recognition** and as **receptors** or **antigens** (see Glycocalyx section below). Proteins are particularly important in **transporting** substances across the bilayer. They aid transport by acting as:

   - **channels** – These proteins span the membrane and work by creating a hydrophilic channel that allows polar molecules to bypass the hydrophobic centre of the bilayer. These channels may be permanently open or have their opening controlled (gated).
   Gated channels are very important in controlling the passage of ions into and out of neurones during nervous conduction.

   - **carriers** – These proteins carry specific ions and molecules across the membrane. This may be because the molecules have charged groups, such as glucose, or because the molecules or ions have to be moved against the concentration gradient. The carrier protein can change shape to carry the substance from one side of the membrane to the other.

4. **Glycocalyx** – The polysaccharides that bind to membrane protein (glycoprotein) or phospholipid (glycolipid) are always found on the outside of the cell-surface membrane and are always peripheral to the protein or phospholipid. Glycoproteins and glycolipids are involved in **cell-to-cell recognition**, important in allowing cells of similar type to recognise each other and group together to form tissues. Consequently, some glycoproteins acts as **antigens**. They can also act as **receptor sites**. Receptor sites provide sites on the cell-surface membrane that particular molecules fit – this can only occur because the receptor sites and the specific molecule or substance concerned are complementary in shape to each other. Receptor sites are very important in hormone action and in the passage of neurotransmitters between neurones. As glycoproteins and glycolipids can form hydrogen bonds with water molecules outside the membrane, they help **stabilise** the membrane.

Viruses

Viruses are very small and unlike cells they are measured in nm not μm, varying in size between 10 nm and 300 nm.

All viruses have a **protein coat** (capsid) that surrounds **nucleic acid**. Depending on the virus concerned, the nucleic acid can be DNA or RNA.

There are several different types of virus. These include:

- **bacteriophages** – Commonly called **phages**, these viruses have a **DNA** core and are parasitic on bacteria. Inside their host cells (bacteria) the viral DNA codes for the production of new protein – for new protein coats. The DNA itself replicates to make copies that are then packaged within the protein coats, forming new viruses. In due course, the bacterial cell is destroyed as it ruptures and many new viruses are released to continue the cycle.

- **the human immunodeficiency virus (HIV)** – HIV and other similar viruses have a **RNA** core. Outside the RNA core they have the typical protein coat, but in addition, have a **lipid bilayer** containing **glycoprotein**. HIV viruses deliver the RNA into the host cell together with the enzyme reverse transcriptase. The **reverse transcriptase** catalyses the synthesis of DNA from RNA. The DNA then makes new viruses by synthesising new protein coats and viral RNA.

These viruses are known as **retroviruses**, as the viral RNA is used as a template to make DNA. This is the reverse of the normal transcription process, where DNA is used to make RNA as part of protein synthesis.

> **Note:** transcription and protein synthesis will be covered in detail in A2.

In humans, HIV invades a type of **lymphocyte** called **helper T-cells**. These T-cells are very important in the immune system when protecting against disease. As progressively more T-cells are destroyed, the immune system becomes critically compromised and the medical condition AIDS can develop.

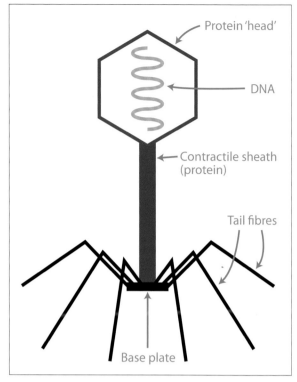

A bacteriophage

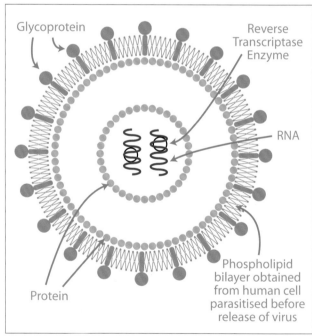

The HIV virus

Viruses are not true cells; they do not have cytoplasm and the organelles associated with it. Crucially, viruses are inert unless they gain access to a living cell. In effect, they do not exhibit the characteristics normally associated with living organisms.

Practical work

In this section you should be able to recognise the main cell structures from photomicrographs, electron micrographs and drawings. You should also be able to calculate the true size (in µm) of cells and cell structures, and also work out the magnification used.

The next section shows annotated electron micrographs of an animal cell and part of a plant cell.

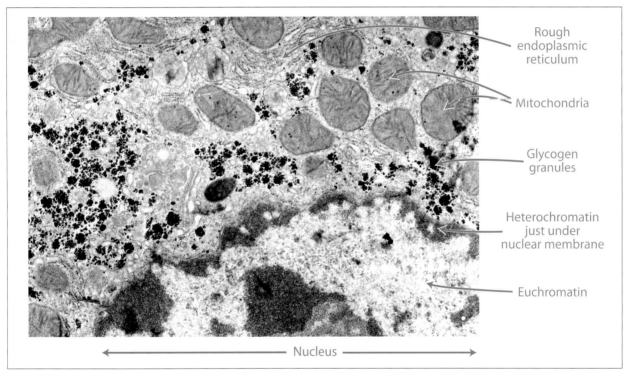

Liver cell

Image courtesy of Dr Gerard Brennan, School of Biological Sciences, Queen's University, Belfast

Liver cell (TEM)

This TEM image of a liver cell shows many of the features of animal cells you need to know. The level of detail of the cell ultrastructure suggests a high magnification is involved and absence of a 3-D appearance suggests that this is a TEM as opposed to a SEM electron micrograph.

As is expected with liver cells, there are numerous glycogen granules and the high density of mitochondria suggests that this cell has a high rate of metabolic activity. Many of the mitochondria are transverse sections (TS) as opposed to longitudinal (LS) sections and are therefore round in appearance as opposed to the more characteristic 'bean' shape.

Chloroplast in a plant cell (TEM)

The chloroplast is embedded in a thin layer of cytoplasm running round the edge of the cell, with the bulk of each cell in the image below appearing to be vacuole, as is typical with many mature plant cells. The cell walls separating the two cells shown are held together by the middle lamella (seen as the slightly more opaque central area).

Chloroplast in a plant cell (TEM)

Dr Jeremy Burgess/ Science Photo Library

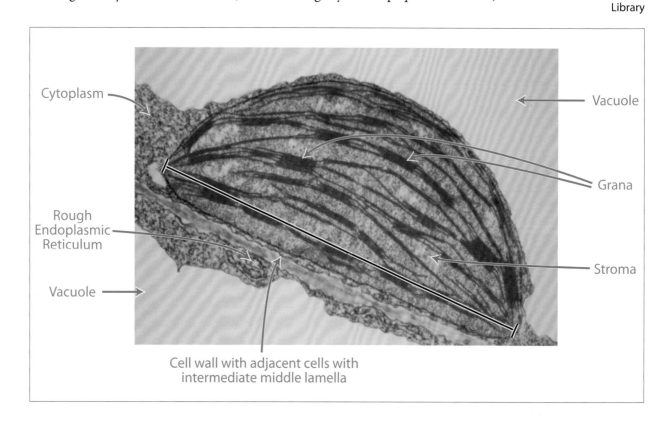

Cytoplasm

Vacuole

Rough Endoplasmic Reticulum

Grana

Vacuole

Stroma

Cell wall with adjacent cells with intermediate middle lamella

Typical calculation

The magnification used is × 20,000. Calculate the actual size of the chloroplast shown in the image in μm.

Size of chloroplast = size of chloroplast in image / magnification

$$= 105 \text{ mm} / 20{,}000$$

$$= 105 \times 10^3 \text{ μm} / 20{,}000$$

$$= 5.25 \text{ μm}$$

You could also be asked to calculate the magnification used. You would then be given the actual size of the chloroplast.

Magnification = size of chloroplast in image / actual size of chloroplast

$$= 105 \text{ mm} / 5.25 \text{ μm}$$

$$= 105{,}000 \text{ μm} / 5.25 \text{ μm}$$

$$= \times 20{,}000$$

Exam Questions

1. A lysosome and other cellular structures are shown in the diagram below. The lysosome may contain over 40 different hydrolytic enzymes.

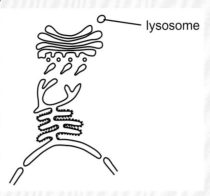

Describe the sequence of events which occur from the initial synthesis of the enzymes until their encapsulation within the lysosome. [3]

Question taken from CCEA's Biology Assessment Unit AS 1, Module 1: Cell Biology, January 2009, © CCEA 2012

2. Fungi are composed of eukaryotic cells, similar to both plant and animal cells. The cellular structure of a fungus is represented in the diagram.

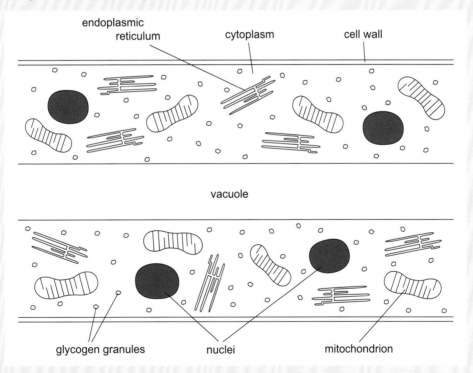

(a) Identify which structures labelled in the diagram above are also found
   - in both plant and animal cells.
   - in plant cells but not in animal cells.
   - in animal cells but not in plant cells. [3]

(b) Identify one feature which is unique to the cells of fungi. [1]

Question taken from CCEA's Biology Assessment Unit AS 1, Module 1: Molecules and Cells, June 2011, © CCEA 2012

3. The cell-surface membrane is mainly composed of phospholipids and proteins.

   (a) The symbol below represents a phospholipid molecule.

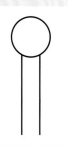

   Using the symbol above, draw a diagram to show how phospholipids are arranged in a cell-surface (plasma) membrane. [2]

   (b) Describe **two** roles for proteins in the cell-surface membrane. [2]

   (c) Name **one** other component of the cell-surface membrane. [1]

   Question taken from CCEA's Biology Assessment Unit AS 1, Module 1: Molecules and Cells, June 2010, © CCEA 2012

4. The diagram below shows a yeast (fungal) cell in the process of producing a daughter cell by budding.

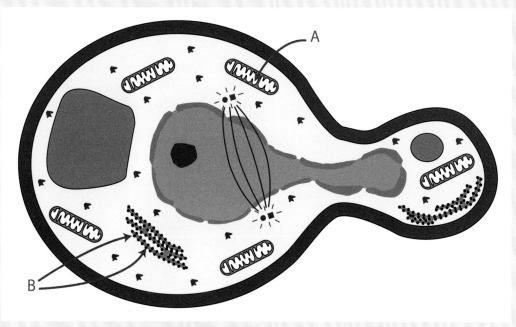

   For copyright reasons this diagram has replaced the diagram from CCEA's Biology AS1, January 2010 paper.

   (a) (i) Identify structures **A** and **B** in this cell. [2]

   (ii) State **two** features, other than **A** and **B**, which show that this cell is eukaryotic. [2]

   Question taken from CCEA's Biology Assessment Unit AS 1, Module 1: Molecules and Cells, January 2010, © CCEA 2012

5. The photograph below is an electromicrograph of parts of two adjacent spongy mesophyll cells found in the leaf of a geranium plant.

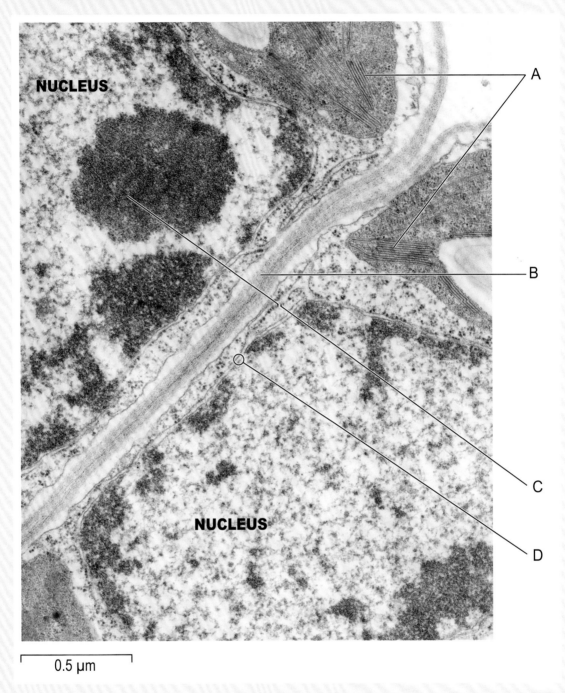

0.5 µm

Dr Jeremy Burgess/Science Photo Library

(a) (i) Identify the structures labelled **A** to **D**. [4]

   (ii) Explain the position of the nuclei in these mesophyll cells. [1]

(b) Use the scale bar to calculate the magnification of this electron micrograph (show your working). [3]

Question taken from CCEA's Biology Assessment Unit AS 1, Module 1: Molecules and Cells January 2011, © CCEA 2012

6. Quality of written communication is awarded a maximum of 2 marks in this section. [2]

   Give an account of the structure of proteins and their roles in the cell-surface membrane. [13]

   Question taken from CCEA's Biology Assessment Unit AS 1, Module 1: Molecules and Cells, June 2011, © CCEA 2012

Chapter 4 – Cell Physiology

1.6.1   Understand the mechanisms by which substances move across membranes.

1.6.2   Account for membrane permeability.

1.6.3   Calculate the water potential of a cell.

1.6.4   Practical work to include calculating the water potential of cells in a plant tissue and determining the average solute potential of cells at incipient plasmolysis.

Movement of substances across the cell-surface membrane

(Simple) Diffusion

Non-polar molecules, such as lipid soluble oxygen and carbon dioxide can pass through the membrane unaided, ie protein molecules are not involved. Very small molecules, such as water, can also pass through due to their very small size. Water soluble substances generally are unable to pass through by simple diffusion due to the hydrophobic nature of the centre of the phospholipid bilayer.

Diffusion can be defined as the net movement of a substance from where it is in a higher concentration to where it is in a lower concentration. Diffusion is not restricted to occurring across membrane surfaces, for example, the spread of smoke in a room is an example of diffusion, but many important examples of diffusion in biological systems involve movement across a membrane surface.

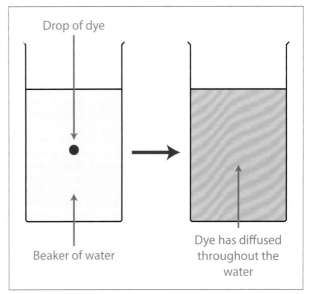

Diffusion

Diffusion across membranes is affected by a number of factors including:

- **the concentration gradient** – The greater the concentration gradient across the membrane, the faster the diffusion.

- **the size** of the molecule – Small molecules diffuse faster than larger molecules.

- **the temperature** – Diffusion normally takes place quicker at higher temperatures, as the higher temperatures give the diffusing molecules more kinetic energy.

- **the thickness** of the exchange surface – Biological membranes are generally very thin therefore ideal for rapid diffusion.

- **the surface area** of the membrane – The greater the surface area, the faster the diffusion. In many cells where diffusion is important, the cell-surface membrane is extended to increase the area across which diffusion can take place, for example, by the presence of microvilli.

Facilitated diffusion

This is the type of diffusion involved when the diffusion process is supported or 'facilitated' by **protein carriers**. These protein carriers have binding sites that match specific molecules and they assist the movement of these molecules across the membrane.

There are two types of protein that are involved in facilitated diffusion:

- **carrier proteins** – They take in the diffusing molecule, such as glucose, change shape and release the molecule on the other side of the membrane (see A).

- **(ion) channel proteins** – These channels are formed by proteins with a central pore that enables charged particles (ions) to pass through. Some of these ion channels are permanently open but others are gated. Gated channels can open or close allowing control of ion movement (see B).

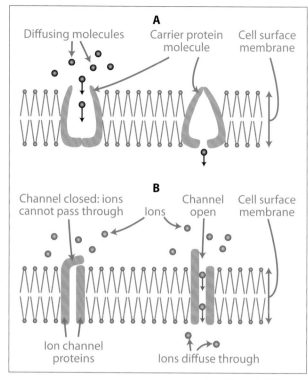

Facilitated diffusion

The rate of facilitated diffusion is dependent on the number of carrier or channel proteins in the membrane.

Note: both diffusion and facilitated diffusion only transport molecules down the concentration gradient and neither involves the expenditure of energy (ie they are passive processes).

Active transport

Active transport

Sometimes molecules need to be moved across the membrane **against the concentration gradient** (ie from low to high concentration). Consequently, **energy** is required. Active transport involves **protein carrier molecules** (sometimes called **pumps**). The substance to be transported binds to the carrier protein. As with carriers in facilitated diffusion, the carrier changes shape and releases the transported substance on the other side of the membrane. Again, as with facilitated diffusion, the carriers are specific to a particular type of molecule or ion.

There are two key differences compared to facilitated diffusion:

1. substances are moved against the concentration gradient.

2. energy is required.

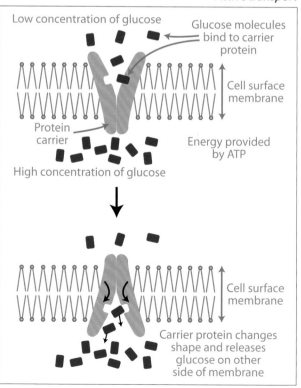

Cells that carry out a lot of active transport usually have a large number of **mitochondria** in their cells. The mitochondria supply the **ATP** (energy) needed for active transport.

Cytosis

Some substances can be transported into or out of the cell without having to pass through the membrane itself. The process of cytosis is important in transporting:

1. large molecules that are too big for the carriers.

2. the bulk transport of smaller molecules (for example, water).

Endocytosis is the movement of substances into the cell and **exocytosis** is the movement of substances out of the cell.

In **endocytosis**, the cell-surface membrane **invaginates** (infolds) around substances entering the cell from the outside to form a membrane-bound sac or **vesicle**, which then pinches off on the inside of the cell-surface membrane. When the vesicles are taken into the cell, the fluid nature of the cell-surface membrane allows it to reform and close the gap created by cytosis.

There are two types of endocytosis: **phagocytosis** and **pinocytosis**.

- **Phagocytosis** involves the transport of **solid** material into the cell. A good example is the engulfing of bacteria by phagocytes.

- **Pinocytosis** ('cell drinking') involves the transport of **fluid** into the cell.

Exocytosis is the movement of substances out of the cell. **Secretory vesicles** (possibly having budded off from the Golgi apparatus) move to and fuse with the cell-surface membrane. The contents of the vesicle are then released outside the cell. As with endocytosis, the creation of the gap in the cell-surface membrane is followed by the reforming of the membrane.

Exocytosis is important in the secretion of many proteins from cells, including digestive enzymes and many hormones.

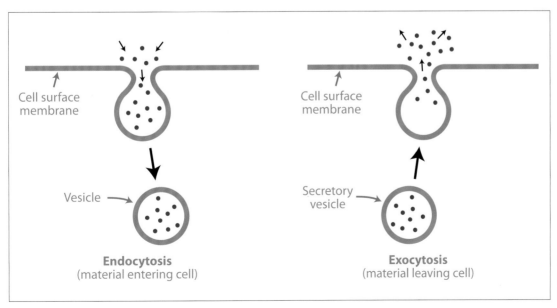

Cell surface membrane

Vesicle →

Endocytosis
(material entering cell)

Cell surface membrane

Secretory → vesicle

Exocytosis
(material leaving cell)

Endocytosis and Exocytosis

Osmosis

Osmosis can be defined as the net movement of water from a high water concentration (dilute solution) to a lower water concentration (more concentrated solution) across a selectively (differentially) permeable membrane.

> **Note 1:** it is described as the **net** (or overall) movement, as individual water molecules can move in either direction across the membrane.

> **Note 2:** Water can move through the selectively or differentially permeable phospholipid membrane in osmosis but much of it moves through special channel proteins called **aquaporins**.

Useful terms to know are hypotonic, hypertonic and isotonic. When comparing two solutions the stronger solution is **hypertonic** to the weaker **hypotonic** solution. If two solutions are of equal concentration (and therefore osmosis is not occurring), the solutions are described as being **isotonic**.

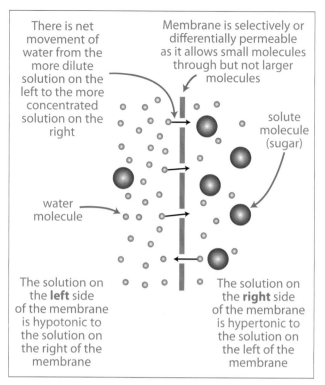

There is net movement of water from the more dilute solution on the left to the more concentrated solution on the right

Membrane is selectively or differentially permeable as it allows small molecules through but not larger molecules

solute molecule (sugar)

water molecule

The solution on the **left** side of the membrane is hypotonic to the solution on the right of the membrane

The solution on the **right** side of the membrane is hypertonic to the solution on the left of the membrane

Osmosis

Water potential

At 'A' level, osmosis must be considered in terms of water potential.

The **water potential** of a solution may be regarded as its **tendency to take in water** by osmosis from pure water across a selectively permeable membrane. Water potential is measured in **kilopascals** (kPa). Pure water has a water potential of zero (0 kPa), ie it is unable to take in any more water by osmosis.

The water potential is an indication of the free energy of the water molecules. The water potential of pure water is 0 kPa because all the water molecules are 'free' – they are not forming associations with other molecules. In solutions, some of the water

The formation of hydration shells in solutions

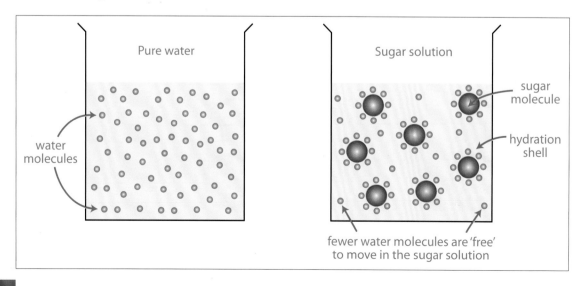

Pure water

Sugar solution

water molecules

sugar molecule

hydration shell

fewer water molecules are 'free' to move in the sugar solution molecules are not 'free', as they form **hydration shells** around the solutes. The presence of solutes also reduces the ability of water molecules to diffuse throughout the solution.

A solution **always** has a negative water potential – it will always have some water in hydration shells. The more concentrated a solution is, the more negative its water potential is, as more water is bound up in hydration shells and not 'free'. It is also increasingly more likely to take in water by osmosis. A solution with a water potential of -600 kPa will take in less water by osmosis from pure water than a solution of -1000 kPa.

A better definition of osmosis, taking account of water potential is:

Osmosis can be defined as the net movement of water through a selectively (differentially) permeable membrane, from a solution of less negative water potential to a solution of more negative water potential.

Note: in osmosis questions candidates often get confused over the terms higher and lower water potential – a water potential of -700 kPa is lower than a water potential of -600 kPa.

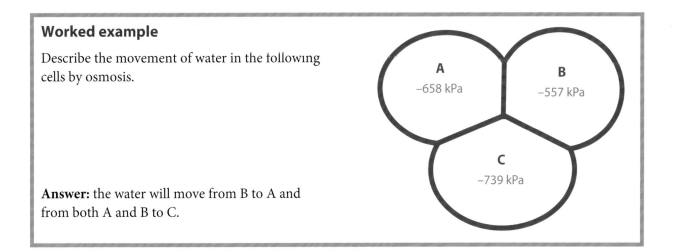

Worked example

Describe the movement of water in the following cells by osmosis.

A −658 kPa

B −557 kPa

C −739 kPa

Answer: the water will move from B to A and from both A and B to C.

There are other terms relating to water potential you need to be familiar with.

Solute potential – This is the **potential** of a solution to take in water. The potential may or may not be the same as the **tendency** to take in water (water potential). The potential relates to the **solute concentration only** but the tendency (water potential) is affected by other factors, such as the space available within a cell. For example, a turgid cell will still have the potential to take in water, as it is still more concentrated than pure water, but because it is turgid it may be unable to take in water, as there is simply no space.

Pressure potential – This is the effect of **pressure** on the solution. A plant cell that is turgid will exert considerable pressure on its cell wall, whereas one that is not will exert much less pressure. This pressure influences the ability of the cell to take in or lose water by osmosis. The pressure potential is usually positive (although it can be 0).

The three terms water potential, solute potential and pressure potential are often written as variations of the Greek letter ψ, (psi). The equation below summarises the relationships between the three components in a cell:

Water potential of the cell (ψ_{cell}) = solute potential (ψ_s) + pressure potential (ψ_p)

Osmosis in plant cells

The following diagram shows the respective changes in water potential, solute potential and pressure potential as a plant cell takes in, or loses water, by osmosis.

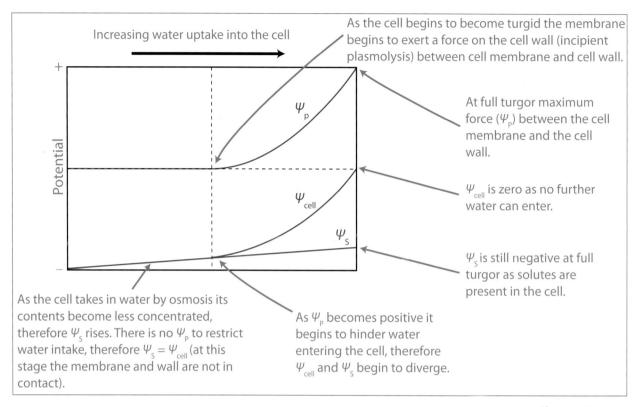

Changes in water potential, solute potential and pressure potential in a plant cell as it takes in (or loses) water by osmosis

Plant cells rely on **turgor** for support. Herbaceous (non-woody) plants are almost totally reliant on turgor pressure. The plant cell wall has a very important role to play, as its strength limits the expansion of the cell membrane as water enters the plant cell by osmosis. The opposing forces of the cell membrane and cell wall on each other help create the turgor support itself.

If plant tissue suffers a shortage of water, the cells will cease to be turgid and the tissue is described as being **flaccid**. If a large number of cells are flaccid, the phenomenon of **wilting** occurs.

If a plant cell loses too much water by osmosis, its vacuole can shrink to the extent that the cell membrane (or protoplast) can pull away from the cell wall (except at points where adjacent protoplasts are joined via plasmodesmata). This is described as **plasmolysis** and the cell is **plasmolysed**.

Note: protoplast is the term used to describe the cytoplasm (including the vacuole) and the surrounding cell membrane.

Note: the above diagram is hypothetical to some extent. If a plant cell is plasmolysed (the left hand side of the diagram) it is unlikely to survive. The right hand side of the diagram more typically reflects the changes that take place in most plant cells as they gain or lose water.

In nature, plasmolysis seldom occurs, which is just as well as plant cells are unlikely to survive if they have become plasmolysed. However, the following examples give situations in which it can occur:

- Plants growing in a field that has been given too much fertiliser.

- A seed from a woodland tree being carried to a salt marsh and starting to germinate in this environment.

The point at which the cell membrane just begins to lose contact with the cell wall is called **incipient plasmolysis**.

Osmosis in animal cells

Animal cells do not have a cell wall and therefore there is nothing to stop the expansion of the cell membrane until it bursts (lysis). **Lysis** will take place if animal cells, for example, red blood cells, are placed in hypotonic solutions.

If animal cells are placed in a hypertonic solution, the cells lose water by osmosis, shrink and shrivel up (**crennation**).

In healthy animals, the blood and tissue fluid is kept at the correct water potential to ensure that neither lysis nor crennation take place.

Practical work

It is important to be familiar with the practical activities associated with osmosis.

There are two main types of investigations involved at AS level.

1. Measuring the average water potential of cells in a plant tissue

Sections of plant tissue are placed in a range of concentrations of a solution. Some of the sections of plant tissue will gain water and some will lose water by osmosis. When the solute potential of the external solution is equal to the water potential of the plant tissue there will be no change in mass of the plant tissue.

Normally, the data is presented graphically and the critical value can be identified from the graph.

The following example is a typical procedure used:

- Add water and a series of sucrose solutions of different concentrations, each to separate beakers.

- Use a cork borer to cut sections of potato tuber. Use the same cork borer to ensure the thickness of each potato cylinder is equal. The potato cylinders should be cut to the same length as far as possible.

- The potato cylinders should be surface dried and weighed.

- A potato cylinder (or a set number if cut into small slices) should be added to each of the solutions.

- After a set period of time (for example, 24 hours) the potato cylinders are surface dried and reweighed.

- The percentage change in mass should be calculated for the cylinder(s) in each solution.

- The percentage change in mass is plotted against the concentration of the sucrose solution (or the solute potential of the sucrose solution, which can be worked out from a conversion table).

- Where the line of best fit crosses the x-axis, the solute potential of the immersing solution is equivalent to the water potential of the potato tissue (ie ψ cell = ψ external). At this point there is no net osmosis taking place between the potato tissue and the sucrose solution.

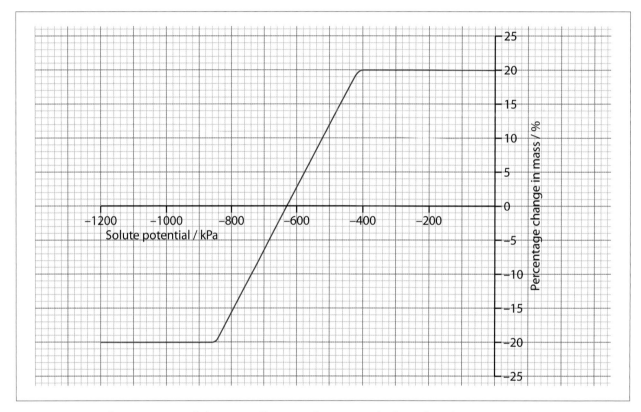

Percentage change in mass of plant tissue (for example, potato cylinders) plotted against the solute potential of the immersing sucrose solution for the determination of the water potential of the plant tissue

The line of best fit is sigmoidal (S shaped). This is due to the fact that at high (or less negative) solute potentials of the immersing sucrose solution (right side of graph) the cells will all be fully turgid, therefore there will be little or no difference in the percentage gain in mass between the different samples. Similarly, at low (or more negative) solute potentials (left side of graph) the cells become fully dehydrated due to loss of water by osmosis into the immersing solution. The tissue cannot lose any more water if in more concentrated immersing solutions, therefore the curve levels off.

Some experimental graphs will be less sigmoidal and the line of best fit may be (much closer to) a straight line. The actual shape of the line of best fit drawn will depend on a number of factors including:

- the **range** of immersing solution values used. In the graph *(left)* the line of best fit would be a straight line if the solute potential of the immersing solution only ranged from –400 kPa to –850 kPa.

- the **number** of immersing solution concentrations used.

Different tissues will have different water potential values. This depends on a number of factors including the main carbohydrate storage compound used in the cells – the water potential of carrot cells is very different to potato cells, as carrots store sugar instead of starch. Other factors are important too in contributing to different water potential values in the same type of tissue – these include factors such as the age of the tissue.

2. Measuring the average solute potential of cells at incipient plasmolysis

Incipient plasmolysis is the point where the cell membrane is just beginning to pull away from the cell wall in plant cells. At this point the pressure potential (ψ_p) is zero, ie the membrane is not exerting pressure on the wall. Therefore, using the following equation, the cell water potential is the same as the solute potential:

$$\text{water potential} = \text{solute potential} + \text{pressure potential}$$

However, incipient plasmolysis in plant cells is very hard to judge. How can you tell whether the membrane is just pulling away or not? The compromise is that the point of incipient plasmolysis is taken to be the point where 50% of the cells are clearly plasmolysed (and 50% are not).

The following example is a typical procedure used:

- Add sections of onion epidermal tissue to pure water. This ensures that all the cells are turgid at the start of the experiment.

- Place sections of onion epidermal tissue in beakers, each beaker containing either water or one of a range of sucrose solutions.

- Leave the onion epidermal tissue in the solutions for a set period of time, for example, 30 minutes.

- Remove the onion epidermal sections and mount on microscope slides, with each onion epidermal section immersed in the same concentration of sucrose solution that it was immersed in.

- Use a microscope to observe a number of cells. A tally should be made of the number of cells plasmolysed and also the number turgid (not plasmolysed).

- A graph should be drawn of the percentage plasmolysis against solute potential of the immersing solution. Use the graph to identify the point at which 50% of cells are plasmolysed. At this point the solute potential of the immersing solution is the same as the average solute potential of the onion cells.

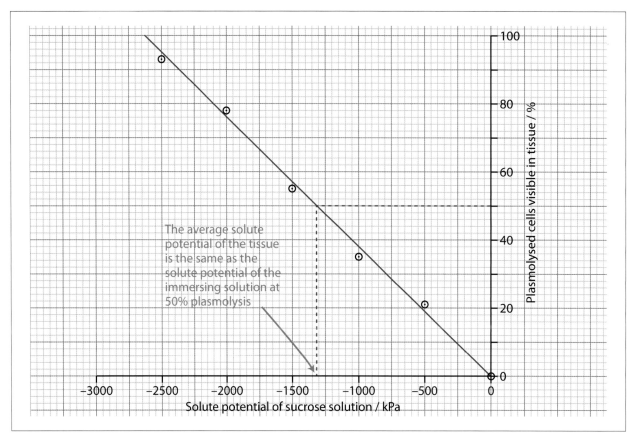

The average solute potential of the tissue is the same as the solute potential of the immersing solution at 50% plasmolysis

Percentage plasmolysis in plant tissue (for example, onion epidermis) plotted against the solute potential of the immersing sucrose solution for the determination of average solute potential of the plant tissue

Note: the above diagram may be slightly diagrammatic. In reality the graph will probably be sigmoidal, as plasmolysis will not occur in very dilute solutions and 100% plasmolysis may occur over a number of the more concentrated solutions.

The same principles apply in this experiment as to whether the best fit line will be sigmoidal or a straight line, as applied in the previous experiment. Similarly, the solute potential giving 50% plasmolysis in the cells in different tissues and even within the one type of tissue can vary for reasons similar to those discussed on the previous page.

Exam Questions

1. The diagram below represents the fluid mosaic model of membrane structure and three mechanisms (labelled **1**, **2** and **3**) by which substances may move across the membrane. The concentration gradient across the membrane is also shown.

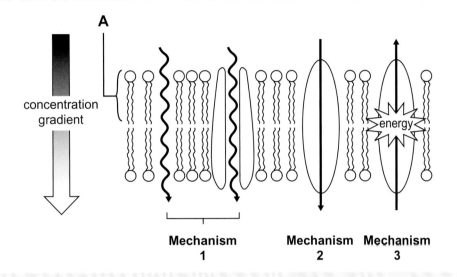

(a) Identify the structure labelled **A**. [1]

(b) Identify each mechanism of membrane transport and, in each case, give a reason for your identification.

   (i) Mechanism 1 [2]

   (ii) Mechanism 2 [2]

   (iii) Mechanism 3 [2]

(c) Mechanism 1 involves two different paths across the membrane. Explain why there are two paths for this mechanism of membrane transport. [2]

   Question taken from CCEA's Biology Assessment Unit AS 1, Module 1: Cell Biology, June 2009, © CCEA 2012

2. (a) The diagram below represents the fluid mosaic model of the cell-surface membrane.

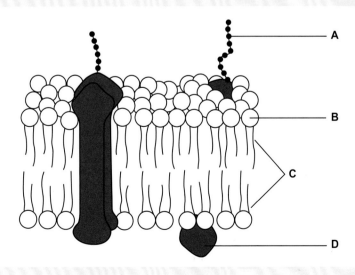

(i) Identify the structures labelled **A** to **D**. [4]

(ii) Make a copy of the diagram. Place an X on the diagram to indicate the outer surface of the membrane. Give a reason for your answer. [1]

(b) The table below shows the effect of changing conditions on three different mechanisms of membrane transport.

Change in conditions	Effect of changing conditions on rate of movement		
	Mechanism 1	Mechanism 2	Mechanism 3
Increased oxygen levels	Rate increases significantly	No effect on rate	No effect on rate
Addition of cyanide (a respiratory poison)	Rate decreases significantly	No effect on rate	No effect on rate
Increased numbers of membrane carriers	Rate increases	Rate increases	No effect on rate

Using the information in the table, identify each mechanism of membrane transport and, in each case, give a reason for your identification.

(i) Mechanism 1 [2]

(ii) Mechanism 2 [2]

(iii) Mechanism 3 [2]

Question taken from CCEA's Biology Assessment Unit AS1, Molecules and Cells, January 2011, © CCEA 2012

3. The diagram below represents a plant cell immersed in a bathing solution with a solute potential of -1200 kPa ($\psi_{external}$). The solute potential (ψ_s) and pressure potential (ψ_p) of the cell are also shown.

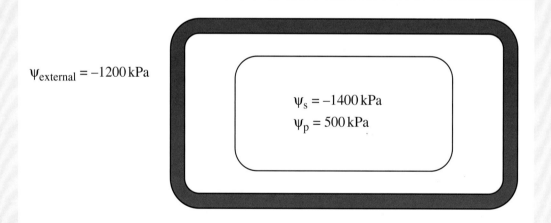

$$\psi_{external} = -1200 \, \text{kPa}$$

$$\psi_s = -1400 \, \text{kPa}$$
$$\psi_p = 500 \, \text{kPa}$$

(a) Calculate the water potential (ψ_{cell}) of the cell. [1]

(b) Describe and explain the movement of water between the cell and its bathing solution. [2]

(c) Draw a diagram of the cell to show its final appearance in the bathing solution. [2]

Question taken from CCEA's Biology Assessment Unit AS1, Molecules and Cells, January 2011, © CCEA 2012

4. The diagram below shows two adjacent plant cells, **A** and **B**. The solute potential (ψ_s) and pressure potential (ψ_p) of both cells are given.

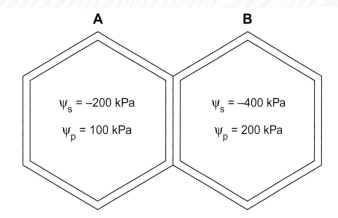

A   B

$\psi_s = -200$ kPa $\psi_s = -400$ kPa

$\psi_p = 100$ kPa $\psi_p = 200$ kPa

(a) Write an equation which summarises the relationship between solute potential (ψs), pressure potential (ψ_p) and water potential (ψ_{cell}) of a plant cell. [1]

(b) Water movement will take place between the two cells. In which direction will this movement take place? Explain your answer. [3]

(c) The pressure potential of cell **B** is higher than the pressure potential of cell **A**. Suggest **one** reason for the difference in the pressure potentials of the two cells. [1]

Question taken from CCEA's Biology Assessment Unit AS1, Molecules and Cells, January 2010, © CCEA 2012

5. In an experiment to determine the solute potential (ψ_s) of leaf tissues by means of the incipient plasmolysis method, tissues from two plants were immersed in a series of sucrose solutions of different concentrations. Samples of the tissue were observed under a microscope, the total number of cells counted and the number of plasmolysed cells recorded for each sample.

The two leaf tissues were onion bulb leaves and leaves from the pondweed, *Elodea*. The onion leaf cells are modified for storage of sugars. The *Elodea* is a common freshwater aquatic plant, found in many ponds and lakes.

It was predicted that the onion cells would have a lower solute potential than the *Elodea* cells.

(a) (i) Unstained onion cells can be difficult to see under a microscope unless the light is reduced. Describe **one** method of reducing the light passing through the onion tissue. [1]

(ii) Describe how you would recognise a plasmolysed onion cell under a microscope. [1]

(b) Plasmolysed *Elodea* cells were identified by a clumping of chloroplasts in the centre of the cell. Explain why the chloroplasts clumped in the centre of a plasmolysed cell. [1]

(c) (i) Use the graph overleaf to determine the solute potentials of the onion and *Elodea* cells.

Onion cells _____ kPa

Elodea cells _____ kPa [2]

(ii) Explain the basis of the method used to determine the solute potential of the tissues. [2]

(iii) Suggest **one** reason for the difference in the solute potentials determined in (**i**) above. [2]

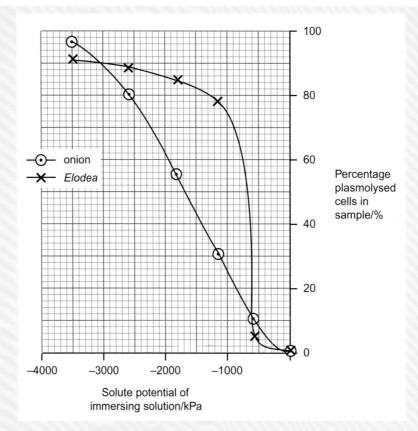

(d) Explain why the pondweed, *Elodea*, cannot survive in seawater which has a high concentration of salts. [1]

Question taken from CCEA's Biology Assessment Unit AS1, Molecules and Cells, June 2010, © CCEA 2012

6. Cylinders of potato tissue were immersed in sucrose solutions, differing in their solute potential, for 24 hours and the percentage change in length determined. The results are shown in the graph below.

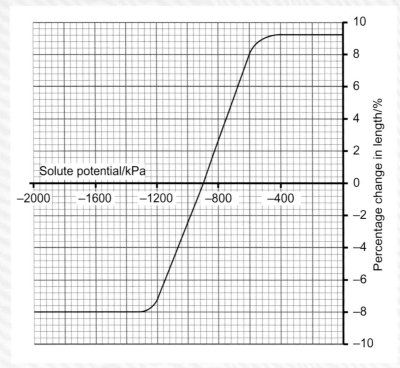

(a) With reference to water potential, explain the change in length that occurred when the cylinder of potato tissue was immersed in a sucrose solution of solute potential -600 kPa. [2]

(b) Using the information in the graph, determine the water potential of the potato tissue. Explain your reasoning. [2]

(c) The initial length of the potato cylinder immersed in a solution of water potential -1600 kPa was 50 mm. Calculate its final length. (Show your working out.) [2]

(d) Draw a potato cell as it might appear when immersed (for 24 hours) in a sucrose solution of solute potential -1200 kPa. [1]

Question taken from CCEA's Biology Assessment Unit AS1, Module 1: Cell Biology, January 2009, © CCEA 2012

7. (a) The water potential of a cell (ψ_{cell}) has two components, the solute potential (ψ_s) and the pressure potential (ψ_p).

   (i) Explain why the solute potential of a cell's contents is always less than zero. [1]

   (ii) State the term which is used to describe a plant cell when its pressure potential (ψ_p) is zero. [1]

(b) The solute and pressure potentials of carrot tissue were determined after immersion in five external solutions (differing in their solute potential). These are shown in the graph below.

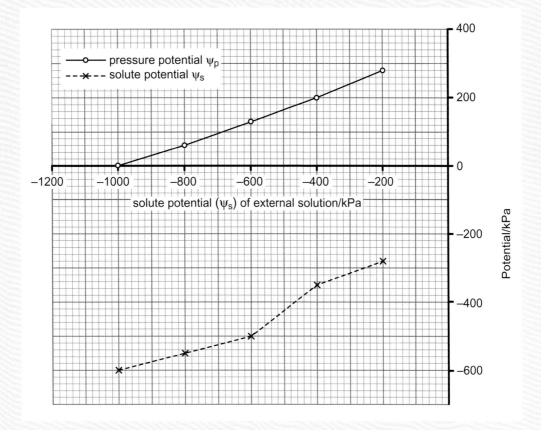

   (i) The water potential of the carrot tissue was calculated using the values for solute and pressure potentials shown in the graph above. Three of the values are shown in the table on the following page. Make a copy of the table and complete it by calculating the two missing values. [2]

Solute potential of the external solution /kPa	Water potential of the carrot tissue /kPa
-200	0
-400	-150
-600	-370
-800	
-1000	

(ii) Make a copy of the graph on page 71. Plot the water potential values, including those you have calculated, on this graph and draw an appropriate line of best fit. [2]

Full turgor occurs when no more water can enter the tissue.

(iii) Using the graph, determine the solute potential of the external solution at the point of full turgor. [1]

(c) A weighing method can be used to determine the average water potential (ψ_{cell}) of plant tissues, such as potato.

(i) Briefly describe the procedure for the weighing method. [3]

(ii) Explain how you would analyse the results to obtain an estimate of the water potential of potato cells. [2]

(iii) Explain the biological basis of the weighing method as a means of determining the average water potential of the cells in a plant tissue. [2]

Question taken from CCEA's Biology Assessment Unit AS1, Molecules and Cells, June 2011, © CCEA 2012

8. Give an account of the process of osmosis and its effect in animal and plant cells. [15]

Question taken from CCEA's Biology Assessment Unit AS 1, Module 1: Cell Biology, June 2009, © CCEA 2012

Chapter 5 – Nucleic Acids and DNA Technology

1.1.6	Recognise the occurrence, structure and function of nucleic acids.
1.1.7	Understand the replication of DNA.
1.3.1	Explain the polymerase chain reaction (PCR).
1.3.2	Understand the use of DNA probes to locate a specific section of DNA.
1.3.3	Understand that differences in nucleotide sequences can be identified.
1.3.4	Explain genetic fingerprinting and show an appreciation of its potential uses.

The structure and function of nucleic acids

The sub-unit of nucleic acids is the **nucleotide**. Each nucleotide consists of three components:

- a **pentose** (5 carbon) **sugar**.
- a **phosphate** group.
- a nitrogenous **base**.

The three components are combined as a consequence of **condensation reactions** to form the nucleotide. A **phosphodiester bond** forms between the sugar molecule and the phosphate of the next nucleotide. Adjacent nucleotides can be combined (again by condensation reactions) to create the nucleic acid. The nucleic acid is a chain of nucleotides (**polynucleotide**) which has a free 5′ end (with 'free' phosphate) and a free 3′ end (with 'free' sugar).

Nucleic acids can also be broken down (as in digestion) through hydrolysis reactions to nucleotides.

DNA and RNA

There are two types of nucleic acid; **deoxyribonucleic acid (DNA)** and **ribonucleic acid (RNA)**.

DNA – A molecule of DNA consists of two **anti-parallel** strands with the two strands being held together by hydrogen bonds between adjacent bases. Anti-parallel means the two strands are running in opposite directions (note the orientation of the sugar molecules in each strand in the diagram on page 74).

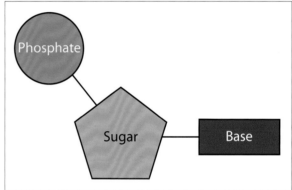

A nucleotide

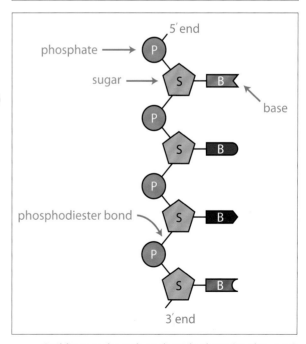

Building up the polynucleotide chain (nucleic acid)

The nature of base pairing always ensures that:

- **adenine** only pairs with **thymine** (by two hydrogen bonds).
- **guanine** only pairs with **cytosine** (by three hydrogen bonds).

The DNA molecule is organised as a **double helix**. The backbone of the DNA (**phosphate** and **deoxyribose sugar**) are wound round each other like a twisted ladder, linked and held together by the **bases**, following **base pairing** rules as noted above. The organisation of the DNA is very regular, with there being ten base pairs for each complete turn of the helix.

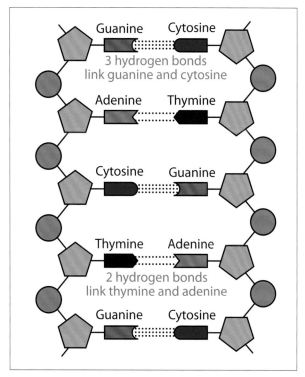

A section of DNA

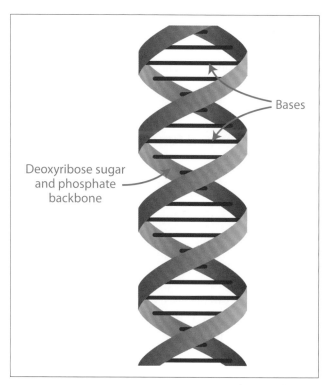

The Double Helix

RNA – As its name suggests, RNA has the sugar **ribose** (not the deoxyribose as associated with DNA). RNA molecules are **single stranded** and invariably much **shorter** than DNA. In RNA the base **uracil** replaces thymine: therefore the RNA bases are A, U, C and G.

There are three types of RNA:

- **messenger RNA (mRNA)**
- **transfer RNA (tRNA)**
- **ribosomal RNA (rRNA)**

Functions of DNA and RNA

DNA is the **genetic code** of living organisms and, with very few exceptions, is found in all cells. It regulates the development of living organisms through the control of **protein synthesis**, in particular, the regulation of enzymes, the key catalysts in metabolism. Specifically, the sequence of DNA bases determines the **amino acid**

sequence (primary structure) of **polypeptides**. A **gene** can be described as a sequence of DNA that codes for a polypeptide.

One of the DNA strands is the **coding (template)** strand, which functions as the genetic code. In effect, the code is read as the sequence along the length of the coding strand of the DNA, for example, AAGTCCCTTA. Each sequence of three bases, such as AAG, is a **base triplet** and codes for one amino acid.

The different types of **RNA** also have crucial roles in protein synthesis:

- **Messenger RNA** – carries the code from the DNA in the nucleus (the DNA remains protected in the nucleus) to a ribosome in the cytoplasm where protein synthesis takes place.

- **Transfer RNA** – carries the amino acids to the mRNA/ribosome where the protein synthesis takes place. It is a single chain folded into a 'clover leaf' shape. There are as many different types of tRNA as there are amino acids. Their structure is similar except for the part that links with the appropriate amino acid and the part that links with the mRNA.

- **Ribosomal RNA** – is made in the nucleolus and forms over half the mass of each ribosome.

DNA replication

DNA is a stable molecule, which can be replicated and pass unchanged from parent to daughter cells as an organism grows. It also can pass unchanged through the generations from parent to offspring. **DNA replication** is the process that replicates the DNA molecule. It is important to appreciate that the DNA replication takes place **before** the chromosomes duplicate during the processes of mitosis and meiosis.

The enzyme **DNA helicase** 'unzips' the two strands of the DNA by breaking the hydrogen bonds between the bases. This allows **each** of the **original strands** to become a **template** for the formation of two DNA molecules. **Free nucleotides** are linked to the template strands in the correct sequence as a consequence of bases on the 'free' nucleotides following **base pairing** rules with the bases on the template strands. The 'new' strand is joined together by the enzyme **DNA polymerase**.

DNA Replication

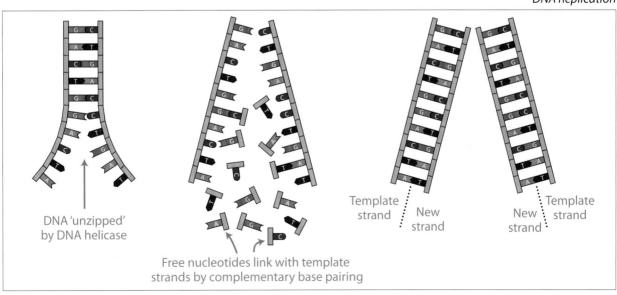

DNA 'unzipped' by DNA helicase

Free nucleotides link with template strands by complementary base pairing

Template strand   New strand

New strand   Template strand

Each of the new DNA molecules contains one original (template) strand and one new DNA strand. This is why the process of DNA replication described above is called **semi-conservative replication**.

The Meselson and Stahl (1958) experiment

It was only in the middle of the last century that Watson and Crick worked out the structure of DNA. It very quickly became apparent that for DNA to function as the molecule of heredity, it had to replicate. There were two obvious alternative methods of replication:

- **the conservative model** – This model proposed that the parental DNA remained intact but copied the new DNA molecule (analogous to a photocopier).
- **the semi-conservative model** – As described at the start of this section.

One of the most famous experiments in the history of biology was carried out by Meselson and Stahl, who proved that the **semi-conservative model** is the process involved.

Meselson and Stahl cultured the bacterium *Escherichia coli* using the 'heavy' isotope of nitrogen, ^{15}N. The ^{15}N nitrogen was incorporated into the bases of the DNA in all the bacteria over time, as older bacteria (containing the normal ^{14}N) died and were replaced.

The bacteria were then transferred to a medium containing the lighter (normal) ^{14}N. Following the transfer the bacterial DNA was extracted and analysed at intervals. Key stages were:

- **bacteria growing in ^{14}N** (before transfer to the ^{15}N).
- **bacteria growing in ^{15}N** (many generations after transfer from ^{14}N).
- **one generation after transfer to ^{14}N.**
- **two generations after transfer to ^{14}N.**

Density-gradient centrifugation was used to separate the bacterial DNA following sampling at the stages listed above. DNA containing the 'lighter' ^{14}N accumulated in a zone near the top of the centrifuge tube, whereas DNA consisting of 'heavy' ^{15}N formed a zone near the bottom of the centrifuge tube.

Meselson and Stahl's results

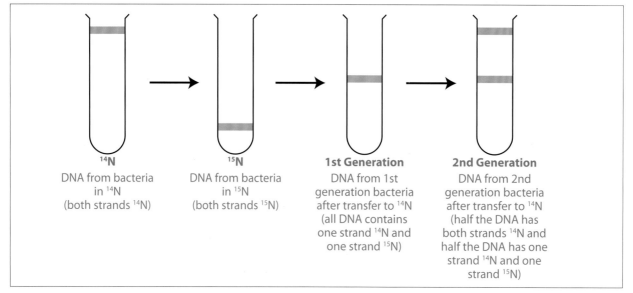

^{14}N	^{15}N	1st Generation	2nd Generation
DNA from bacteria in ^{14}N (both strands ^{14}N)	DNA from bacteria in ^{15}N (both strands ^{15}N)	DNA from 1st generation bacteria after transfer to ^{14}N (all DNA contains one strand ^{14}N and one strand ^{15}N)	DNA from 2nd generation bacteria after transfer to ^{14}N (half the DNA has both strands ^{14}N and half the DNA has one strand ^{14}N and one strand ^{15}N)

Explanation of Meselson and Stahl's results:

- **after one generation** – The intermediate position of the DNA can be explained by **all** the DNA consisting of **one strand** that has bases containing ^{15}N and **one strand** having bases containing ^{14}N.

- **after two generations** – About half the DNA consisted of 'mixed' DNA of both ^{14}N and ^{15}N but the other half was DNA that only contained ^{14}N.

These results can only be explained by the **semi-conservative model**. After one generation the new generation of bacteria had DNA that contained one parental strand and one new strand formed using ^{14}N from the medium in which the parental bacteria had been transferred. In the second generation each strand from the 'mixed' DNA of first generation bacteria acted as a template to produce bacteria, half of which contained 'mixed' DNA and the other half only DNA with ^{14}N.

> **Note 1:** In the third (and subsequent) generations the same pattern would be evident as with the second generation. However, there would be proportionally fewer bacteria containing the 'mixed' DNA and much more containing only the 'lighter' DNA. Consequently, the lighter band (zone) in the centrifuge tube would get denser as the mixed band would get lighter.

> **Note 2:** When we say one strand has ^{14}N and one strand has ^{15}N it is important to remember that it is the nitrogenous bases in the strands that has the ^{14}N or the ^{15}N.

DNA Technology

DNA technology is one of the fastest growing areas of biology and includes the areas of genetic engineering, GM crops, gene therapy, genetic (DNA) fingerprinting, genetic screening and personalised medicine. Many of these topics will be covered in A2 but AS focuses on some of the key **techniques** involved:

- **amplifying DNA** (making large quantities available for analysis) – the **polymerase chain reaction**.

- **comparing DNA** – the identification and use of specific **marker sites** using special enzymes (**restriction endonucleases**) and **DNA probes**.

The Polymerase Chain Reaction (PCR)

Often in forensic science (genetic fingerprinting) or in medical research (researching a disease-causing allele) it is necessary to make many copies of the DNA that is available. The PCR can produce many copies of the selected section of DNA in a very short time.

The PCR technique is a modified version of the process of DNA replication that takes place in cells naturally.

1. The DNA section to be amplified is **heated to around 95°C**. This breaks the hydrogen bonds holding the two strands together.

2. The DNA is **cooled to 40–60°C**. This is necessary to allow **primers** to bind (anneal) to each strand at specific points – they could not form bonds if it remained at 95°C. The primers are short chains, approximately 20 nucleotides long, which are

complementary to the bases in the part of the DNA strand selected. The primers have a number of functions:

- they stop the two DNA strands rejoining.
- they 'bracket' the section of DNA to be copied.
- DNA replication can only start within a double stranded region.

In addition to primers being added, **free nucleotides** and **DNA polymerase** must be introduced to complete the rest of the copying process.

3. The mixture is **heated again**, this time to around **70°C**. DNA polymerase copies each strand, starting at the primers. At temperatures of around 70°C normal DNA polymerase would be denatured. The DNA polymerase used must be **thermostable**. Thermostable DNA polymerase has been isolated from the *Thermus aquaticus* bacterium found in hot springs. This *Taq* polymerase allows the process to occur rapidly at the higher temperatures involved. Other thermostable DNA polymerase enzymes have been isolated and a trade off appears to exist between speed of replication and the ability to proofread and correct mistakes in the DNA being copied. The particular DNA polymerase used in a given situation will depend on whether the emphasis is on accuracy or speed of replication.

4. The two DNA molecules formed following the PCR process can be used as templates as the process is repeated. Millions of copies of the original DNA can be produced in a very short time.

The Polymerase Chain Reaction

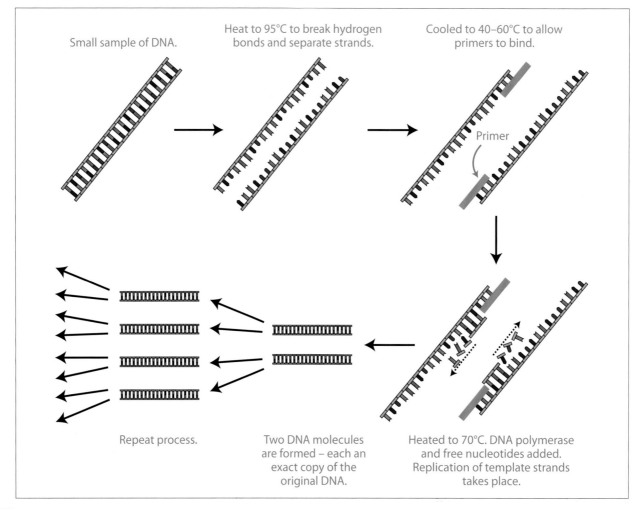

Small sample of DNA.

Heat to 95°C to break hydrogen bonds and separate strands.

Cooled to 40–60°C to allow primers to bind.

Primer

Repeat process.

Two DNA molecules are formed – each an exact copy of the original DNA.

Heated to 70°C. DNA polymerase and free nucleotides added. Replication of template strands takes place.

Role of PCR

Often a crime scene may contain as little as a speck of blood or a fragment of a hair from a suspect. PCR allows the DNA to be amplified to produce sufficient quantities for forensic analysis. PCR is also widely used in medical and scientific research. For example, investigating the DNA of extinct organisms to elucidate relationships with living species, genetic screening and research involving many genetic diseases all rely heavily on the PCR process. The Human Genome Project was also very dependent on PCR producing the quantities of DNA necessary.

In all these examples a key requirement is avoiding contamination of the DNA – contaminated DNA will copy every bit as well as the original uncontaminated DNA sample! DNA evidence in many famous legal cases involving genetic fingerprinting has been disallowed because of possible contamination.

Genetic markers

Much of the latest DNA technology involves sections of DNA acting as **markers**. An obvious example is a section of DNA that is associated with particular genetic diseases. The identification of a particular DNA sequence will indicate that someone has that particular disease – this is the basis of genetic screening. However, there are a number of techniques used to compare DNA sequences among different people and identify specific sequences. These include:

The action of the restriction enzyme EcoRI

restriction endonuclease enzymes – are enzymes that cut DNA at specific nucleotide sequences. They were originally obtained from bacteria, which used them to dismantle the DNA of attacking bacteriophages.

*Eco*RI – is a well known restriction enzyme that recognises the sequence GAATTC and cuts each strand of the DNA between the G and the A. As the G and A do not lie opposite each other (due to base pairing rules) on the DNA, the DNA is cut in a way to produce **sticky ends**.

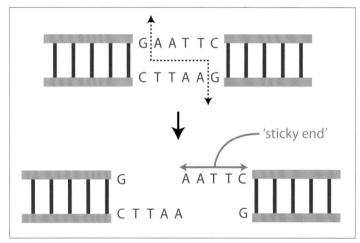

Other restriction enzymes, and there are hundreds, may or may not produce sticky ends depending on the sequences they recognise and cut.

Restriction enzymes can be used to compare DNA of different individuals or even between different species. The restriction enzyme will cut the DNA into a **number** of fragments depending on the number of recognition sites in the sample. The **size** of the fragments will depend on how far apart the recognition sites are.

Restriction Enzyme	Recognition Sequence	Sticky Ends
*Bam*I	G↑GATCC / CCTAG↓G	Yes
*Hae*III	G↑GCC / CC↓GG	No

Other examples of restriction enzymes

If a section of DNA has four recognition sites for a particular restriction enzyme, then five fragment lengths are produced.

If two samples of DNA are identical, treatment with a **particular** restriction enzyme will produce the same number of DNA fragments, each of similar size.

However, different individuals (with different DNA sequences) will produce different patterns when equivalent sections of DNA are treated with a particular restriction enzyme. The different fragment sequences produced from different samples of DNA, when equivalent sequences are treated with the same restriction enzyme, are referred to as **restriction fragment length polymorphisms (RFLPs)**.

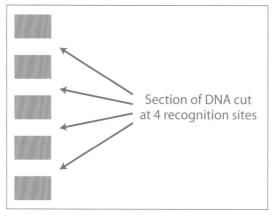

Section of DNA cut at 4 recognition sites

Section of DNA cut at four recognition sites

Microsatellite repeat sequences (MRSs) – Only around two percent of our DNA actually codes for protein; another three percent has a regulatory role. The remaining 95% has no function or an, as yet, unknown role. The non-coding or 'junk' DNA has many sections where a small number of bases (for example, 2–3) are repeated many times (for example, ATCATCATCATCATCATCATCATC etc). The number of repeats of these microsatellite repeat sequences (also called **short tandem repeats – STR**) are unique in each individual. The uniqueness of MRSs in each individual forms the basis of DNA (genetic) fingerprinting.

Single nucleotide polymorphisms (SNPs) – Although humans are 99.9% similar at the DNA level there are small changes between different individuals. The variation can be as little as one nucleotide in a section of DNA (a SNP). SNPs can give rise to the existence of different alleles (an alternative form of a gene) for the same gene. Some alleles, such as the allele for cystic fibrosis, vary from the normal allele by more than one nucleotide. In this example there is usually a difference of three nucleotides but often the difference is only one nucleotide, such as with the allele for sickle cell anaemia.

Note: only some genes have different alleles. Most genes come in one form only; therefore the gene will be exactly the same in all individuals across the human population. Nonetheless, there are about 10 million human SNPs.

DNA (Gene) Probes

DNA probes are used to identify specific gene sequences. In reality, they can identify whole genes or just short sections of DNA. The general principle involves:

- treating the cell so that the DNA strands separate.
- the probe will form base pairs with a complementary sequence of DNA.
- the probe is usually marked with dye, is fluorescent or radioactive in order that its position can be identified.
- detection of the target sequence using X-ray film for radioactive probes or a laser scanner for a fluorescent probe.

DNA probes have many applications. They can be used to identify the presence of some inherited diseases. Many inherited diseases are caused by the presence of single alleles with known base sequences. If a probe complementary to the disease allele binds to an individual's DNA, the disease is present; if binding does not occur, the harmful allele is not present. DNA probes are also used in genetic (DNA) fingerprinting, as explained in the following section.

Genetic (DNA) fingerprinting

The technique of DNA fingerprinting was developed by Alec Jeffreys at the University of Leicester just over 30 years ago. The key features of genetic fingerprinting involve:

- **extracting DNA from a sample** (this could be from a crime scene or from the cells of any living or dead organism). Often PCR is involved to produce enough DNA for analysis.

- **restriction enzymes cut the DNA into different sized fragments** (in the early days of DNA fingerprinting RFLPs were used but this has now been replaced by the use of microsatellite repeat sequences – MRSs – or short tandem repeats, as these can be measured more accurately than RFLPs). Primers are needed to 'flank' the microsatellite region involved to ensure that the fragments only come from the region required.

- the fragments of DNA are separated on the basis of size by **gel electrophoresis**. DNA has a negative charge due to the phosphate ions in the backbone of the helix and the DNA will tend to move towards the positive electrode. In gel electrophoresis an electrical current running through the gel enables the DNA to move and this separates the DNA fragments with smaller fragments travelling further than larger fragments during the process.

DNA fragments being separated by gel electrophoresis

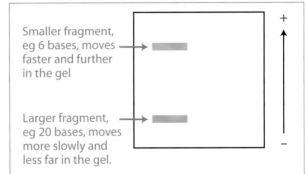

Smaller fragment, eg 6 bases, moves faster and further in the gel

Larger fragment, eg 20 bases, moves more slowly and less far in the gel.

- The DNA is treated (for example, heated) to make it **single stranded**.

- The DNA fragments are transferred to a nylon membrane (Southern blotting). **Radioactive (or fluorescent) DNA probes are added** to the membrane. These attach by base pairing to complementary bases present in the DNA fragments. The probes used will be complementary to the DNA sequences in the microsatellite region selected. DNA that does not form base pairs with the probe will be washed off and not used in the analysis.

- The labelled DNA is added to an X-ray film and appears as a pattern of bars, recognisable as a **DNA fingerprint**.

Note: the thickness/density of the bars is an indication of the **number** of DNA fragments of a particular size. This is **not** linked to fragment size. The **smaller** the fragment size the further it travels in the gel.

Role of genetic fingerprinting in society – Genetic fingerprinting is now commonplace in criminal justice systems but it has many other uses. It is also used to solve paternity and relationship disputes, and is very important in establishing evolutionary relationships between species, including extinct species. Genetic fingerprinting has been used to establish ancient human migratory pathways, tissue typing for transplants and identifying victims from many types of catastrophes (wars, air crashes and terrorist incidents).

The principle of genetic fingerprinting is that everyone has a unique DNA fingerprint (except identical twins) and the closer the relationship between individuals (or species), the closer the match. The uniqueness of the DNA fingerprint is due to the fact that each individual will have a unique number of MRSs (microsatellite repeat sequences) in at least some of their 'junk' DNA. The DNA repeating sequence may not change, for example, ACTAACTAACTAACTAACTA, but the **number** of repeats varies between individuals and the greater number of repeat sequences, the longer the

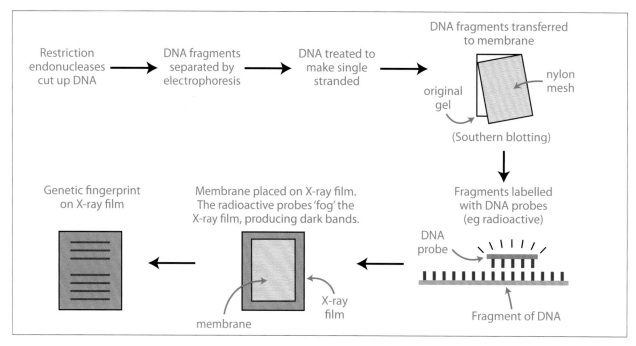

Genetic fingerprinting

piece of DNA. The process is made robust by analysing many microsatellites in different parts of the DNA. For example, the USA CODIS database system uses 13 specific STR sequences.

As with many advances in DNA technology, ethical issues must be considered. DNA fingerprinting is only effective if contamination is avoided. The development of DNA databases in many countries has raised data protection concerns.

Exam questions

1. (a) The diagram below represents the structure of DNA.

   Identify the part of the DNA structure shown in the box X. [1]

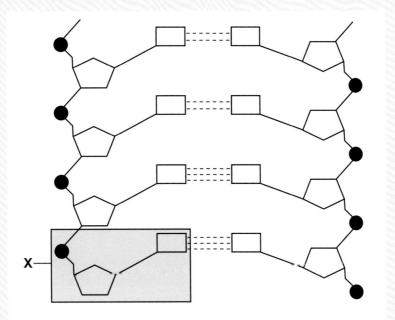

(b) In a classic experiment, Matthew Meselsöhn and Frank Stahl grew bacteria in a medium where the nitrogen source contained the 'light' nitrogen isotope, ^{14}N. The bacteria were then placed in a medium with a nitrogen source containing the 'heavy' nitrogen isotope, ^{15}N, and allowed to reproduce. After many generations, all DNA in the bacteria contained this 'heavy' ^{15}N isotope. This DNA was termed 'heavy' DNA.

DNA extracted from bacterial cells was centrifuged and observed under ultra-violet light. The DNA appeared as a black band in the centrifuge tube. The band produced by 'heavy' DNA was much lower in the centrifuge tube than that produced by 'light' DNA. They are shown in the diagrams below.

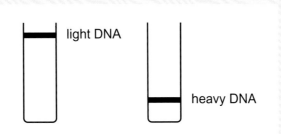

The bacteria containing 'heavy' DNA were then transferred to a medium with a nitrogen source containing the 'light' nitrogen isotope, ^{14}N and allowed to reproduce. After one generation, samples of the bacteria were removed and their DNA was extracted and centrifuged. This process was repeated after a further generation.

(i) Make a copy of the diagrams below and complete them to show the position of the extracted DNA by **drawing appropriate bands**. [2]

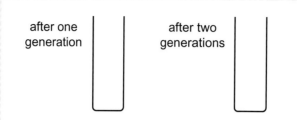

(ii) Explain the result produced after one generation. [2]

Question taken from CCEA's Biology Assessment Unit AS1, Molecules and Cells, June 2011, © CCEA 2012

2. The diagram below represents the processes involved in the polymerase chain reaction (PCR). This technique allows forensic scientists to analyse and potentially match DNA samples left at the scene of a crime.

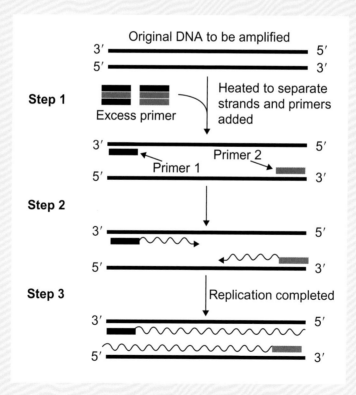

(a) What advantage does PCR offer to forensic scientists? [1]

(b) (i) In **step 1**, what is the purpose of heating the DNA sample to 95°C? [2]

(ii) Primers, each containing roughly twenty bases are also added to the DNA sample in **step 1**. What is the purpose of these primers in the process? [1]

(iii) Name the enzyme that would be added to the DNA sample in **step 2**. [1]

(iv) What else should be added to the process in **step 2** to allow successful replication of the DNA sample? [1]

(c) In **step 3**, replication of the DNA is completed. Describe the sequence of events, following the separation of the DNA strands in **step 1**, which lead to the DNA being replicated. [3]

The heating of the DNA sample to 95°C in **step 1** could denature the enzymes involved.

(d) (i) Describe precisely how high temperatures could denature the enzymes. [1]

(ii) Suggest how scientists have solved this potential problem. [1]

(e) In some legal cases, the use of PCR has been discredited. Suggest **one** possible source of error in the PCR process. [1]

Question taken from CCEA's Biology Assessment Unit AS1, Module 1: Cell Biology, June 2009, © CCEA 2012

3. (a) Nucleic acids are composed of nucleotides. Make a copy of the table below and complete it to give **two** ways in which the structure of a DNA nucleotide differs from that of an RNA nucleotide. [2]

	DNA nucleotide	RNA nucleotide
1.		
2.		

(b) The polymerase chain reaction (PCR) enables many copies of DNA to be made from a small sample. The diagram below summarises the procedure.

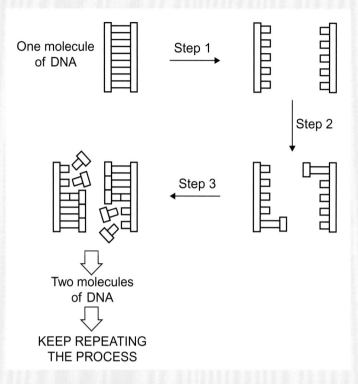

(i) Explain what is happening at each of the steps indicated. [3]

(ii) At the end of the first cycle, there are two molecules of DNA. How many molecules will there be at the end of five cycles? [1]

(c) Explain, precisely, how restriction endonucleases cut DNA molecules into fragments. [2]

(d) A DNA fragment, consisting of 24 base pairs, was analysed for the number of different bases on each strand. The table below shows some of the results. Make a copy of the table and determine the missing values to complete it. [2]

	Number of bases			
	A	G	T	C
Strand 1	7	8		
Strand 2	4			

Question taken from CCEA's Biology Assessment Unit AS1, Module 1: Cell Biology, January 2009, © CCEA 2012

4. The diagram below summarises the polymerase chain reaction (PCR).

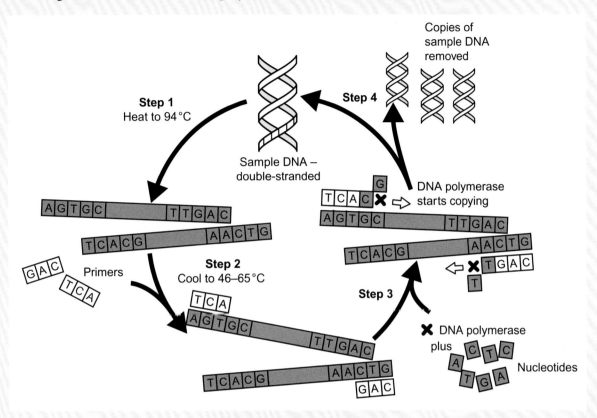

(a) (i) Explain the role of heating the sample DNA to 94 °C in **step 1**. [2]

(ii) State **one** function of the primers added in **step 2**. [1]

(iii) Explain why the DNA sample is cooled during the addition of the primers in **step 2**. [1]

(b) Describe the structure of the nucleotides added in **step 3**. [2]

(c) Restriction endonuclease enzyme cuts DNA into fragments. The restriction endonuclease enzyme *Eco*RI recognises the sequence of bases GAATTC (from the 5′ end to the 3′ end) in a DNA molecule and cuts the DNA between G and A bases.

(i) Make a copy of the diagram below and show the position of the cuts in the sequence of bases. [1]

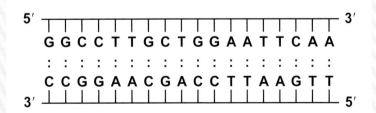

(ii) State the type of end that is produced. [1]

(d) Outline how a DNA probe is used to locate a specific DNA fragment. [3]

Question taken from CCEA's Biology Assessment Unit AS1, Molecules and Cells, June 2010, © CCEA 2012

5. The technique of DNA fingerprinting is based on the uniqueness of each person's genetic make-up. Enzymes are used to cut the DNA at specific points to create different sized fragments, eg *Eco*RI recognises the base sequence GAATTC. These DNA fragments are separated by gel electrophoresis to create a series of bands. Because each person's DNA is different, each person's DNA will produce a different series of bands.

(a) (i) Name the type of enzyme used to cut DNA into fragments. [1]

   (ii) Explain how different sized fragments are produced after this type of enzyme cuts the DNA. [2]

The results of a DNA fingerprint can be used as evidence to link a suspect with a crime. The DNA fingerprints below show the bands obtained from DNA on a hair found at the crime scene along with those obtained from the DNA of three different suspects.

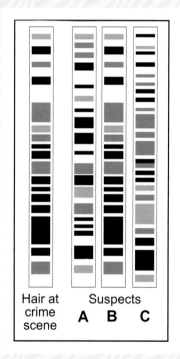

Hair at crime scene   Suspects
A   B   C

(b) Which suspect is most likely to have committed the crime? Explain your choice. [2]

Question taken from CCEA's Biology Assessment Unit AS1, Molecules and Cells, January 2010, © CCEA 2012

6. Quality of written communication is awarded a maximum of 2 marks in this section. [2]

(a) Give an account of the structure of the nucleic acids, DNA and RNA. [8]

(b) Describe the process of DNA replication. [5]

Question taken from CCEA's Biology Assessment Unit AS1, Molecules and Cells, January 2011, © CCEA 2012

Chapter 6 – Continuity of Cells

Students should be able to:

1.7.1   Describe the cell cycle.

1.7.2   Understand chromosome structure.

1.7.3   Describe the process of mitosis.

1.7.4   Understand the chromosome number of a cell and its significance in haploidy and diploidy.

1.7.5   Describe the process of meiosis and understand its significance in producing haploid cells and genetic variation.

1.7.6   Practical work to include preparing and staining root tip squashes, and identifying the stages of mitosis and meiosis from prepared slides and photographs.

Most living organisms grow by increasing cell number. It is relatively straightforward for cells to divide in two (thereby increasing cell number). The complex part is ensuring that the DNA is duplicated and then accurately distributed between the new cells.

The processes of mitosis and meiosis ensure that this takes place.

The cell cycle

Mitosis ensures that the daughter cells produced during cell division have exactly the same chromosome makeup as the parent cell. Mitosis is only part of the sequence of events, called the **cell cycle**, that includes a cell's formation, its growth, mitosis and the cell physically dividing into two (**cytokinesis**).

In reality, **mitosis** is the division of the **chromosomes** and **cytokinesis** is the division of the **cell**.

> **Note:** the diagram shows that mitosis itself may be a relatively short part of the cell cycle (perhaps as little as 10%). However, **interphase** (incorporating the **G1**, **S** and **G2** phases) is also an active phase, with many metabolic processes taking place that prepare the cell for its metabolic role and also for division. The diagram shows the specific events that take place during G1, S and G2.

> **Note:** G stands for **gap** and S stands for **synthesis**.

A summary of the cell cycle

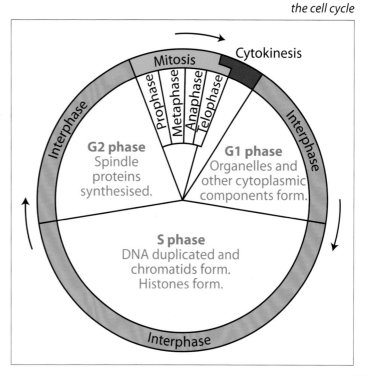

Mitosis
Cytokinesis
Prophase
Metaphase
Anaphase
Telophase
Interphase

G2 phase
Spindle proteins synthesised.

G1 phase
Organelles and other cytoplasmic components form.

S phase
DNA duplicated and chromatids form. Histones form.

Interphase

DNA and the cell cycle

In preparation for mitosis, the DNA content of a cell doubles. This is to provide enough DNA for the new chromosomes that need to be synthesised. The DNA doubles during the **S phase** and only returns to its normal cellular level during cytokinesis.

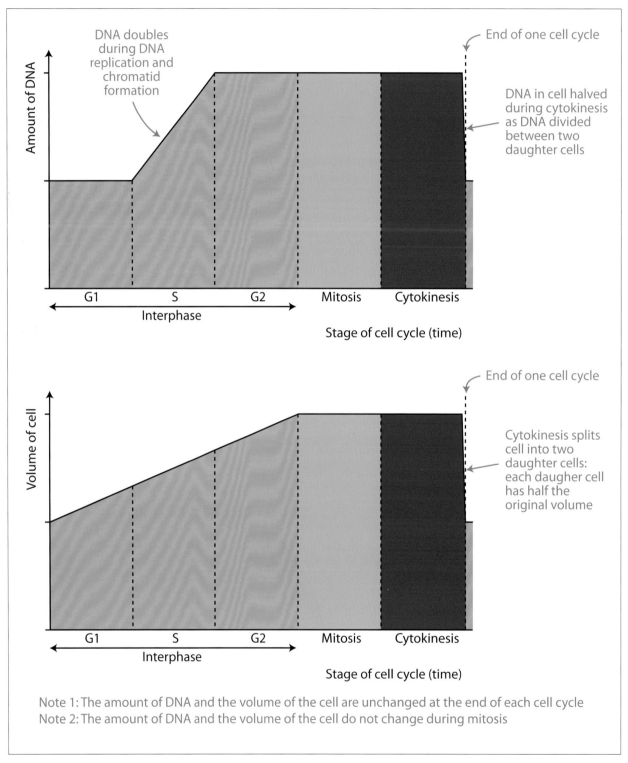

Note 1: The amount of DNA and the volume of the cell are unchanged at the end of each cell cycle
Note 2: The amount of DNA and the volume of the cell do not change during mitosis

The amount of DNA in a cell and the cell volume at different stages of the cell cycle

Revisiting chromosomes

Chromosomes consist of an extended **DNA** molecule supported by special proteins called **histones**. The histones are particularly important in providing support for the DNA when the chromatin condenses to form visible chromosomes during nuclear division.

Humans, and most other complex organisms, are described as being **diploid**. Diploid organisms have their chromosomes arranged in **homologous** pairs within their cells. Homologous chromosomes are very similar to each other; they carry the same genes in the same sequence along their length, as their partner chromosome does. However, they are not identical, as the **alleles** for a small number of the genes may differ in the two chromosomes.

Humans have 46 chromosomes arranged as 23 pairs – a **karyotype** shows the chromosomes, arranged in homologous pairs. It also shows that while the two chromosomes from each pair are similar in size, they differ from other chromosome pairs. This is because each homologous pair carries different genes compared to other pairs. In humans, homologous pairs are numbered according to the length of the chromosomes (with the exception of the sex chromosomes) – ie chromosome pair 1 contains the longest chromosomes.

> **Note:** how each chromosome is divided to form two chromatids held together by a centromere. As the karyotype shows two X chromosomes this is from a female.

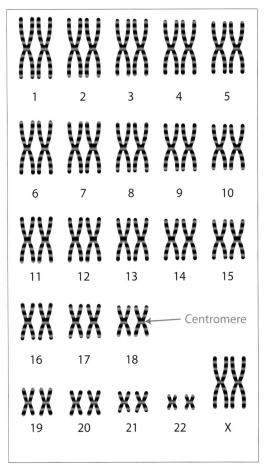

A karyotype showing the chromosomes in a human female

The process of mitosis

Although it is a continuous process, for explanatory purposes mitosis can be subdivided into four stages: prophase, metaphase, anaphase and telophase.

Prophase – at the start of mitosis the chromatin in the nucleus becomes **condensed**. During interphase some of the DNA, the euchromatin, remains unwound to facilitate the process of protein synthesis. When condensed the chromatin has much greater strength, important in preventing damage during mitosis. As the chromosomes continue to condense, they become more visible – this is why you can observe chromosomes only during nuclear division but not at other times. At this stage the **nucleolus disappears**. In animal cells, the **centrioles** move towards opposite ends (poles) of the cell.

Prophase in an animal cell

Centrioles are involved in the formation of the **spindle** (in plant cells spindle formation takes place without the presence of centrioles). By late prophase, each chromosome can be seen to consist of **two chromatids**, joined by a **centromere**.

Metaphase – by this stage the **nuclear membrane** will have broken down and the **spindle** will have formed (in animal cells the centrioles will have completed their migration to opposite poles). The **microtubules** of the spindle will have extended to attach to the **centromeres** of each chromosome. The spindle pulls the chromosomes into position along the equator of the cell.

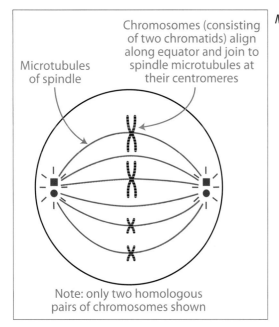

Metaphase

Chromosomes (consisting of two chromatids) align along equator and join to spindle microtubules at their centromeres

Microtubules of spindle

Note: only two homologous pairs of chromosomes shown

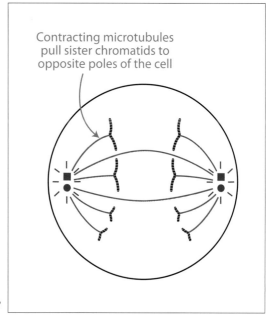

Contracting microtubules pull sister chromatids to opposite poles of the cell

Anaphase

Anaphase – the centromeres attaching the two chromatids of each chromosome split and the contraction of the spindle fibres pulls the chromatids apart. As anaphase progresses the two chromatids of each chromosome are pulled further apart to opposite ends of the cell.

Telophase – sister **chromatids** end up at opposite poles of the cell and are now usually referred to as chromosomes again. Many of the processes that took place at the start of mitosis now happen in reverse – the **chromosomes decondense** and become less visible, the **nucleolus reappears**, the **nuclear membrane reforms** around the two groups of chromosomes and the **spindle disappears** as it is broken down.

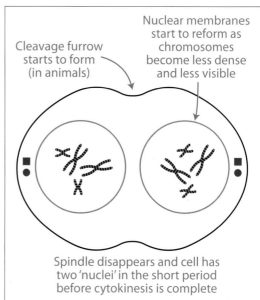

Cleavage furrow starts to form (in animals)

Nuclear membranes start to reform as chromosomes become less dense and less visible

Spindle disappears and cell has two 'nuclei' in the short period before cytokinesis is complete

Telophase

Cytokinesis – at the end of mitosis, the cell divides during cytokinesis to form two daughter cells, each with the identical chromosome makeup that the parent cell had. The process of cytokinesis is different in animal and plant cells due to their different cell structures.

In **animal** cells, a **cleavage furrow** forms as the cell-surface membrane invaginates and eventually splits the cell into two. In **plant** cells, a **cell plate**, precursor to a new cell wall, is laid down along the centre of the cell. The Golgi apparatus play an important role in synthesising the materials needed in the formation of the new wall.

In summary, mitosis is the process of **nuclear** division, a necessary prerequisite for cell division, important in growth and tissue repair.

Meiosis

Mitotic cell division maintains the state of **ploidy**, for example, a diploid cell will produce two **diploid** cells (diploid can be represented as **2n**, ie having both chromosomes in a homologous pair). In some situations, this could be a problem. During fertilisation, the chromosomes of the two gametes are combined in the zygote. Consequently, if human gametes were diploid (with 46 chromosomes) then the zygote and new individual would have 92 chromosomes, and so on. **Meiosis** is a necessary process in organisms that carry out sexual reproduction to maintain constancy of chromosome number. Meiosis produces **haploid** cells (**n**), having only one chromosome from each homologous pair.

Note: although gametes are haploid, not all haploid cells are gametes. Moss plants contain haploid cells and when a moss plant grows the cells divide by mitosis.

Meiosis is the process of **reduction division**, which is cell division that halves the number of chromosomes in gametes. Of course, it is not just any half, but it is one chromosome from each homologous pair that enters a gamete. This ensures that when male and female gametes fuse, the normal diploid number is restored, with each homologous pair of chromosomes gaining one chromosome from the male parent and one from the female parent. Therefore, meiosis can only take place in diploid cells, cells that have homologous pairs to start with.

The process of meiosis

Meiosis differs from mitosis in a number of ways, including:

- it only takes place in reproductive organs (testes and ovaries in humans and pollen grains and ovules in plants).
- it involves two divisions resulting in four daughter cells.
- chromosome arrangements in the daughter cells are both different from each other and different from the parent cell.

During the first meiotic division (**meiosis I**), the chromosomes are separated into two sets. One set contains one chromosome from each homologous pair, the other set contains the other homologous chromosome from each pair – with the two daughter cells containing a set each. During the second meiotic division (**meiosis II**) the two chromatids of each chromosome split and go into the two new cells produced by each 'daughter' cell.

Meiosis I

Prophase I – homologous chromosomes have paired up to form **bivalents** (the actual pairing up takes place during interphase prior to meiosis starting). This is another difference from mitosis – in mitosis the chromosomes behave as single units and not as homologous pairs. Other features of prophase are similar to the events of prophase in mitosis (for example, chromosomes condensing and becoming visible with each chromosome consisting of two chromatids, the nucleolus becoming less obvious, in animal cells the centrioles migrating to opposite poles).

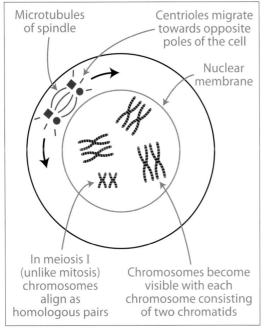

Prophase I in an animal cell

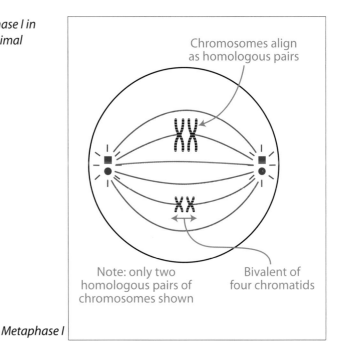

Metaphase I

Metaphase I – as with mitosis by this stage the nuclear membrane breaks down and the microtubules of the spindle attach to the centromeres of the chromosomes. The chromosome pairs (bivalents) are aligned along the 'equator' of the cell.

Anaphase I – as the microtubules of the spindle contract they pull *chromosomes* (each consisting of two chromatids) to opposite poles of the cell. Note the key difference with mitosis – in anaphase of mitosis it is the chromatids that are pulled to opposite ends of the cell. With the two chromosomes in each bivalent (a homologous pair) pulled apart, this ensures that one chromosome from each homologous pair will end up in a daughter cell.

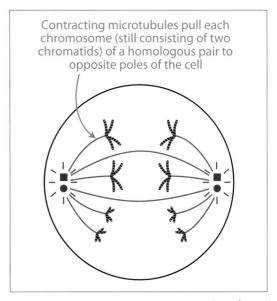

Telophase I – the chromosomes are pulled to opposite ends of the cell, with each chromosome still consisting of two chromatids and the nuclear membrane reforms. Once the chromosomes become invisible, telophase I of meiosis appears similar to telophase of mitosis.

Anaphase I

Cytokinesis – produces two daughter cells, each containing the haploid number of chromosomes.

Meiosis II

Normally prophase II continues in each daughter cell immediately after the completion of meiosis I. The spindles are formed at right angles to the angle of division of meiosis I and the outcome is the separation of each of the chromosomes into its two chromatids. In effect, meiosis II is very similar to mitosis.

Following meiosis II, cytokinesis occurs with each of the original 'daughter' cells producing two new daughter cells. Therefore, meiosis produces four haploid cells, each different from each other (as explained below), in two cell divisions.

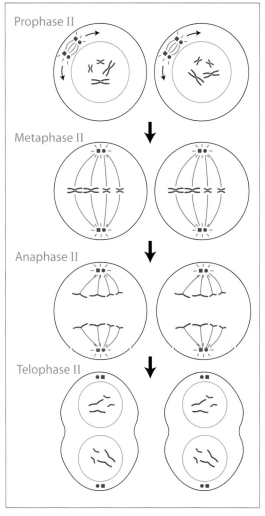

Meiosis II

Meiosis and genetic variation

Although meiosis is necessary to ensure constancy of chromosome number in sexually reproducing organisms, it is very important in producing **variation**. Variation is produced as a consequence of two specific processes, independent assortment and crossing over.

Independent assortment – the golden rule in meiosis is that only one chromosome from each homologous pair can enter a gamete (this is necessary as it is reduction division). However, for any one gamete it can be **either** of the two homologous chromosomes from **any** particular pair. The chromosome of a homologous pair that actually enters a particular gamete is dependent on the random nature of how the chromosomes line up at the cell equator at the start of **metaphase I**. The way one chromosome pair lines up (ie which chromosome is closer to a particular pole of the cell) is totally independent of how any other pair aligns.

With 23 pairs of chromosomes in humans, there are millions of possible chromosome combinations in any one gamete. This process of **independent assortment** is very important in producing variation in the next generation.

Crossing over – we have already noted that the two chromosomes of a homologous pair align themselves side by side as interphase progresses. As each chromosome separates into two chromatids, following DNA replication, the resulting **bivalent** consists of four chromatids lying side by side.

Sometimes two chromatids (from different chromosomes in the homologous pair) may break and exchange sections with each other. This happens during **prophase I** and is called **crossing over**. The points where the chromosomes cross over are called **chiasmata** (singular **chiasma**).

Why is crossing over significant?

Note 1: the two **chromosomes** of a homologous pair have identical genes but some alleles may differ between the two chromosomes.

Note 2: the two **chromatids** of each chromosome are identical (before crossing over) – they possess the same genes and the same alleles.

Crossing over exchanges sections of genes between the two chromatids from different chromosomes – this can work because the genes will be the same. However, the alleles may not be. The consequence:

- the two chromatids of the **same** chromosome are no longer genetically identical.
- some chromatids, as a consequence of crossing over, may contain unique sequences of alleles that did not exist in the parental chromosome. Remember, one chromosome in each homologous pair comes from the male parent and the other from the female parent. The two chromatids (which eventually become chromosomes) involved in crossing over are referred to as **recombinants**.

To understand crossing over it is important that you understand fully what homologous chromosomes and chromatids are, their similarities and differences, and how they behave during meiosis.

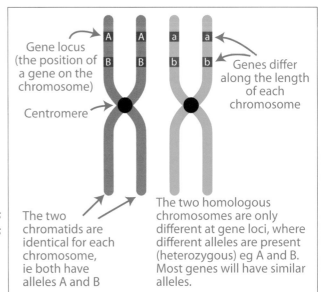

Gene locus (the position of a gene on the chromosome)

Centromere

Genes differ along the length of each chromosome

The two chromatids are identical for each chromosome, ie both have alleles A and B

The two homologous chromosomes are only different at gene loci, where different alleles are present (heterozygous) eg A and B. Most genes will have similar alleles.

Homologous chromosomes and chromatids

Crossing over

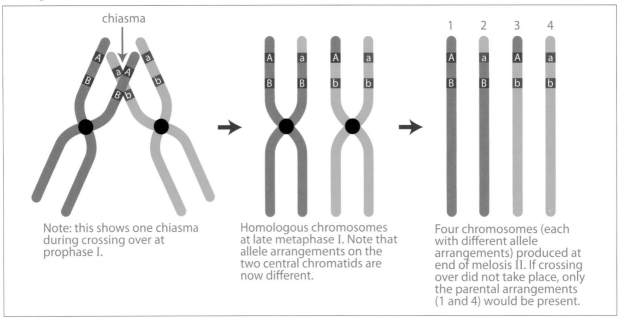

chiasma

1 2 3 4

Note: this shows one chiasma during crossing over at prophase I.

Homologous chromosomes at late metaphase I. Note that allele arrangements on the two central chromatids are now different.

Four chromosomes (each with different allele arrangements) produced at end of melosis II. If crossing over did not take place, only the parental arrangements (1 and 4) would be present.

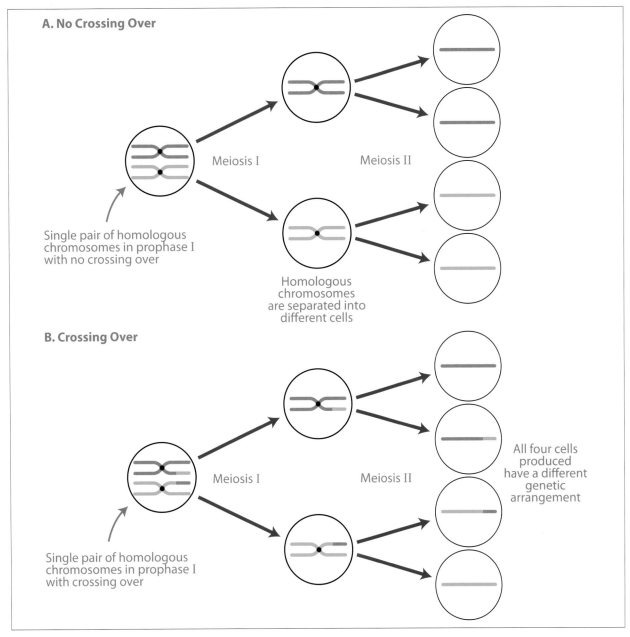

Summary showing gametes produced (a) without crossing over, (b) with crossing over (only one pair of homologous chromosomes shown).

Note 1: the diagrams showing crossing over in this chapter show only one chiasma. In reality there are often many chiasmata occurring in a bivalent.

Note 2: the diagrams show the effect of crossing over in one homologous pair of chromosomes. Remember that crossing over takes place in other homologous pairs, therefore significantly increasing the number of new allele combinations in gametes.

Independent assortment and crossing over produce significant variation in **gametes**. The process of fertilisation itself adds to the variation, as it is totally random which gamete from each parent is actually involved in fertilisation.

Practical work

You need to be able to identify the different stages of mitosis and meiosis from **photographs** or diagrams. You need practice at this but there are some useful tips.

- It is very difficult to tell the difference between mitosis and meiosis II – in both cases chromosomes are splitting into chromatids. You will usually be given some extra information if you have to distinguish between the two in a photograph, for example, the diploid number of chromosomes in that organism or where the section was taken from.

- Crossing over results in the homologous chromosomes becoming twisted or bowed – if you see paired chromosomes in a range of strange shapes or twists, it is likely to be a photograph of late prophase I (or metaphase I) of meiosis.

- Anaphase I of meiosis will show chromosomes, each consisting of two chromatids. As the chromosomes are pulled by their centromeres towards the poles of the cell, the centromere region can be seen leading with **4** chromatid tails being pulled behind. Anaphase II of meiosis (or anaphase of mitosis) will only show 2 'tails' being pulled behind the centromere.

- If identifying a particular stage of meiosis in an examination, from either a photograph or a diagram, make sure you identify the division (**I** or **II**) as well as the stage.

Preparing root tip squashes of mitosis

There are many different techniques for preparing root tip squashes to show mitosis. While you will not be expected to know a range of methods, you will be expected to know the general principles.

Growth in plants takes place in very specific regions or meristems. Most meristems are located at the shoot and root tips, just behind the root cap. As shoot and root tips are regions of concentrated growth, it is here that cell division will be occurring. Consequently, mitosis will be taking place in the cells of these parts of the plant.

Traditionally, root tips are used as they are practically more suitable and it is often the short side or lateral roots of a fast growing young seedling, such as from a broad bean, that are used for preparing root tip squashes.

Usually a number of healthy looking lateral roots are cut off and placed in a suitable stain, for example, acetic orcein. The acetic orcein is necessary to stain the chromosomes. The lateral roots are added to acetic orcein in a boiling tube and heated in a water bath (for example, at 60°C for 20 minutes). The 'cooking' in the water bath both allows the stain to permeate the cells and also softens the plant root tissue.

After the lateral roots are removed from the boiling tube, all but the few mm at the tip are discarded. The root tip is placed on a microscope slide, irrigated with acetic orcein, a cover slip added, and then gently tapped with the blunt end of a pointed needle. The purpose of this is to 'squash' the root tip into a single layer of cells in order that they can be examined using a microscope.

Even if only the last few mm of the shoot tip are used, it will be difficult to find cells undergoing mitosis for two main reasons:

- Mitosis only occurs in a specific part of the shoot tip (**the zone of division**).
- Even within the zone of division only a very small number of cells will be undergoing mitosis – most will be at the interphase stage and therefore appear as non-dividing.

Note: the staining process will have killed the cells so the cells in the root tip will show cells 'arrested' at particular stages of mitosis – you cannot see the events taking place in sequence in a particular cell.

However, the process can be made easier by using low power to identify the zone of division. In this region, the cells are smaller and cuboidal, with relatively large nucleus/cell volume ratios. This region is often flanked by a **root cap** (at the very tip) and the **zone of elongation**, where cells are elongating behind the zone of division (see plant root tip diagram).

Note: growth in root (or shoot) tips involves both cell division (in the zone of division) and elongation (in the zone of elongation) but mitosis only takes place in the former.

Once the zone of division has been identified, switch to high power to examine individual cells for mitosis. As already noted, most cells will be in interphase, so will not show mitosis taking place. Metaphase and anaphase are relatively short stages, so few cells may show these stages. However, prophase (nucleus resembling 'balls of wool') and telophase (resembling two cells together but without an obvious common cell wall between them) are often much more common, but more difficult to spot.

Cells in the zone of elongation are more elongated and larger

Zone of elongation

Zone of division

Root cap

Cells in the zone of division are cuboidal and smaller

Plant root tip

The different stages of mitosis are shown in sequence, from left to right, starting with the top row and finishing with the bottom.

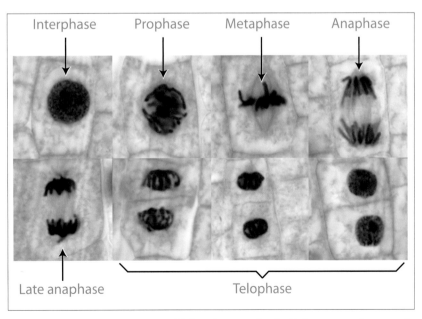

Interphase   Prophase   Metaphase   Anaphase

Late anaphase   Telophase

Light micrograph of cells from an onion root tip showing the different stages of mitosis

Steve Gschmeissner/Science Photo Library

99

Exam questions

1. The diagrams below represent some important stages (labelled **A** to **D**) during mitotic cell cycle in an animal cell.

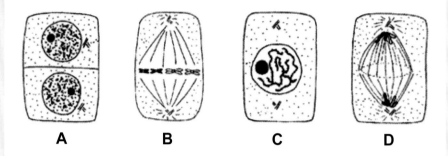

(a) Identify stage **B**. [1]

(b) The diagrams are not in the correct sequence. Rearrange the letters to illustrate the correct sequence of the stages. [1]

(c) Give **one** piece of evidence which suggests that the diagrams represent animal cells and not plant cells. [1]

(d) Give **two** pieces of evidence from the diagrams which suggest that the stages take place during mitosis and not meiosis. [2]

Question taken from CCEA's Biology Assessment Unit AS1, Molecules and Cells, June 2010, © CCEA 2012

2. The following statements describe events within stages of meiosis.

Identify the stage in each case.

• Bivalents are formed when homologous chromosomes pair

• Chromatids separate and are pulled to opposite poles

• Four haploid nuclei are formed

• Chiasmata occur

Question taken from CCEA's Biology Assessment Unit AS1, Molecules and Cells, June 2011, © CCEA 2012

3. The graph on page 101 shows changes in both cell mass and DNA mass per nucleus during several mitotic cell cycles in a mammalian embryo.

(a) Between which times shown on the graph does the G1 phase (first growth phase) occur during the first cell cycle? [1]

(b) State what is occurring during the phase indicated by **X** on the graph. [1]

(c) Explain the changes in the DNA mass per nucleus during one cell cycle. [3]

(d) The DNA mass per nucleus during a **meiotic** cell cycle follows a similar pattern to that shown opposite, but with one major difference.

Describe and explain this difference. [2]

Question taken from CCEA's Biology Assessment Unit AS 1, Module 1: Cell Biology, June 2009, © CCEA 2012

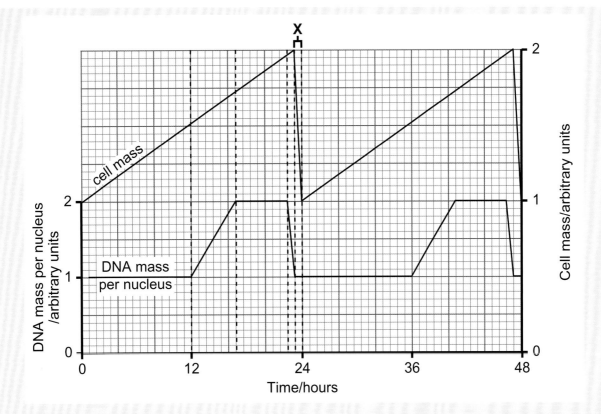

4. (a) **Photographs A** to **D** show light micrographs of bluebell cells at different stages of mitosis.

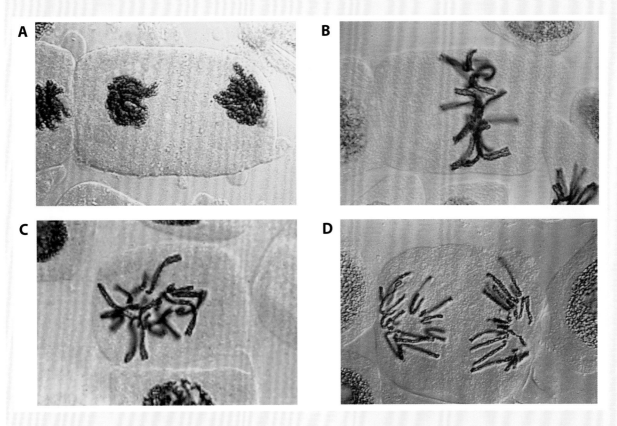

Pr G Gimenez-Martin/Science Photo Library

(i) Identify the stage of mitosis shown by each of the cells A to D. [4]

(ii) Arrange the letters A to D to give the correct sequence of stages during mitosis. [1]

(b) The diagram below shows an homologous pair of chromosomes (bivalent) during prophase I of meiosis.

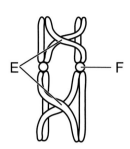

(i) Name the features labelled **E** and **F** in the diagram. [2]

(ii) Explain how feature **E** results in genetic variation. [2]

Question taken from CCEA's Biology Assessment Unit AS 1, Module 1: Cell Biology, January 2009, © CCEA 2012

5. Quality of written communication is awarded a maximum of 2 marks in this section. [2]

(a) Describe the behaviour of the chromosomal material during a cell cycle involving mitosis. [8]

(b) Describe how the behaviour of chromosomes differs during the processes of mitosis and meiosis. Explain the consequences of these differences. [5]

Question taken from CCEA's Biology Assessment Unit AS 1, Module 1: Cell Biology, January 2010, © CCEA 2012

Chapter 7 – Tissues and Organs

Students should be able to:

1.8.1   Appreciate the specialisation of cells in tissues and organs.

1.8.2   Understand the structure and function of the ileum (a mammalian organ).

1.8.3   Understand the structure and function of a mesophytic leaf (a plant organ).

1.8.4   Practical work to include examining sections of the ileum and the mesophytic leaf and making accurate drawings of these to show the tissue layers.

Multicellular living organisms consist of more than one cell, and can contain anything from a relatively small number to many millions of cells. They also have specialised cells, with different cells being adapted for particular functions.

Tissues are composed of groups of cells that carry out the same (or a very small number of) functions. Not surprisingly, the cells in any one tissue are often very similar in structure. The palisade layer in a plant leaf contains palisade cells; cells that are all very similar in shape and all adapted to carry out the same function (photosynthesis).

Several different types of tissue can be grouped together to form an **organ**, a structural unit that carries out one or more functions. The **leaf** is an organ which is highly specialised for photosynthesis but has a number of other functions, including being the site of transpiration through the stomatal pores. The leaf contains palisade tissue, but also vascular tissue (xylem and phloem), epidermal and spongy mesophyll tissue. The boundary between different types of tissue is not always clear: it could be argued that the mesophyll tissue in a leaf is one tissue containing two types of cells (palisade cells and spongy mesophyll cells).

The **ileum** is an example of an organ in humans. Its primary role is the absorption of digested food, although some digestion takes place also and the ileum has an important role in moving undigested food through to the colon. As with all organs, the ileum contains a range of tissues (for example, epithelial tissue that forms the boundary between the ileum and the lumen of the gut, muscle, blood tissue).

Organs seldom work in isolation – they tend to work as **organ systems**. The ileum is part of the digestive system with other organs including the mouth, oesophagus, stomach, pancreas, liver and colon.

The ileum

The alimentary canal is the part of the digestive system that forms the long hollow tube that runs from the mouth to the anus. It is regionalised with highly adapted organs in specific regions. However, all the organs, including the ileum, are modifications of the same basic five-layered structure.

The diagram opposite identifies the **serosa**, the **muscularis externa**, the **submucosa**, **muscularis mucosa** and the **mucosa** as the different layers, working from the outside in.

Each of these layers is formed of different tissues and they have specific roles in the functioning of the ileum. Some can even be further subdivided as seen in the next section.

- **serosa** – This outer layer of connective tissue provides a very thin protective and supportive lining for the alimentary canal.

- **muscularis externa** – This consists of an outer layer of **longitudinal muscle** (muscle that runs along the length of the alimentary canal) and an inner layer of **circular muscle** (muscle that runs around the alimentary canal). Contractions of the longitudinal muscle cause **pendular movement** and contractions of the circular muscle cause **local constrictions** – actions which help churn and mix the food. Contractions of the circular muscle help push food along the gut in a series of **peristaltic** waves.

- **submucosa** – This region is largely composed of connective tissue and contains many blood vessels and lymphatic vessels – vessels that are crucial in transporting absorbed food products.

- **muscularis mucosa** – This thin layer of muscle lies between the submucosa and the mucosa. It is important in moving the villi that are present in the mucosa, thus increasing contact with digested food in the gut lumen. It is able to do this as small strands of muscle extend from the main muscularis mucosa layer up through the mucosa into each villus, with contractions of these strands helping to produce the characteristic 'wafting' movement of the villi.

- **mucosa** – This is the layer in contact with the food in the gut lumen. It is highly specialised with a substantially increased surface area due to the presence of **villi** and **microvilli**.

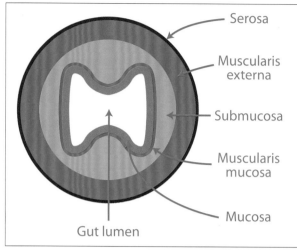

A section through the ileum

The villus

The diagram opposite shows a light micrograph section through part of the ileum showing villi, with the diagram on page 105 showing a diagrammatic representation of the structure of the villi and surrounding layers.

The **columnar epithelial** cells of the villus have their surface area extended by the presence of numerous **microvilli** that give a **brush border** appearance. Although many digestive enzymes are secreted into the lumen of the gut, many occur within the cell-surface membrane of ileum epidermal cells, where the presence of microvilli further increases surface area, increasing the number of these enzymes that can make

The villus

Biophoto Associates/
Science Photo Library

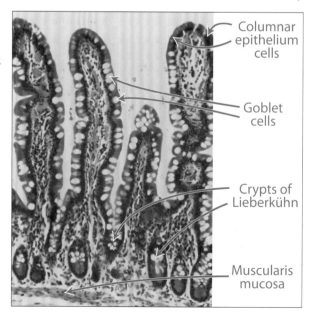

contact with the food. The columnar epithelium cells are particularly rich in the presence of **mitochondria** for the active transport of some absorbed food products.

The absorption of some products involves both **active transport** and (facilitated) **diffusion,** involving protein carrier molecules. **Glucose** and **amino acids** are taken into the epithelial cells by active transport, and once there, can diffuse into the **capillary network** due to the concentrations that can build up in the cells.

Lipid soluble products such as glycerol and fatty acids can simply diffuse into the cells lining the villi. **Lipids** are transported out of villi by the **lacteals**, which are part of the lymphatic system.

Pinocytosis is also involved in absorption of some substances. For example, in babies, antibodies, which are proteins, can pass from breast milk into their blood system without being digested.

The diagram shows a vertical section through part of a villus to show the cells and structures that are important in absorption.

Note: villi are up to 1 mm in length and consist of many cells. Microvilli are sub-cellular and many occur in each villus epithelial cell – they both function to increase the surface area for digestion and absorption. Together, villi and microvilli enable the surface area of the internal lining of the ileum to be about 300 times greater than its external area.

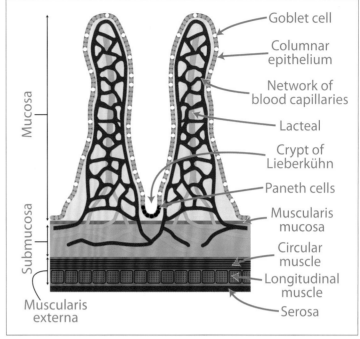

The structure of the villus

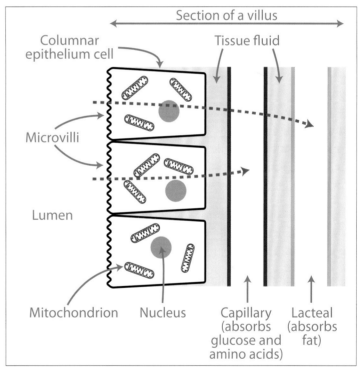

Vertical section of part of a villus

Dotted within the columnar epithelium cells are **goblet** cells. These secrete **mucus**. Mucus provides a slimy protective layer that lubricates the lining of the alimentary canal, facilitating the movement of food and also protects against the actions of digestive enzymes on the epithelial cells.

The **capillaries** within the villi are important for transporting **amino acids** and **monosaccharides** out of the villi. These capillaries eventually combine to form the venules of the hepatic portal vein, which transports these digested products to the liver. **Lipids** are not absorbed into the capillary network but are instead transported away by **lacteals**, which are part of the lymphatic system.

Crypts of Lieberkühn are intestinal glands that lie embedded in the tissue between villi. The cells at the bottom of the crypts are continually dividing by mitosis to produce new cells that continually move up the surface of the villi, like a conveyer belt, as new cells are produced below them. By the time they reach the tip of the villus – usually after a few days – they are sloughed off and replaced. **Paneth cells**, at the base of the crypts, have an anti-microbial function in protecting their neighbouring actively dividing cells. Other cells lining the crypts are involved in mucus secretion.

The leaf

The tissue layers in the leaf are clearly organised into discrete layers or zones, these being the upper epidermis, palisade mesophyll, spongy mesophyll, vascular tissue (xylem and phloem) and the lower epidermis (with stomata).

The leaf is primarily an organ for photosynthesis. It is also well adapted for gas exchange (to enable both photosynthesis and respiration to take place in the cells) and many leaves are highly adapted to reduce water loss by transpiration.

The **upper epidermis** is the upper protective layer of the leaf and it has no chloroplasts so is not directly involved with photosynthesis. It is covered with a **waxy cuticle** to reduce water loss. The waxy cuticle is thickest in the leaves of those plants best adapted to reduce water loss, but, being transparent, it does not significantly impede the passage of light.

The **palisade mesophyll** is the primary photosynthesising region in the leaf and to maximise the harvesting of light energy, it occurs immediately beneath the upper epidermis – the surface of the leaf that receives most light. The palisade cells are arranged regularly in order to pack in as many as possible. Each cell has many chloroplasts to maximise photosynthesis. Depending on the species, there may be one or more layers of palisade cells in the palisade mesophyll. The large vacuole in palisade cells helps the light to pass down through the layers with minimum shading.

Orientation of palisade cells

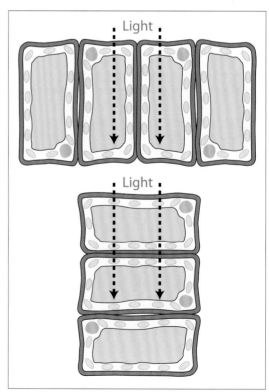

The diagram opposite shows the benefits of having palisade cells perpendicular to the upper epidermis, as opposed to having their long axis parallel to the epidermal cells.

As well as the benefits of maximising the incident light on each cell, there are other advantages with this arrangement. For example, sugars moving to the phloem have to pass through fewer cells, as do the gases diffusing to and from the intercellular air spaces.

The **large surface area** of most leaves is a further adaptation for photosynthesis, both through providing more palisade cells in close proximity to the upper leaf surface and also to facilitate gas exchange with no cell being too far from a gas exchange surface. However, the leaf surface area is a compromise between maximising photosynthesis and restricting water loss. In plants such as cacti, adapted to arid habitats, the leaves can be reduced to needle shaped to reduce the surface area across which water loss can occur.

The **spongy mesophyll** lies immediately beneath the palisade layer. The spongy mesophyll cells are much more loosely and irregularly arranged. This arrangement leads to the formation of intercellular air spaces that encourages the diffusion of gases for gas exchange. While spongy mesophyll cells do photosynthesise, they have fewer chloroplasts than palisade cells, and consequently have a less significant photosynthetic role than the palisade cells. They are important in gas exchange and the carbon dioxide and oxygen required by the palisade cells diffuses through the spongy mesophyll cells on their way to and from the palisade layer. The loose and irregular arrangement of these cells gives a large **gaseous exchange surface** in the leaf.

Note: the gas exchange surface in leaves is the cell-surface membrane of the spongy mesophyll cells, not the stomata!

Within the spongy mesophyll lies the **vascular tissue**. The vascular tissue is often evident as the leaf veins that branch from the leaf midrib. **Xylem vessels** transport water and inorganic ions (minerals) up through the plant and into the leaves. **Phloem sieve-tubes** transport sugars, usually sucrose, produced in photosynthesis away from the leaf to plant storage regions, such as bulbs or tubers, where it can be converted to starch, or to actively growing regions where it is used in respiration.

The **lower epidermis** is also covered with a waxy cuticle but it is usually much thinner than the cuticle on the upper epidermis, as less transpiration tends to occur through the lower epidermis. **Stomata** are present and their opening and closing is controlled by the presence of guard cells. **Guard cells** are unusual for epidermal cells in that they do possess chloroplasts. When turgid, the guard cells expand and open the pore of the stomata, thereby facilitating gas exchange. When less turgid, the pore closes and reduces water loss.

In most plants the stomata are closed at night to reduce water loss. While evaporation losses are usually greater during the day (compared to night) when it is warmer, the stomata need to remain open to allow the gases involved in photosynthesis and respiration to enter and leave. During darkness, leaf metabolic activity is much

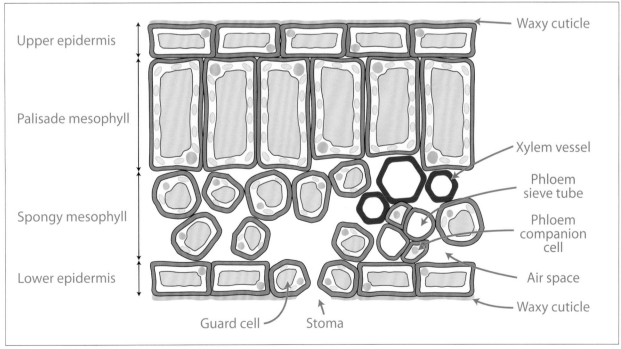

A section through a typical mesophytic leaf

reduced, with only respiration taking place and there is usually enough oxygen within the leaf to allow respiration to take place even with the stomata closed.

Some plants, such as many grasses, have stomata on both leaf surfaces and others, such as water lilies, have stomata on the upper leaf surface only.

Practical work

You need to be able to identify the key layers/tissues and cells in sections of the ileum and the leaf. These can take the form of diagrams or photographs in examination questions. You also need to be able to draw block diagrams of the tissues within the ileum and the leaf.

The block diagrams do not require drawing of individual cells or cell detail but they need to be an accurate representation of the photograph (or diagram used) – the layers present need to be included and need to be proportional – likewise anything not in the photograph should not be included in your block diagram. Continuous (not sketchy) lines should be drawn and the tissue layers must be labelled as required. You could also be asked to draw individual cells from a photograph or diagram (as opposed to a block diagram).

Exam questions

1. The ileum is an organ which makes up part of the mammalian digestive system.

   (a) (i) Why can the ileum be described as an organ? [1]

   (ii) Why can the digestive system be described as a system? [1]

   (b) Describe the role of the following structures in the functioning of the ileum.
   - muscularis mucosa
   - goblet cells
   - muscularis externa [3]

   Question taken from CCEA's Biology Assessment Unit AS1, Module 1: Cell Biology, June 2009, © CCEA 2012

2. The photograph below is a section through part of the ileum.

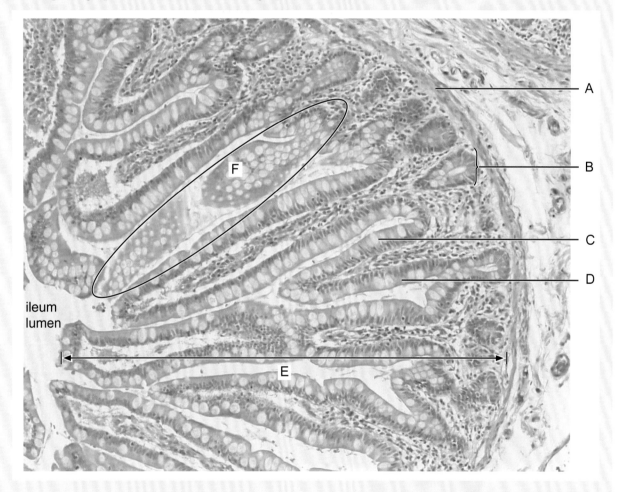

© School of Anatomy and Human Biology, The University of Western Australia

   (a) Identify the structures labelled **A** to **E**. [5]
   (b) Suggest an interpretation for the area labelled **F**. [1]
   (c) Describe the role of the lacteal within each villus of the ileum. [1]

   Question taken from CCEA's Biology Assessment Unit AS1, Molecules and Cells, June 2011, © CCEA 2012

3. The diagram below shows the tissues present in a mesophytic leaf.

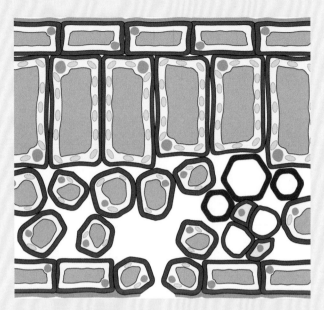

For copyright reasons this diagram has replaced the diagram from CCEA's Biology AS1, June 2010 paper.

The leaf is an organ with adaptations for maximising photosynthesis while minimising transpiration. Describe these adaptations for:

- maximising photosynthesis [3]
- minimising transpiration [2]

Question taken from CCEA's Biology Assessment Unit AS1, Molecules and Cells, June 2010, © CCEA 2012

4. Quality of written communication is awarded a maximum of 2 marks in this section. [2]

In complex organisms, cells are organised into tissues which are then organised into organs. The ileum is an example of an organ. Describe the structure and function of the different tissue layers in the ileum and, where appropriate, their constituent cells. [13]

Question taken from CCEA's Biology Assessment Unit AS1, Molecules and Cells, January 2012, © CCEA 2012

Unit AS 2: Organisms and Biodiversity

Chapter 8 – The Principles of Exchange and Transport

Students should be able to:

2.1.1 Understand the relationship between an organism's size and its surface area to volume ratio.

2.1.2 Understand the features of exchange surfaces which aid passive and active transport.

2.1.3 Understand the principle of mass transport.

2.1.4 Understand factors affecting the rate of gas exchange.

2.1.5 Understand gas exchange in plants.

2.1.6 Understand gas exchange in a mammal.

2.1.7 Understand the structure and functioning of the breathing system of a mammal.

2.1.8 Practical work to include an understanding of the J-tube, respirometer, Audus apparatus and demonstration of compensation point using hydrogencarbonate indicator.

Transport and exchange in living organisms

Cells in living organisms need to be able to obtain essential substances (such as oxygen and glucose for respiration, or nitrate ions in plants to provide the nitrogen needed for amino acid synthesis) from their surroundings and also be able to remove waste or toxic products (such as carbon dioxide from respiration, or urea in many animals as a waste product from protein metabolism). In unicellular organisms this **exchange** takes place through the cell-surface membrane. Multicellular organisms often have specialised exchange surfaces that take in or remove materials. In the more complex organisms there is a **transport** system that links the specialised exchange surface (such as gills in fish) to the cells throughout the organism.

The link between surface area and volume in living organisms

The surface area of an organism may be regarded as the total number of cells in direct contact with the environment and its volume may be regarded as the three-dimensional space occupied by metabolically active tissues.

If we consider the relationship between the surface area of a cube and its volume (the surface area to volume ratio), as cube size increases we can appreciate the relationship between the surface area and volume of living organisms.

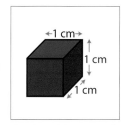

A cube with 1 cm sides

Each side of the cube has a surface area of 1 cm^2 (1 cm × 1 cm) but as the cube has 6 sides it has a surface area of 6 cm^2. The volume of the cube is the height × length × breadth, (ie 1 cm × 1 cm × 1 cm) = 1 cm^3.

Therefore the surface area to volume ratio of a cube with 1 cm sides is 6.

What happens to this ratio as the cube gets larger?

The relationship between size and the surface area to volume ratio

Cube side length/cm	Area of cube/cm²	Volume of cube/cm³	Surface area to volume ratio
1	6	1	6
2	24	8	3
3	54	27	2
4	96	64	1.5
5	150	125	1.2
6	216	216	1
7	294	343	0.86
8	384	512	0.75

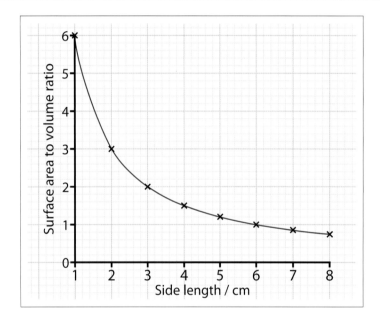

The graph above shows that with increasing size the surface area to volume ratio decreases. The consequence of this is that small organisms are able to gain all their requirements (metabolites) through their body surface and remove all waste and toxic products by the same route. This is most obviously exemplified by single cell organisms, where the cell-surface membrane fulfils this role.

However, in large organisms the surface area is simply not large enough to meet the metabolic needs of the large number of cells that occupy the proportionally larger volume within the organism's body. Furthermore, in large multicellular organisms the majority of cells are not in direct contact with the surrounding environment. Consequently, large organisms must have specialised exchange surfaces in order that the rate of exchange of substances into and out of the organism can be increased to meet its greater metabolic needs. The importance of specialised exchange surfaces is even greater in organisms that are very active and have high metabolic rates.

Features of exchange surfaces that aid passive and active transport into and out of organisms

1. Increasing the surface area of the exchange surface

Increasing the surface area of the exchange surface is an obvious method of increasing the surface area to volume ratio of an organism.

In some organisms this is achieved by having a **flattened shape**, as in the multicellular flatworms (Phylum Platyhelminthes). The flattened shape increases the surface area to volume ratio, through increasing the surface area, and respiratory gases can diffuse through the body surface in sufficient quantities to meet the organism's needs. Flatworms therefore do **not** have **specialised respiratory exchange surfaces**, as gases can diffuse through the increased surface area of the entire surface. Having a flattened shape also decreases the distance over which substances have to diffuse to reach any cell in the body.

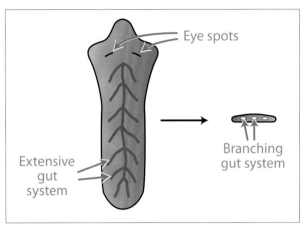

Λ flatworm

In many large organisms the body surface area to volume ratio is not large enough to enable enough respiratory gases to enter and leave. Therefore, specialised exchange (respiratory) surfaces are needed. These specialised respiratory surfaces very significantly increase the surface area across which exchange can take place.

The position is additionally complicated by the fact that most terrestrial organisms (organisms that live on land) have an impermeable body covering necessary to minimise water loss, further increasing the need to have specialised respiratory surfaces across which sufficient respiratory gases can diffuse. These respiratory surfaces cannot be water proofed – a moist surface is required for gas diffusion. This influences the type and position of the respiratory surfaces in particular organisms, as will be seen in the following sections.

The specialised exchange surface can be external or internal to the body surface.

External exchange surfaces, such as the folded external membranes of the **external gills** of young tadpoles, increase the surface area across which respiratory gases can diffuse.

Internal exchange surfaces include **alveoli**, found in mammalian lungs, and fish **gills**. Alveoli and gills have very large surface areas due to the extensively folded internal membranes.

Note: in larger and more complex organisms, such as mammals, food enters through an opening (mouth) to the gut and waste is eliminated through a specialised excretory system. Therefore the specialised (external) exchange surface is primarily dealing with respiratory gases. Large organisms invariably have gut adaptations that provide large surface exchange surfaces deep within the body (for example, villi in the ileum).

2. Thin separating surface

Exchange surfaces are **thin** so that the rate of diffusion is maximised. In alveoli, for example, oxygen diffusing from the lungs into a blood capillary only has to diffuse through two layers of cells: the alveolar lining and the capillary endothelium.

3. Large concentration gradients

Diffusion will only occur across an exchange surface if there is a concentration gradient. In small unicellular or multicellular organisms, the use of oxygen in respiration in the tissues creates low levels of oxygen in the cell(s), therefore a concentration gradient exists that enables oxygen to diffuse in from the atmosphere. Carbon dioxide diffuses out by the same principle.

In larger organisms with specialised exchange surfaces, unaided diffusion is usually not sufficient to deliver, or remove, the volumes of respiratory gases involved. In these organisms, a ventilation system is usually required to maintain the concentration gradient, for example, breathing in mammals.

The principles of a large surface area, a thin separating distance and a concentration gradient are important in all exchange surfaces, irrespective of the nature of the materials being exchanged. The diagram below shows examples of exchange surfaces and summarises their main adaptations.

Other exchange surfaces (the leaf, alveoli and capillaries) will be studied in detail in the next section.

Examples of exchange surfaces

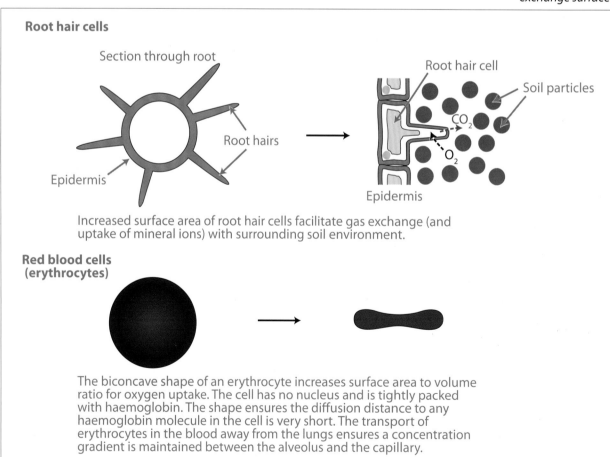

Root hair cells

Section through root

Root hair cell

Soil particles

Root hairs

CO_2

O_2

Epidermis

Epidermis

Increased surface area of root hair cells facilitate gas exchange (and uptake of mineral ions) with surrounding soil environment.

Red blood cells (erythrocytes)

The biconcave shape of an erythrocyte increases surface area to volume ratio for oxygen uptake. The cell has no nucleus and is tightly packed with haemoglobin. The shape ensures the diffusion distance to any haemoglobin molecule in the cell is very short. The transport of erythrocytes in the blood away from the lungs ensures a concentration gradient is maintained between the alveolus and the capillary.

Mass flow transport

As well as requiring specialised exchange surfaces, large organisms (such as flowering plants and mammals) require an internal transport system to carry substances to and from the cells. The transport of substances within large organisms occurs by **mass flow**. Mass flow is brought about by **pressure differences** existing within the organism. Materials are moved by the pressure difference between the area where the pressure is generated (source) and areas where the pressure is much less (sink).

Some examples of mass flow systems in flowering plants and mammals are given in the table below.

Mass flow system	Generation of pressure difference	Functions of system
Xylem tissue (flowering plant)	Water evaporating from the leaf creates a tension (negative pressure) that pulls water up through the xylem as part of the transpiration stream.	Transports water and mineral ions from the roots to the leaves.
Phloem tissue (flowering plant)	Energy expenditure is involved in moving the sucrose into the phloem. ATP is used to move sucrose from the companion cell to the phloem sieve tube.	Transport of sucrose (**translocation**) to roots (for storage of carbohydrate) and to growing regions (to provide energy for growth).
Circulation in mammals	High pressure is generated by the pumping of the heart.	Transport of substances including oxygen, carbon dioxide, glucose, amino acids, lipids and urea in the blood system around the body.
Ventilation (breathing) in mammals	Reduction of pressure in the thorax causes air to enter the lungs (inhalation) and increased pressure in the thorax causes air to be expelled from the lungs (exhalation).	Ventilation of the lungs by bringing fresh air (rich in oxygen and low in carbon dioxide) into the lungs and removing air with raised carbon dioxide levels and low oxygen levels. Ventilation ensures that diffusion of respiratory gases can take place between the alveoli and the capillaries.

Gaseous exchange in flowering plants and mammals

Gaseous exchange is necessary to ensure that sufficient oxygen reaches all the cells in an organism and that carbon dioxide is excreted. As already noted, gaseous exchange may take place across the surface of the entire (or a significant part of the) organism or may involve specialised exchange surfaces that are particularly adapted for the diffusion of gases.

Gas exchange surfaces have the same features as exchange surfaces in general but tend to have some specific features.

To maximise the rate of exchange, gas exchange (respiratory) surfaces:

- have a **large surface area.**
- have a **moist surface** into which the respiratory gases dissolve.
- have **diffusion gradients** for both oxygen and carbon dioxide.

- must also be **permeable** to oxygen and carbon dioxide.
- have a short diffusion path – this is aided by exchange surfaces being very **thin**.

The relationship between some of these factors can be summarised by **Fick's law**, which can be expressed as:

$$\text{Rate of diffusion} \propto \frac{\text{Surface area} \times \text{difference in concentration}}{\text{thickness of membrane (length of diffusion path)}}$$

Gas exchange in plants

There are two processes involving gas exchange in plants; respiration and photosynthesis. All living cells in plants carry out **respiration** to produce energy and it is a process that takes place all the time (ie during night and day). As in animals, this involves the use of oxygen and the production of carbon dioxide as a waste product.

Some (but not all, for example, root hair cells) plant cells also carry out photosynthesis – most photosynthesis takes place in the **palisade mesophyll** cells of the leaf. **Photosynthesis** requires light energy – it occurs during the daytime and is most rapid when light intensities are high. The process of photosynthesis uses carbon dioxide and produces oxygen as a waste product.

In effect, most plants carry out respiration only during the night, when light energy is not available but carry out **both** respiration and photosynthesis during the daytime, when light energy is available. When a lot of light energy is available (for example, early afternoon) the rate of photosynthesis in photosynthesising cells is much greater than the rate of respiration, thus there will be net diffusion of carbon dioxide into the leaves (and oxygen out of the leaves). When respiration only is occurring, oxygen will diffuse into the cells and carbon dioxide out.

At low light levels, the rate of photosynthesis will be the same as the rate of respiration, which is likely to happen in very early morning (dawn) and late in the evening (dusk). This is known as the **compensation point**. At the compensation point, the rate of carbon dioxide used in photosynthesis is the same as the rate of carbon dioxide produced in respiration (or the rate of oxygen used in respiration is the same as the rate of oxygen produced by photosynthesis).

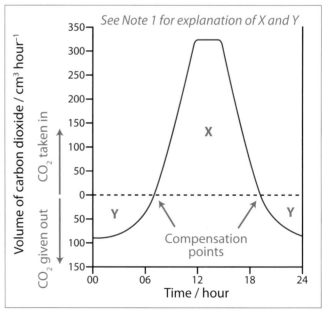

The net volume of carbon dioxide produced (and used) by a plant over a 24 hour period

Note 1: For a plant to grow, the production of carbohydrate in photosynthesis must exceed the loss of carbohydrate as a respiratory substrate. In effect this means that over a period of time (for example, a 24 hour cycle) the net intake of carbon dioxide must exceed the net production of carbon dioxide. In the graph above, this is represented by area X exceeding the combined totals of areas Y.

Note 2: The term 'net' can be used, as even when photosynthesis is taking place at maximum rate and there is a net intake of carbon dioxide, some carbon dioxide will be produced by the cells in respiration (although in leaves it all may be quickly used in photosynthesis).

Leaf adaptations for gas exchange – The leaf is an organ highly adapted for the process of photosynthesis in general. It is also very well adapted for gas exchange – necessary for both respiration and photosynthesis – but the high level of adaptation is particularly important for the diffusion of carbon dioxide into the leaf during periods of rapid photosynthesis.

These adaptations include:

- Most leaves are usually **thin**. This ensures that the overall surface area to volume ratio is high but also that there is a short diffusion distance, with no cell being far from an exchange surface.

- The **large** and **moist gas exchange surfaces** of the **spongy mesophyll** cells. It is the cell-surface membranes of the spongy mesophyll cells that form the metabolic contact with the air spaces within the spongy mesophyll, and they are the gas exchange surfaces. The loose arrangement of these cells ensures that there is a large surface area across which gases can diffuse. Due to their positioning within the leaf, the gases involved in photosynthesis and respiration can easily diffuse between the cells of the spongy mesophyll and the palisade cells.

- The **intercellular air spaces** of the **spongy mesophyll** facilitates diffusion within the leaf.

- **Stomata** (singular: stoma) are pores in the leaf surface that allow respiratory gases to diffuse in and out of the leaf easily. Most stomata are found in the lower leaf surface. In most plants the stomata are open during the daytime, when the diffusion of gases into and out of the leaf is at its greatest. The stomata may be closed during the night when there is no photosynthesis and there will be enough oxygen inside the leaf for respiratory needs. Closing the stomata during the night ensures that water loss from the leaf is reduced. The opening and closing of a stoma is controlled by two **guard cells** that can change shape. Depending on the degree of turgor (and shape) of the guard cells, a stomatal aperture (pore) may be present or not – stomata are open when the guard cells are turgid and closed when they are not. Guard cells, unlike other epidermal cells contain chloroplasts.

Surface view of a stoma

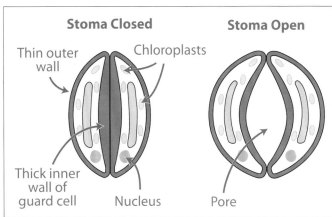

Stoma Closed — Thin outer wall, Chloroplasts, Thick inner wall of guard cell, Nucleus

Stoma Open — Pore

Note: most water loss from leaves (transpiration) is during the day, when it is usually warmer. However, the stomata are unable to close then without significantly compromising the rate of photosynthesis (and growth).

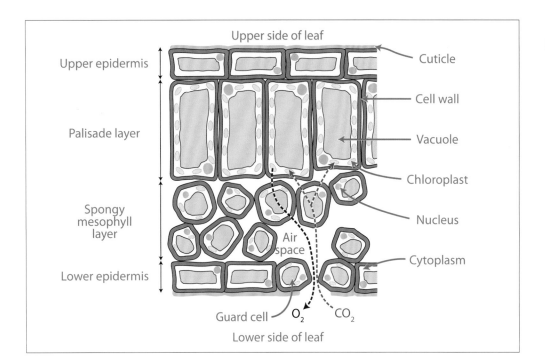

Gas exchange in a photosynthesising leaf

Gas exchange in mammals

Mammals have relatively **small surface area to volume ratios** and have an **impermeable body covering**. These two facts mean that highly specialised exchange surfaces have evolved to ensure that each of the cells in the body receives sufficient oxygen and that carbon dioxide is eliminated.

The factors that affect the rate of diffusion (see Fick's law, page 118) are at their optimum for the rapid diffusion of gases, as noted in the following sections.

Mammals have a pulmonary (lung) respiratory system and the gas exchange surface is the **alveolar wall**.

The squamous epithelial cells lining the alveoli are very thin (approximately 0.2 µm thick) and are surrounded by a dense network of capillaries, with an endothelial lining consisting of a single layer of squamous epithelial cells (also around 0.2 µm thick). This creates a **very short diffusion distance** between the alveolus and the blood, as the capillaries sit tight against the alveolar walls. The red blood cells (erythrocytes) have to squeeze their way through the narrow capillaries, ensuring that they are in contact with the endothelial wall, which further reduces the diffusion pathway.

The lungs have approximately 700 million alveoli, with the total **surface area** of the alveoli being around 75 m², which is over 30 times greater than the surface area of the body. This is achieved by there being around 350 million alveoli in each lung and the spherical shape of each alveolus. The contact surface area between the alveoli and the blood is maximised by the degree of proliferation of capillaries around each alveolus, to the extent that there is almost a continuous layer of blood surrounding each alveolus.

A **steep concentration gradient** is created by the ventilation of the lungs, which both brings oxygen into the lungs and removes carbon dioxide from the lungs. The flow of blood through the capillaries helps maintain the gradient as it continually brings carbon dioxide-rich blood to the alveoli and removes oxygen-rich blood from the alveoli.

The alveoli (and respiratory system) have many other adaptations. The position of the alveoli deep inside the body reduces water loss by evaporation (remember respiratory surfaces must be moist and permeable). Surfactant-secreting cells in the alveolar wall produce a **surfactant** that reduces the surface tension in the moisture coating of the alveoli and prevents their collapse, which would reduce the surface area for gas exchange.

The diagram opposite shows the flattened squamous epithelial cells lining the alveolus and a surfactant-secreting cell responsible for producing surfactant. Other cell types are present in the alveoli, including **macrophages** (originating from monocytes – see page 157), that protect against infection by digesting microbes through phagocytosis.

The diagram below shows the structure of the respiratory tree (system) of a mammal (human). The other structures (apart from the alveoli) shown in the diagram are concerned with ensuring that the alveoli are well ventilated.

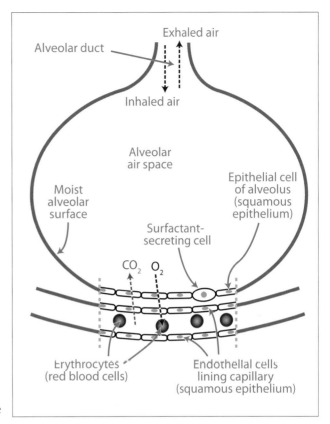

Gas exchange in an alveolus

The respiratory system

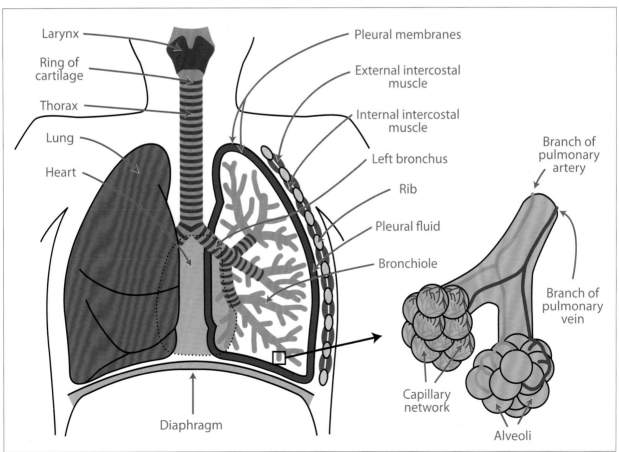

Breathing – is the term used to describe the processes involved in ventilating the lungs and the alveoli.

Inspiration (or inhalation)– describes the process of breathing in. The external intercostal muscles contract (as the internal intercostal muscles relax) and the ribs are pulled upwards and outwards. Simultaneously, the diaphragm muscle contracts, causing the diaphragm to flatten from its domed shape. Both these actions increase the volume of the thorax, which in turn reduces the pressure around the lungs. The pressure differential between the atmosphere and the lungs causes air to enter the lungs until a pressure equilibrium is achieved (see reference to mass flow and ventilation, page 117).

Expiration (exhalation) or breathing out – is really inspiration in reverse. The external intercostal muscles relax (as the internal intercostal muscles contract) causing the ribs to move downwards and inwards. The relaxation of the diaphragm muscles causes it to return to its domed position. The return of the ribs and the diaphragm to their original positions causes the volume of the thorax to reduce, consequently increasing the pressure around the lungs. With the thorax now having a higher pressure than the atmosphere, air is forced out of the lungs.

Additionally, the natural elasticity of the lungs produces an elastic recoil, which helps force air out of the lungs during expiration.

Summary of inspiration and expiration

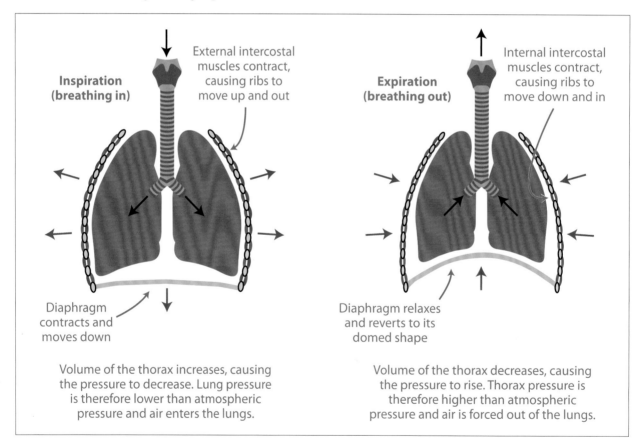

Inspiration (breathing in)
External intercostal muscles contract, causing ribs to move up and out
Diaphragm contracts and moves down
Volume of the thorax increases, causing the pressure to decrease. Lung pressure is therefore lower than atmospheric pressure and air enters the lungs.

Expiration (breathing out)
Internal intercostal muscles contract, causing ribs to move down and in
Diaphragm relaxes and reverts to its domed shape
Volume of the thorax decreases, causing the pressure to rise. Thorax pressure is therefore higher than atmospheric pressure and air is forced out of the lungs.

The effect of smoking on the lungs

Tobacco smoke is rich in toxic substances. **Tar** is the general name given to the collection of toxic chemicals in cigarette smoke, many of which are **carcinogens** (cause cancer). The tar can damage the DNA in the epithelial cells lining the lungs and cause

lung cancer. In lung cancer some of the cells of the lungs (often the cells lining the bronchial tubes) divide uncontrollably, producing a **tumour**. Once the tumour reaches a certain size, it can block the airways and/or damage large sections of the lungs themselves. Not surprisingly, there is a close correlation between the risk of lung cancer and the number of years as a smoker and the number of cigarettes smoked per day.

Emphysema is another lung condition common in heavy smokers. Irritation from the tar in cigarette smoke damages the alveolar lining to the extent that the walls of many alveoli break down. Fewer alveoli mean that the surface area of the lungs is reduced, resulting in less diffusion of respiratory gases. In addition, cigarette smoke breaks down the elastic lining of the alveoli, reducing the ability of the alveoli (and lungs) to recoil during expiration. Air in damaged alveoli cannot be effectively expelled during expiration, leaving a layer of residual air in the alveoli that prevents inhaled fresh air reaching the gas exchange surfaces. People with advanced emphysema may find it difficult to walk more than a few steps due to a severe shortage of oxygen for respiration. Often by the time emphysema is diagnosed, the individual's lungs are irreversibly damaged.

Many smokers also suffer from **bronchitis**. Bronchitis is caused by inflammation of the bronchial tubes. Narrower bronchial tubes (caused by the inflammation) and associated increased mucus production significantly reduces air flow into and out of the lungs. The tar also paralyses the **cilia**, which help remove mucus and microbes from the respiratory tract, increasing the risk of infection. Not surprisingly, people with bronchitis suffer from breathlessness, coughing and increased susceptibility to infection.

Practical work

In this section you are expected to be familiar with the following apparatus:

- the J-tube.
- a respirometer.
- the Audus apparatus.
- and be able to use hydrogencarbonate (bicarbonate) indicator to demonstrate a compensation point.

The J-tube

The J-tube can be used to calculate the percentages of oxygen and carbon dioxide in air.

The procedure normally involves:

- using the syringe (or screw attachment) to trap an air column between water columns within a capillary tube. This is done by filling the J-tube with water, using the syringe to introduce air, then sucking in more water to trap and seal the air bubble.
- measuring the length (**A**) of the air column trapped between the water columns.

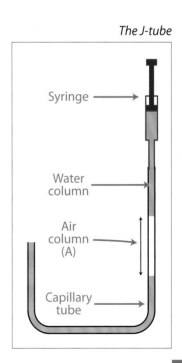

The J-tube

Syringe

Water column

Air column (A)

Capillary tube

- most (but not all) of the water below the air column is expelled and then **potassium hydroxide** is drawn into the tube. Shuttling the air column several times up and down the tube allows the air column to come in contact with the sides of the capillary tube wetted with potassium hydroxide – this then **absorbs the carbon dioxide** in the air column. The air column is then re-measured (**B**). The percentage of carbon dioxide in the air column is **A-B/A × 100**.

- most (but not all) of the potassium hydroxide is now expelled and **pyrogallol** drawn up into the tube. The potassium hydroxide and pyrogallol react to form **potassium pyrogallate**. Again the air column is shuttled up and down the tube using the syringe. This time the air column comes in contact with capillary sides wetted with potassium pyrogallate, which **absorbs the oxygen** in the air sample. The air column is then re-measured (**C**). The percentage of oxygen is **B-C/A × 100**.

The J-tube is typically used to compare the composition of inhaled (fresh) and exhaled air. Due to the small volumes of gas involved (particularly CO_2), it is important that temperature fluctuations are avoided (for example, through not handling the J-tube at the position of the air column and by setting it up under water) and that a number of repeat samples are taken for reliability. Additionally, it is important that the tube is allowed to equilibrate, for a number of minutes, at each stage before measurements are accurately taken.

The respirometer

Respirometers can be used to calculate CO_2 production and O_2 consumption in living organisms. There are many different types of respirometer but they all operate using the same principles as evident in the diagram opposite.

A simple respirometer

Calculating oxygen uptake – The carbon dioxide produced in respiration by the blowfly larvae is absorbed by the **potassium hydroxide (KOH)** in the respirometer. Oxygen taken in leads to a reduction in volume of air in the closed system and therefore the pressure falls. The oil droplet (or bubble within liquid) is drawn along the capillary tube due to the reduction in pressure. The distance moved by the oil droplet represents the oxygen used in respiration.

The actual quantity of oxygen used can be calculated by measuring the volume of the lumen of the capillary tube travelled by the oil droplet.

The volume of a cylinder is $\pi r^2 l$, where r is the radius of the lumen and l is the distance travelled by the oil droplet. If the mass of the blowfly larvae is known the oxygen uptake per gram can be calculated. Calculations often involve working out the oxygen consumption per gram per unit time (for example, per hour). Some respirometers have the scale calibrated for volume, simplifying the calculation of oxygen uptake.

Calculating carbon dioxide production – Repeat the process with the KOH replaced by **water**. Carbon dioxide produced in respiration is not absorbed as there is no KOH present. If over time the oil droplet does **not** move this means there is no pressure change, therefore the carbon dioxide produced in respiration must be **exactly the same** as the oxygen taken in. For example, if the respiring tissue originally used 20 mm^3 of oxygen (calculated with KOH present) in 10 minutes, then if the same tissue (organism(s)) is used for 10 minutes with water replacing the KOH, it can be assumed that 20 mm^3 of carbon dioxide is produced.

In practice, there may be more or less carbon dioxide produced than oxygen used, therefore the oil droplet may move a small distance in either direction from its starting position. If the oil droplet moves **away** from the respirometer there is **more carbon dioxide produced than oxygen taken in** but if it moves **closer** to the respirometer there is **less carbon dioxide produced than oxygen taken in** (ie the carbon dioxide produced does not compensate for the pressure reduction caused by the oxygen uptake). In our example (above), if the oil droplet moved 3 mm^3 away from the respirometer, when the water is used, the amount of carbon dioxide produced is 20 + 3 = 23 mm^3 (assuming that 1 mm distance in this respirometer = 1 mm^3).

In this type of experiment it is critical that **all possible variables are controlled**. Where possible it is often best to use the same apparatus for calculating the oxygen uptake (with KOH) and for calculating carbon dioxide production (with water) with the same living organisms (this ensures factors such as age and metabolic rate of the organisms are controlled as far as possible). Other variables such as temperature can be controlled by placing the apparatus in a water bath at the same temperature for both parts of the experiment. The control of temperature is important as changes in temperature can affect both rate of respiration and gas volume in the system. It is also important to calculate oxygen uptake and carbon dioxide production over the same time period.

The Audus apparatus

The Audus apparatus can be used to measure the rate of photosynthesis in different environmental conditions. For example, it can be used to measure the rate in different light intensities. This is achieved either by moving a light source in steps away from the apparatus or measuring the rate of photosynthesis in different wavelengths of light by using filters to produce the required wavelengths.

The gas produced (mainly oxygen) from photosynthesising pondweed is collected at the flared end of the capillary tube for a **set period of time** (for example, 5–10 minutes). After this time, the gas collected is drawn into the capillary tube by pulling the plunger on the syringe until the **volume** (or length) of the bubble of oxygen produced can be measured on the scale. The experiment can be repeated with the independent variable changed as required.

The Audus apparatus

As with many biology experiments, it is important to **control all variables** not being investigated. For example, if the effect of light intensity on the rate of photosynthesis is being investigated, it is important to ensure that temperature is controlled by the use of a water bath and that carbon dioxide levels are not limiting by using hydrogencarbonate solution to produce carbon dioxide. The experiment should be **repeated** at least three times for each value of the independent variable to increase **reliability**.

> **Note:** some types of apparatus used in this experiment do not have the capillary tube calibrated to volume. If the capillary tube is calibrated for distance only, the volume of oxygen produced can be calculated if the diameter of the capillary bore is known using the formula for the volume of a cylinder discussed on page 124.

Using hydrogencarbonate (bicarbonate) indicator to demonstrate a compensation point

In normal atmospheric levels of carbon dioxide, hydrogencarbonate indicator solution is **orange-red**. Increasing acidity (more carbon dioxide added due to increasing carbon dioxide levels in the atmosphere) turns the indicator **yellow** and decreased acidity (carbon dioxide lost from the solution due to less carbon dioxide in the atmosphere) causes the solution to turn **purple**.

If living organisms are placed in a closed container containing hydrogencarbonate indicator, the processes of respiration (and photosynthesis if plant material is used) can be monitored through the net exchange of carbon dioxide between the living organism(s) and the atmosphere in the closed container.

Results:

In boiling tube A – the hydrogencarbonate indicator turned **purple** as photosynthesis was taking place at a much faster rate than respiration, therefore there was a reduction in the level of carbon dioxide in the tube.

In boiling tube B – the indicator turned **yellow** as respiration only was taking place (no photosynthesis due to the foil), therefore there was an increase in carbon dioxide.

In boiling tube C – the indicator remained **orange-red** as the muslin provided partial shading. Enough light reached the pondweed to allow photosynthesis to take place at a reduced rate. The indicator remained orange-red as the rates of photosynthesis and respiration were equal, with the volume of carbon dioxide produced in respiration being equal to the volume of carbon dioxide used in photosynthesis. This shows the **compensation point**.

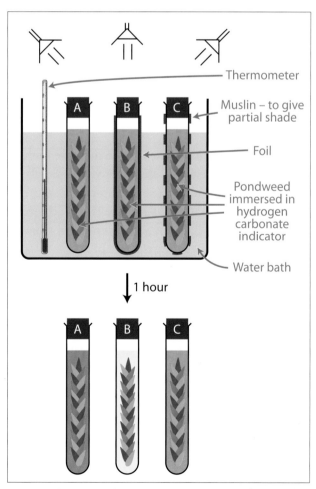

Using hydrogencarbonate indicator in monitoring the exchange of carbon dioxide

Exam Questions

1. Describe how gas exchange is facilitated in the lungs of a mammal. [3]

   Question taken from CCEA's Biology Assessment Unit AS2, Organisms and Biodiversity, June 2011, © CCEA 2012

2. The diagram below shows a magnified view of a section of lung tissue.

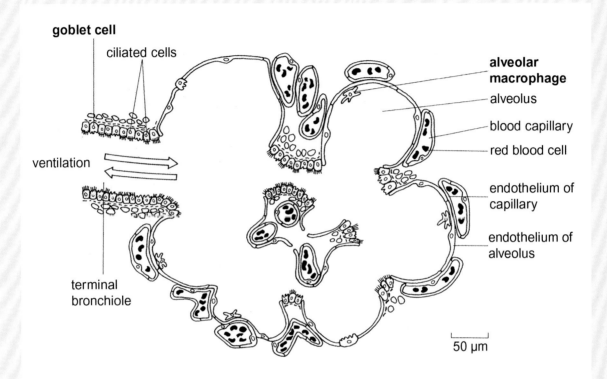

Figure from A Level Biology by WD Phillips & TJ Chilton (OUP, 1994) © Oxford University Press, reprinted by permission of Oxford University Press

   (a) Using the information in the diagram, describe **three** features of the lung tissue which facilitate gas exchange. [3]

   (b) Suggest a role for each of the following.
   - goblet cell
   - alveolar macrophage [2]

   Question taken from CCEA's Biology Assessment Unit AS2, Organisms and Biodiversity, January 2010, © CCEA 2012

3. The diagram at the beginning of page 128 represents a transverse section through a mesophytic leaf as seen through the light microscope.

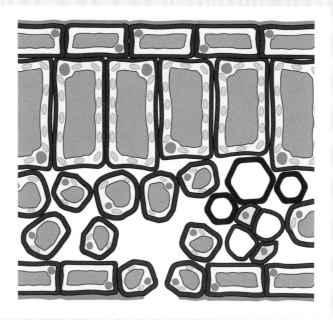

For copyright reasons this diagram has replaced the diagram from
CCEA's Biology AS2, June 2010 paper.

(a) Describe **three** ways in which the mesophytic leaf is adapted for the uptake of carbon dioxide. [3]

Hydrogencarbonate (bicarbonate) indicator can be used to illustrate changes in the concentration of atmospheric carbon dioxide. The colour changes are illustrated below:

Carbon dioxide ← Normal carbon dioxide levels → Carbon dioxide
levels raised   levels lowered
[YELLOW]   [ORANGE/RED]   [PURPLE]

An experiment was carried out to investigate the light compensation point of a leaf. A pair of tubes, one containing a leaf (**A**) and the other without a leaf (**B**) was set up as shown in the diagram below.

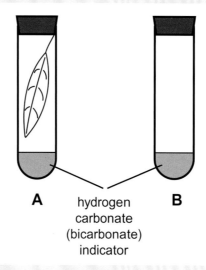

A   hydrogen   B
carbonate
(bicarbonate)
indicator

This was repeated five times, and each pair of **A** and **B** tubes was illuminated at different light intensities for 30 minutes.

The hydrogencarbonate (bicarbonate) indicator was orange/red in both tubes initially, and remained orange/red in tube **B** at all light intensities.

The colour of the solution in tube **A** at different light intensities is shown in the table below.

Resultant colour of indicator in tube A after 30 minutes	Light intensity/arbitrary units				
	1	4	8	16	64
	yellow	orange	orange/red	purple	purple

(b) Explain why the tubes were sealed during the experimental period. [1]

(c) Explain the purpose of tube **B** at each of the light intensities. [1]

(d) Explain the results of the experiment at light intensity **1**. [2]

(e) Use the results of this experiment to determine the light compensation point for this plant. Explain your answer. [3]

Question taken from CCEA's Biology Assessment Unit AS2, Organisms and Biodiversity, June 2010, © CCEA 2012

4. An investigation was designed to determine the effect of light intensity on gas exchange by pondweed. The experiment setup is shown in the diagram below.

In **A**, the lamp was placed close to a test tube containing pondweed immersed in an indicator solution.

In **B**, the lamp was placed further away.

In each case, the indicator was orange-red initially. After 1 hour, the colour was observed and recorded.

The experimental setup and results are shown below.

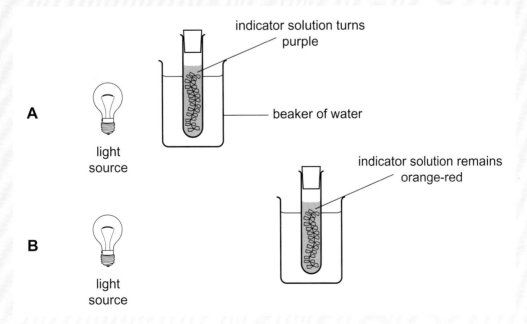

(a) Name the indicator solution used and the gas which caused the change in **A**. [1]

(b) Suggest a reason for the test tube containing the pondweed being placed in a beaker of water. [1]

(c) Explain why the indicator solution remained orange-red in **B**. [2]

Question taken from CCEA's Biology Assessment Unit AS2, Organisms and Biodiversity, January 2011, © CCEA 2012

5. The J-tube apparatus, illustrated below, can be used to analyse the composition of an air column that has been trapped in the capillary tube.

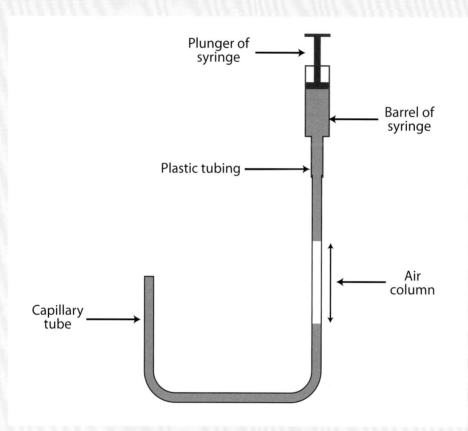

For copyright reasons this diagram has replaced the diagram from
CCEA's Biology AS2, January 2010 paper.

(a) Explain why the analysis of the air column is carried out when the J-tube apparatus is under water. [1]

The following results were obtained using the J-tube apparatus.

Original length of air column: 10.0 cm

Length of air column after potassium hydroxide treatment: 9.6 cm

Length of air column after pyrogallol treatment: 8.0 cm

(i) Use the above results to calculate the percentage of oxygen in the air column. (Show your working.) [2]

(ii) From your result above, what can you conclude about the source of the air sample? [1]

Question taken from CCEA's Biology Assessment Unit AS2, Organisms and Biodiversity, January 2010, © CCEA 2012

6. Quality of written communication is awarded a maximum of 2 marks in this section. [2]

   The relationships between the various factors affecting the rate of gas exchange are expressed in Fick's Law:

   $$\text{Rate of diffusion} \propto \frac{\text{Surface area} \times \text{concentration gradient}}{\text{diffusion distance}}$$

   (a) Explain the influence of each factor on the rate of diffusion. [3]

   (b) With reference to these factors, describe how the mammalian lung is adapted to maximise gaseous exchange. [10]
   - Surface area
   - Concentration gradient
   - Diffusion distance

   Question taken from CCEA's Biology Assessment Unit AS2, Organisms and Biodiversity, June 2010, © CCEA 2012

Chapter 9 – Transport in Plants and Transpiration

Students should be able to:

2.1.9   Recognise and understand plant tissues in relation to water (and ion) transport and translocation.

2.1.10   Understand the uptake of water and mineral ions by root hairs.

2.1.11   Understand the apoplast and symplast pathways through plant tissues.

2.1.12   Understand transpiration and the factors influencing its rate.

2.1.13   Understand the movement of water (and dissolved ions) through xylem.

2.1.14   Understand the translocation of organic solutes through phloem.

2.1.15   Understand the structural adaptations of xerophytes and hydrophytes.

2.1.16   Practical work to include the bubble potometer and its use in the measurement of the rate of water uptake.

As with animal cells, water and other materials can move from cell to cell in a plant by a number of processes. As in multicellular animals, plants have specialised tissues and cells that are adapted for the mass flow of water and other substances.

Plant vascular tissues

1. Structure of plant roots

The cross-section of a typical plant root opposite shows the relative positions of **vascular tissues** specialised for the transport of water and ions (xylem) and organic molecules such as sugars and amino acids (phloem).

The outer layer of the root (as in leaves and stems) is the **epidermis** and vascular tissue is concentrated in a central **stele (vascular cylinder)**. The single layer of cells immediately outside the stele is the **endodermis**. The layer of undifferentiated cells between the epidermis and the endodermis is the **cortex**. Cells in the cortex typically have small air spaces between them and the cells themselves may be rich in starch grains.

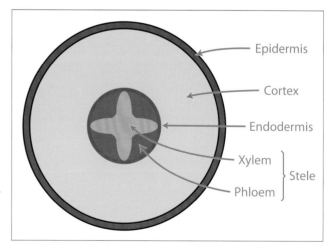

A cross-section of a root

The stele is mainly composed of **xylem** tissue with a smaller amount of **phloem** tissue.

Xylem tissue

The xylem is differentiated into a number of cell types but the main type involved in water and ion transport is the **xylem vessel**. Xylem vessels are highly specialised for transport. They have **no end walls**, **no cell contents** and are **dead** when fully formed. A column of vessels produces a long continuous tube up the plant, ideal for water transport. In addition, the (secondary) cells walls are specially thickened with an impermeable substance called **lignin**.

There are a number of different patterns of lignification in xylem. First-formed xylem (**protoxylem**), typically in the region of elongation behind the root tip, has **annular** or **spiral** thickening (cell wall thickening in the forms of discrete loops or a continuous spiral). Lignin laid down in these patterns does not restrict the elongation of the xylem vessels as growth of root tips takes place.

The xylem vessels in the more mature parts of the root (**metaxylem**) often have a more complete covering of lignin to give a **reticulate** or **pitted** pattern. In pitted vessels there is an almost complete covering of lignin so small **pits** are present (hence the name 'pitted') that allows the movement of water between adjacent vessels and surrounding cells.

The **lignin** has two very important properties:

- it provides great **strength** that prevents the vessels from collapsing when under pressure exerted by the transpiration stream 'sucking' water up the plant. This strength is also important in providing structural support for the plant.

- it is **waterproof**, which prevents the leakage of water.

Note: although protoxylem is typically formed in young growing regions and metaxylem in more mature parts of the plant, the two types of tissue often occur together. New xylem cells are produced in a meristematic region (the **cambium**) between the xylem and the phloem. Consequently, in roots the protoxylem is pushed to the outer edge of the stele as the metaxylem forms behind it. The protoxylem cells are typically smaller and have less thickened walls than the metaxylem.

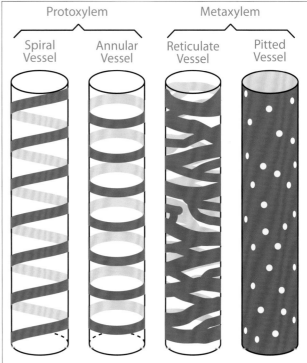

Patterns of lignification in xylem vessels

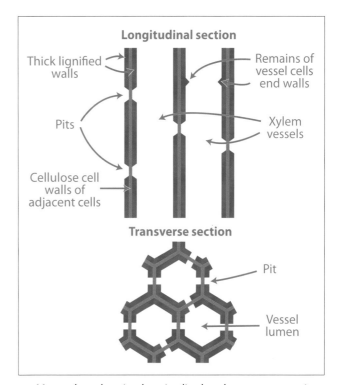

Metaxylem showing longitudinal and transverse sections

Phloem tissue

Phloem tissue also consists of a number of cell types. The cells primarily concerned with transport are the **sieve tube elements**. These are aligned end to end and form a continuous row called the **sieve tube**. Unlike xylem vessels they do have end walls but these are perforated with **sieve pores** to form **sieve plates**. Sieve tube elements are living cells with cell contents. However, by the time they are fully grown they have no nuclei and the reduced volume of cytoplasm is displaced to the side walls and there are few organelles.

Although not visible in the diagram below, sieve elements have **microtubules** that extend between sieve elements and pass through the sieve pores. It is thought that these are involved in the process of translocation of solutes.

Each sieve tube cell (element) is closely associated with one or more **companion cells**. These companion cells have a dense cytoplasm rich in mitochondria and other organelles and have a high metabolic rate. Companion cells are linked to the sieve tube elements by **plasmodesmata**. They act as supporting cells, carrying out many metabolic activities for the highly specialised sieve tube elements, allowing them to be specialised for the transport of organic products through the plant.

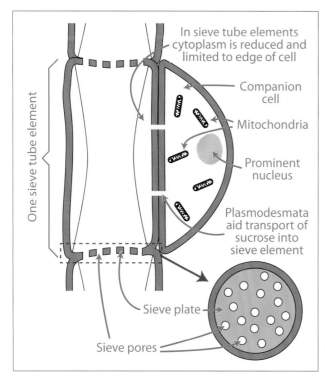

Phloem sieve tube element and associated companion cell

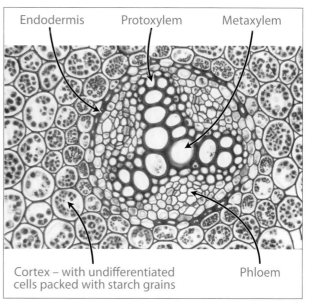

Photograph of a section through a root vascular cylinder

Biodisc, Visuals Unlimited/Science Photo Library

2. Structure of plant stems

The xylem and phloem tissue described in the previous sections has the same structure and function in plant stems. However, the **distribution** of the tissues is different. The vascular tissue is arranged as **vascular bundles** (see cross-section on page 135) around the outside of the stem; one advantage of this arrangement is the provision of the greater support necessary in stems to support branches and leaves. In the vascular bundles the protoxylem is usually in the section of xylem closer to the centre of the stem, with the metaxylem in the section of xylem closer to the outer edge of the stem.

As smaller branches (stems) continually branch they eventually form leaves. A vascular bundle continues into the leaf as the midrib, which branches to form smaller veins that

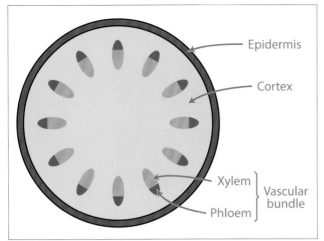

A cross-section through a stem showing the distribution of the main tissues

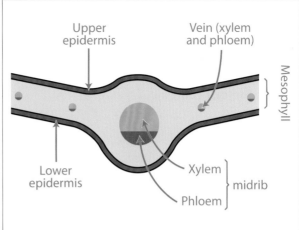

The distribution of vascular tissue in a leaf

are distributed throughout the leaf. The leaf veins are typically found in the spongy mesophyll just below the palisade layer.

Note: the cross-sections of plant roots and stems covered in this section describe the pattern in herbaceous (green) plants. The arrangement is different in woody plants (trees and shrubs). Wood is formed of xylem tissue, therefore woody plants in cross-section are almost all xylem, with very small amounts of phloem and other tissues.

The uptake and transport of water and ions in plants

Plants continually lose water by evaporation. Transpiration is the term used to describe the process of water loss by evaporation in plants. In reality, water continually enters plants (usually through the roots) and passes up through the root, through the stem and evaporates out of the leaves.

It is convenient to consider the movement of water and ions through a plant as having three distinct phases:

1. The transport of water (and ions) into and across the root.
2. Transport up the root and stem in the xylem.
3. Transport through the leaf and the evaporation of water from the leaf.

1. The transport of water and ions into and across the root

Root hair cells have **large surface areas** that facilitate the uptake of water into the root. The water enters by **osmosis**, as in normal circumstances the water in the soil has a higher water potential than the root hair cells due to the sugars and other compounds present in the cells. Uptake of water is aided by the presence of a thin exchange surface. The cell-surface membrane is the effective exchange surface, as the cell wall is permeable and a typical root has many thousand root hairs.

Once into the root hair cell, the water moves across the cells of the cortex and into the xylem in the stele. There are two main pathways involved:

- The apoplast pathway
- The symplast pathway

The apoplast pathway – involves water moving along the **cellulose** microfibrils of the cell walls. This is facilitated by the parallel arrangement of the microfibrils in the cellulose wall, an arrangement that allows water to pass easily between the different layers, rather than through them. The general mesh-like arrangement of the walls further aids movement. As the water moves through the wall, the cohesive properties of the water (aided by hydrogen bonding) help pull the water column along. Due to the limited resistance to water movement by the apoplast pathway, most water tends to move by this method.

Absorption of water by a root hair cell

The symplast pathway – involves water moving by **osmosis** from cell to cell across the cortex. The movement of water across the root creates the water potential gradient necessary for this to take place. For example, as a root hair cell takes in water, its water potential rises and becomes higher than the adjacent cell in the root cortex. Water moves from the root hair cell into the cortex cell by osmosis and so on across the cells of the cortex.

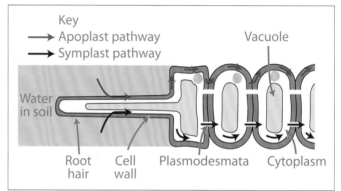

The apoplast and symplast pathways

In the symplast pathway the water moves from cell to cell through **plasmodesmata** that link the cells of the cortex together. The diagram above summarises the two different pathways.

Ions – can enter the root hair cells by **facilitated diffusion** or by **active transport**, depending on the concentration gradient for the particular ion concerned. Intake of ions is often by active transport causing the build up of ions in the plant cells, thereby requiring the ions to be moved against the concentration gradient.

The transport of water and ions into the xylem – the **endodermis** is the layer of cells immediately outside the stele. It has a waterproof layer formed of **suberin** (the **Casparian strip**) embedded in the cellulose cell wall that encircles each cell. The positioning of the Casparian strip prevents the movement of water through the endodermis via the apoplast pathway. At that point, water being transported by the apoplast pathway moves into the protoplast to join the water transported by the symplast pathway. Consequently, all water moving into the stele is transported by the symplast pathway. This ensures that water transport at this point is under metabolic control, an important point in promoting transport into the xylem.

The endodermal cells pump ions into the xylem cells, a process that involves **energy expenditure**. This creates a water potential gradient that draws water from the endodermis into the xylem. The movement of water osmotically into the base of the xylem tissue creates a **root pressure** force that helps to move water up the plant. In large plants (large herbs, shrubs and trees) the force generated by root pressure is not enough to move water up through the entire plant but it can be a significant contribution in many (particularly smaller) plants.

The role of the endodermis in the transport of water into the xylem

Additionally, the cohesive pull of water by the transpiration stream in the xylem helps move water from the endodermis into the xylem.

2. Transport of water up the root and stem in the xylem

In most plants the movement of water (and ions) from root hair to the xylem involves a distance of a few millimetres or centimetres at the most. Movement up the xylem in the root and stem often involve distances of many metres.

As water evaporates out of the stomata in the leaf, it creates a **negative pressure** that pulls the water column up through the xylem as a **mass flow** movement. This process requires the water column to form a continuous unbroken pathway through the xylem (the **transpiration stream**). Water molecules form hydrogen bonds between one another, a feature known as **cohesion**, and this tends to stick the water molecules together. It is the cohesive properties of water that allows the water to be 'sucked' up the xylem in a continuous column, as the water at the leading edge of the column evaporates out of the leaf (analogous to drinking water through a straw).

This theory is known as the **cohesion-tension** theory and the driving force is the evaporation (transpiration) of water out of the leaves, resulting in the **transpiration pull**.

Evidence for the cohesion-tension theory:

- If the water column in the xylem is broken and an air gap appears, water below the gap cannot be pulled up (in reality each column of xylem vessels can be treated as a single column of water, so a water column can be disrupted in one xylem column but continue in others). The same principle applies when keeping cut flowers in containers of water in shops – if the time between buying the flowers and placing them in a vase of water at home is too long, air will enter the bottom of the cut stems as the water column moves up due to loss of water by evaporation. Placing them in water after this has happened will make no difference (as the column is broken) and the flowers will rapidly wilt as they are starved of water even though the stems may be immersed in it.

- During the day, when transpiration is normally at its greatest, there is much more tension, or negative pressure, in the xylem. This negative pressure tends to pull the walls of the xylem vessels in and can reduce the diameter of a tree trunk.

Note 1: changing diameters in tree trunks is more obvious than in herbaceous plants due to the fact that a tree trunk is almost all xylem and therefore much of it is involved in water uptake.

Note 2: remember that the lignin in the xylem vessels gives it two important properties; it is waterproof, avoiding the loss of water and it is very strong, allowing the vessels to withstand the pressures exerted on it by the transpiration pull.

Note 3: the missing end walls and absence of cell contents in xylem vessels make them highly adapted for water transport by the cohesion-tension method.

In most plants the **cohesion-tension** theory is probably the most important process involved in moving water up through the xylem in roots and stems. However, on page 137 we also noted the importance of **root pressure** in some plants and it probably contributes somewhat (albeit in a minor role) in most species.

The **adhesive** property of water is also important. If a drinking straw or a capillary tube is placed in water, the water will move up the tube to some extent. This is due to the adhesive forces between the substances in the straw, or capillary tube, and the water being stronger than the cohesive forces between the water molecules themselves. Adhesion is therefore the attraction of unlike materials. This phenomenon, known as **capillarity**, has a role in water transport in the xylem. It may not have a significant role in moving the water up the xylem but the adhesive forces between the water column and the xylem walls may reduce the forces necessary for the transpiration pull.

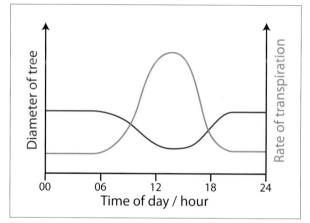

The relationship between rate of transpiration from the leaves and diameter of a tree trunk

3. The transport of water through the leaf and the evaporation of water

Water enters the leaf in the midrib (vascular bundle). In most leaves this midrib splits into a number of veins that distribute water across the leaf. Water passes from the vein to the surrounding cells, where some is used in photosynthesis or in providing turgor but most is lost in transpiration. Transpiration losses are due to water **evaporating from the cell-surface membranes** of the spongy mesophyll cells into the air spaces of the spongy mesophyll, with the water vapour **diffusing** down the concentration gradient out of the **stomata (transpiration)**. This process sets up the water potential gradient that is ultimately responsible for the transpirational pull.

The water travels across the leaf (from the xylem to the spongy mesophyll cells) by the same processes involved in water transport across the root, ie the apoplast and symplast pathways.

Note 1: while most water vapour diffuses out of the stomata, some water is lost through the **waxy cuticle** – cuticular transpiration.

Note 2: if a plant (leaf) is dehydrated the stomata will automatically close, irrespective of whether it is day or night. This is a defensive mechanism to conserve water in times of significant water stress.

The translocation of organic solutes through the phloem

Translocation is the term used to describe the movement of **organic substances** in the phloem. The phloem transports organic substances from the leaves to the growing regions of the plant (for example, carbohydrate for energy and amino acids for growth) and to the roots (for storage).

The main substance transported in the phloem is the disaccharide **sucrose**.

There are two key features associated with translocation: the process is **energy requiring** and **two-way transport** exists, ie translocation can move sucrose both up and down sieve tubes.

Evidence for **energy expenditure** comes from a number of sources:

- **companion cells** have high rates of metabolic activity. They are intimately associated with sieve tube elements and their energy output is linked to processes that take place in the sieve tubes. Companion cells in the phloem in leaf veins are also involved in the uptake of sucrose from adjacent (photosynthesising) cells and the subsequent 'loading' of sucrose into the sieve tube elements via plasmodesmata, before being transported around the plant.
- **metabolic inhibitors**, such as cyanide, that stop respiration in plant cells also disrupts the process of translocation.

Evidence for the **two-way movement** of sucrose in the phloem comes from the use of **radioactively-labelled** sucrose (sucrose produced using $^{14}CO_2$), which shows that the sucrose can move both up and down the stem. A leaf on a branch half way down a stem may send sucrose both up the plant to growing shoot tip regions and also down to the roots for storage as starch. It has also been shown that sucrose can move up in one sieve tube and down in an adjacent sieve tube. Although translocation is another example of a **mass flow** system, the localised build up of sucrose ('**source**') helps create a hydrostatic gradient between some parts of the plant (for example, leaves) and the '**sink**' where sucrose levels are lower (for example, the roots where it is built up into starch for storage **or** a growing region where it is converted into glucose for use in respiration).

Xerophytes and hydrophytes

In most plants a conflict exists between having a large exchange surface for gas exchange and reducing water loss by transpiration. This is complicated by the fact that the same exchange surface (the cell-surface membrane of the spongy mesophyll cells) is responsible for **both** gas exchange **and** the evaporation of water in transpiration. In many typical plants (mesophytes) water conservation measures include adaptations such as a waterproofed cuticle, stomata that can be opened or closed and exchange surfaces that are protected within the leaf from excessive rates of evaporation. These features reduce excessive transpiration but do not overly restrict the rates of gas exchange, which is necessary for rapid photosynthesis and hence rapid growth.

Xerophytes

However, some plants are very highly adapted to reduce water loss by transpiration. These are xerophytes, with the cacti being perhaps the best known example of this group.

The typical structural adaptations found in xerophytes are listed in the following table.

Adaptation	Explanation of adaptation
Leaf curvature	Some xerophytes fold their leaves so that the 'lower' epidermis is enclosed and protected within the leaf, for example, marram grass. This is particularly effective as the stomata are confined to the lower epidermis (as in many species) and it is this layer that lies within the fold. This **folding** creates a layer of humid air within the leaf, significantly reducing the water potential gradient between the inside and the outside of the leaf. This limits the rate of evaporation and consequently transpiration.
Reduced surface area	Many cacti have their leaves reduced to **spines** or **needles**. This reduction in leaf surface area reduces the area across which transpiration can take place. The needles also prevent the plant being grazed by herbivores – particularly important as many cacti have succulent stems. **Note:** in these plants the 'leaves' no longer have a photosynthesising role, the stem carries out this role instead.
Cuticular thickening	A **thick cuticle** makes this waterproofed layer even more efficient in reducing evaporation.
Leaf hairs	Many leaves have a **layer of hairs**, often confined to the lower epidermis. These hairs restrict air flow over the leaf surface and help trap a layer of humid air. Again this serves to reduce the water potential gradient between the inside and outside of the leaf. Most of these hairs are very small and therefore cannot be seen by the naked eye.
Sunken stomata	**Stomata sunk in pits** or grooves is another important method of reducing transpiration losses by creating a layer of humid air around the stomata. The layers or zones of humid air described throughout this table are called **diffusion shells**. Again this works by reducing the water potential gradient between the inside and outside of the leaf. This adaptation is often accompanied by a reduction in the number of stomata in the leaf.
Succulent tissue	Many xerophytes have **succulent** (juicy) leaves that store large quantities of water which can be used in periods of drought, for example, cacti and jade (*Crassula ovata*).
Deep roots	Roots that penetrate **deep** into the soil to reach water well below the ground are common in xerophytes. Another adaptation is very **shallow** roots. Many desert plants have very shallow roots that cover a wide area around the plant but lie just below the surface. This ensures that the infrequent rain water that does fall can be quickly absorbed before it gets a chance to evaporate from the top layers of the soil.

The photograph at the beginning of page 141 shows marram grass growing on sand dunes immediately adjacent to the beach. While there is abundant rainfall, the inability of the sand to retain water means that plants able to colonise these habitats have many xerophytic adaptations.

Marram grass growing in a sand dune system

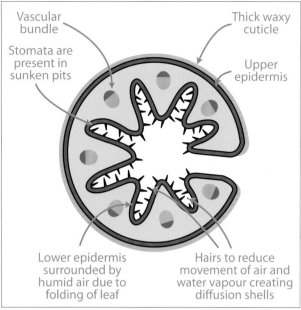

Vascular bundle

Stomata are present in sunken pits

Thick waxy cuticle

Upper epidermis

Lower epidermis surrounded by humid air due to folding of leaf

Hairs to reduce movement of air and water vapour creating diffusion shells

Cross-section through a marram grass leaf

Xerophytic adaptations in jade (left) and a cactus (right).

In jade the leaves are succulent and have a very thick cuticle.

In this cactus the leaves are reduced to sharp spines, which both reduce water loss due to the reduction in leaf area and help protect the succulent stem.

Note: many tree species typically occurring in northern boreal forests, such as pine, show xerophytic adaptations. Although rain/snow may be common in these habitats, the frozen ground reduces water availability. Adaptations in pines include needle shaped leaves and stomata sunk in pits.

Hydrophytes

Hydrophytes are adapted for living in water. These plants have adaptations for growing in or on water, for example, water lilies.

Typical adaptations include the **stomata** being restricted to the upper leaf surface – to prevent them being submerged in water and ensuring that gas exchange with the atmosphere can take place – and the presence of large air spaces (**aerenchyma**) that enables the plant (leaf) to float.

Note: exam questions covering this topic often involve photographs of the leaves of xerophytic plants or hydrophytes. Depending on the degree of adaptation, the leaf may show a small or a wide range of the adaptations listed on page 140.

Practical work

The 'bubble' potometer can both measure the rate of water uptake and compare rates of transpiration in different environmental conditions.

Measuring the rate of water uptake

The potometer measures the amount of **water uptake** into the plant shoot. It is important to note that this is **not** the same as measuring the volume of water transpired out of the leaves. This is because it is impossible to know how much water is used to maintain turgor in the plant cells or is used in photosynthesis or in other ways.

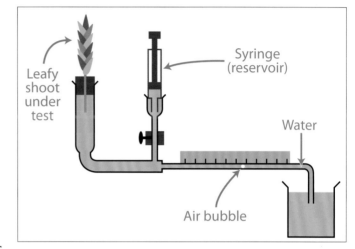

The potometer

The potometer can be a temperamental piece of apparatus to use and often fails to give reliable results unless it is airtight. Many of the procedures used in setting up the potometer help ensure that it remains airtight.

Typical procedure:

- a leafy shoot is cut under water to avoid air bubbles entering the xylem.
- the potometer is filled with water in a basin, again making sure there are no air bubbles.
- the shoot is inserted into the potometer, again under water.
- the potometer is removed from the water and all joints sealed with Vaseline/ petroleum jelly.
- an air bubble is introduced into the end of the capillary tube by exposing the open end of the capillary tube to air for a short period. As the water is drawn up the tube, it creates an air bubble before the capillary is placed back in the water again.
- the syringe (or the tap on the reservoir) can be used to push the bubble back to the start of the scale, to allow for repeat readings to ensure reliability.
- the mean distance moved by the bubble over a set period of time is calculated. This can be converted to volume of water lost per unit time ($\pi r^2 l$ where r is the radius of the capillary tube and l is the mean distance moved by the bubble over a set period of time).

Comparing the rate of transpiration in different environmental conditions

Factors that affect the rate of **evaporation** will affect the rate of transpiration.

Increasing **humidity** (by covering the plant with a clear plastic bag) will decrease transpiration, as humid air will decrease the water potential gradient between the inside of the leaves and the surrounding atmosphere. The sub-stomatal air spaces become more humid due to the build up of water vapour, reducing evaporation from the spongy mesophyll cells – the same principle that applies with many xerophytic adaptations.

Increasing **temperature** gives the water molecules more kinetic energy, increasing the evaporation of water from the spongy mesophyll cells.

Increasing **wind speed** also increases the rate of transpiration, as the wind removes diffusion shells by blowing humid air away from the leaf. This maintains a steep water potential gradient between the inside and the outside of the leaf, allowing water to evaporate rapidly from the spongy mesophyll cells into the air spaces of the spongy mesophyll.

When carrying out investigations of this nature, it is important to ensure that all other factors that affect transpiration are controlled and that the apparatus is given time to acclimatise to the particular environmental condition being investigated. It is also necessary to use the same cut shoot in the potometer throughout the investigation, as changing the shoot would introduce many variables that would be impossible to control, for example, the surface area of the leaves, the number of stomata, the area of the cut shoot in contact with the water.

As **light** has little effect on the rate of evaporation on its own, changing **light intensity** will not have a significant effect on the rate of transpiration. However, the rate of transpiration will be greater during the day (**in light**) compared to during the night (**in darkness**), as the stomata in most plants are often closed when it is dark.

In nature (as in experimental conditions), humidity, temperature, air currents (wind) and light will influence transpiration rate as discussed above but **soil water availability** will also affect transpiration rate.

Note: it is appropriate to use the potometer to compare rates of transpiration (although not absolute values). This is because around 99% of the water taken up by the plant in the potometer is transpired and therefore gives an accurate reflection of the influence of the environmental factors investigated.

Exam questions

1. (a) Xylem and phloem are both composite tissues with a variety of cell types.

   (i) Describe the distribution of xylem and phloem tissues in the stem of a flowering plant. [2]

   (ii) Phloem sieve tubes are the main cell type in phloem tissue.

   Describe **two** major features of phloem sieve tubes. [2]

   (b) The diagram below shows different forms of lignification patterns in xylem vessels.

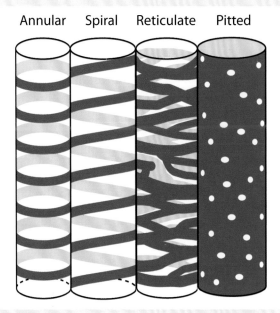

Annular   Spiral   Reticulate   Pitted

For copyright reasons this diagram has replaced the diagram from CCEA's Biology AS2, June 2010 paper.

   (i) Explain why the added strength which lignin provides in the xylem vessels is necessary for their functioning. [2]

   (ii) Suggest why the xylem vessels in young stems have rings or spirals of lignin whereas older stems will have reticulate walls. [2]

   Question taken from CCEA's Biology Assessment Unit AS2, Organisms and Biodiversity, June 2010, © CCEA 2012

2. An investigation was undertaken to determine the relationship between stomatal density and the rate of transpirational water loss in daffodil leaves.

   The stomata of daffodil leaves are found on both surfaces of the leaf.

   (a) A student took five counts of stomata in areas 2 mm × 2 mm (4 mm^2) on both surfaces. The mean number of stomata per 4 mm^2 was then calculated and, for the upper epidermis, this was converted to a count per cm^2. The results are shown in the table on page 145.

   (i) Make a copy of the table and complete it by entering a mean value for the number of stomata per cm^2 in the shaded cell. [1]

	Number of stomata	
	Upper epidermis	**Lower epidermis**
Replicated counts/ 4 mm^{-2}	136	67
	146	81
	132	90
	154	58
Mean count/4 mm^{-2}	142	74
Mean count/cm^{-2}	3550	

(ii) Assess the variation shown within the replicates and comment on reliability of the measurements. [2]

(b) An estimate was made of the amount of transpiration from both surfaces of a daffodil leaf by sticking small pieces of dry cobalt chloride paper on the upper and lower epidermis. The cobalt chloride paper changes from blue to pink as it absorbs water. The graph below shows the colour changes over a period of 60 minutes.

(i) Using the information in the graph and the table above it, explain the colour changes shown. [3]

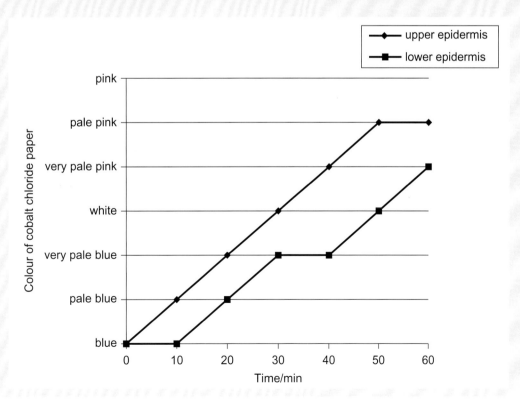

(ii) Covering part of the leaf with the cobalt chloride paper may reduce the transpiration in that part. Suggest **one** reason for this. [1]

(c) Explain how water loss from the leaf provides a means for water transport in the whole plant. [2]

Question taken from CCEA's Biology Assessment Unit AS2, Organisms and Biodiversity, January 2011, © CCEA 2012

3. The photograph below is a photomicrograph of a transverse section through a leaf of heather (genus *Erica*). Heather is a xerophyte.

   (a) Draw a block diagram to show the tissue layers in the leaf as shown in the photograph. Label the tissue layers. [5]

   (b) Explain how each of the following xerophytic features in the heather leaf further limits water loss.
   • The thick cuticle   • Hairs on the surface   [2]

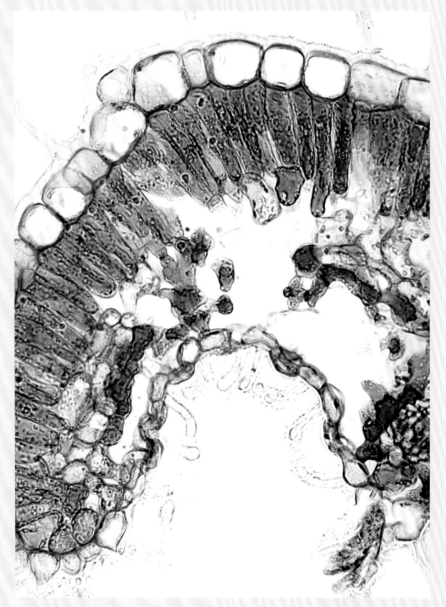

Dr Keith Wheeler/Science Photo Library

Question taken from CCEA's Biology Assessment Unit AS2, Organisms and Biodiversity, January 2011, © CCEA 2012

4. A potometer is a device for investigating the rate of transpiration. Prior to setting up, the potometer and the stem of a leafy shoot are immersed in water. Under water, the bottom centimetre of the stem is cut off and the cut end inserted into the rubber bung. The apparatus is removed from the water, a bubble of air allowed to enter the open end of the capillary tube and that end then inserted into a beaker of water. The completed set-up for a simple potometer is shown below.

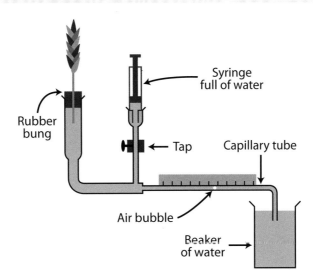

For copyright reasons this diagram has replaced the diagram from CCEA's Biology AS2, June 2009 paper.

(a) What assumption is made when this apparatus is used to investigate the rate of transpiration? [1]

(b) Explain each of the following.
   • why it is necessary to cut the leafy shoot and fit it into the potometer under water
   • how the bubble of air is introduced into the capillary tube
   • why a syringe is attached
   • why the set-up is left for 15 minutes before taking readings [4]

(c) The table below shows some results recorded using the apparatus.

Time/minutes	Distance travelled by bubble/mm		
	"Normal" room conditions	Covered with clear plastic bag	Covered with black plastic bag
0	0	0	0
2	18	10	4
4	36	19	8
6	55	29	11
8	74	38	15
10	90	48	18

(i) Explain, as fully as possible, the results obtained. [3]

(ii) In 'normal' room conditions, the distance moved by the bubble was 90 mm during 10 minutes. The capillary tube has a cross-sectional area of 0.8 mm². Calculate the rate of movement in mm³ minute⁻¹. (Show your working.) [2]

(d) In experiments using a potometer it is usual to use the same shoot throughout. Give **one** limitation of using different shoots in the potometer when investigating the rate of transpiration. [1]

Question taken from CCEA's Biology Assessment Unit AS2, Organisms and Biodiversity, June 2009, © CCEA 2012

5. Quality of written communication is awarded a maximum of 2 marks in this section. [2]

Give an account of the processes involved in the movement of water through a plant, to include:
- the uptake of water into and through the root
- the movement of water through the stem
- the movement of water through and out of the leaf [13]

Question taken from CCEA's Biology Assessment Unit AS2, Organisms and Biodiversity, June 2011, © CCEA 2012

6. Quality of written communication is awarded a maximum of 2 marks in this section. [2]

(a) Describe the process of transpiration. [3]

(b) Explain how the following factors influence the rate of transpiration.
- Temperature
- Humidity
- Wind speed [10]

Question taken from CCEA's Biology Assessment Unit AS2, Organisms and Biodiversity, January 2010, © CCEA 2012

Chapter 10 – Circulatory Systems in Mammals

The mammalian circulatory system and the blood vessels

Mammals have small surface area to volume ratios. A circulatory system is necessary to transport materials to and from the large volume of metabolically active tissue.

Mammals have a **double circulatory system** – this means the blood goes through the heart twice for each complete circuit of the body. In effect, the heart pumps the blood through two circuits (the pulmonary and the systemic circulation). The **pulmonary circulation** supplies the lungs and the **systemic circulation** supplies the other organs and the rest of the body.

The pulmonary circulation is a relatively small circuit (relative to the systemic circulation) and the blood is pumped at a lower pressure. The lower pressure allows the blood to pass relatively slowly through the capillaries in the lungs, allowing more time for gas exchange. In addition, high pressure is not necessary to pump the blood over the shorter distances involved.

A higher pressure in the systemic circuit ensures that blood is pumped to all the other organs in the body at a pressure sufficient to deliver metabolites and remove waste, at the rate required, and also at a pressure that maintains the blood/tissue fluid balance in each organ.

Note 1: blood going through the pulmonary circulation is pumped by the right hand side of the heart and blood going through the systemic circulation is pumped by the left side of the heart. Consequently, the cardiac muscle in the wall of the left ventricle is much thicker than that of the right ventricle.

Note 2: the double circulatory system is a very efficient system, necessary in meeting the high metabolic needs of mammals. In animals with a single circulatory system, such as fish, the blood is pumped through the gas exchange surfaces (the gills) and the rest of the body in the same circuit. This means that following the loss of pressure associated with passage through the gill capillaries, there is no further increase in pressure before the blood continues through the remaining organs.

The blood vessels

Arteries, veins and capillaries are the three main types of blood vessel that occur in mammals.

Arteries carry blood **away from the heart** and **veins** return blood **to the heart**. Arteries subdivide to form **arterioles,** which eventually subdivide to form **capillaries**. The blood is then returned to the heart via **venules** that combine to form **veins**. The main features of these blood vessels are described below.

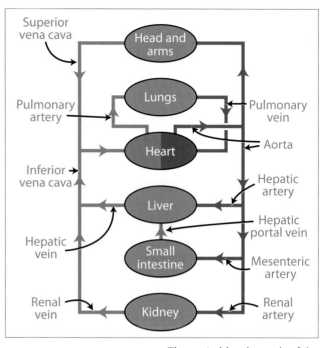

The main blood vessels of the thorax and the abdomen

Feature	Artery	Vein	Capillary
Structure	**Thick wall** (an outer thin layer of fibrous tissue, with a thick middle layer of **muscle** and **elastic tissue**, with an inner endothelial layer formed of squamous epithelium) and a **narrow lumen**. Arteries usually retain an overall **rounded shape**.	**Thin wall** (an outer thin layer of fibrous tissue, with a thin middle layer containing some muscle and very little elastic tissue, with an inner endothelial layer of squamous epithelium). Veins have a **large lumen** and **valves** at intervals along their length. They are much **less regular in shape**.	Microscopic vessels with **one cell thick walls**, consisting of **squamous (pavement or flattened) epithelium**.
Blood pressure	High in pulses	Low	Reduction in pressure across capillary network.
Adaptations	The **elastic tissue** in the thick middle layer allows the artery to **stretch** as the blood pulses out of the heart, through the arterial system, following the contraction of the ventricle muscles. As the elastic tissue **recoils** between heartbeats it helps to push blood along the artery, maintaining blood pressure. The **muscle tissue** in the middle layer provides **support** but, in addition, can **constrict (vasoconstriction) or dilate (vasodilation)**, providing less or more blood to an organ, such as the skin during temperature regulation, depending on metabolic needs. Contraction of the muscle and the narrowing of the **lumen** can help maintain blood pressure, further aided by the small lumen-wall ratios characteristic of arteries.	**Large lumen** offers little resistance to blood flow, which is essential as the blood is at low pressure in the veins. **Valves** prevent the backflow of blood. Due to the low pressures involved, there is much less muscle tissue and very little elastic tissue compared to arteries. However, as with arteries, veins are covered with a layer of **fibrous tissue** for protection and have an **endothelial layer** of squamous epithelium on their inner surface, which creates a smooth surface reducing friction as blood flows through. With blood pressure being very low in the veins it is gravity and the force created by the contraction of surrounding muscles that helps transport the blood.	Its small size allows an **extensive network** of capillaries, providing a **large surface area** for the diffusion of materials (no cell is far from a capillary). A capillary has a **very thin wall** (one cell thick), which facilitates exchange of materials with surrounding cells and tissues through being **permeable** to water and solutes, and providing a **short diffusion distance**. Red blood cells are just about able to 'squeeze' their way though the narrow capillaries, further reducing the diffusion distances between the red blood cells and the lungs or the tissues.

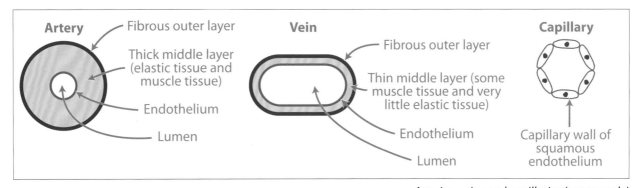

Arteries, veins and capillaries (not to scale)

Note: the proportion of elastic tissue to muscle is relatively high in the arteries close to the heart, but lower in the arteries close to the organs. Can you work out why?

The diagram to the right shows the relative values in mean blood pressure and velocity in relation to the total cross-sectional area of the blood vessels.

Explanation of diagram – The blood remains at high pressure while it travels through the aorta and the main arteries, as it is still close to the heart and there is no significant increase in cross-sectional area. The pulse effect in the blood pressure is not matched by a pulse in the blood velocity, due to the smoothing effects of the elastic and muscle tissue in the artery wall. As the main arteries branch into a large number of smaller arterioles, the increased cross-sectional area causes a significant reduction in pressure. There is a further increase in cross-sectional area as the arterioles subsequently branch into millions of capillaries. The low pressure, and consequent reduction in blood velocity, facilitates the exchange of materials between the blood and the surrounding tissue fluid as the blood flows through the capillaries.

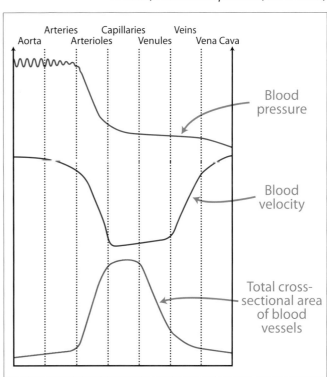

Changes in blood pressure, blood velocity and total cross-sectional area of blood vessels across the circulatory system

When the blood leaves the capillaries it has a low pressure and a low velocity. The overall cross-sectional area of the blood vessels decreases as the capillaries unite to form venules, which in turn unite to form veins. However, the large lumen in each vein ensures that friction between the blood and the wall of the vein is reduced to the extent that the blood velocity can increase even though blood pressure is still low. Valves help to prevent backflow due to the very low blood pressure.

The heart

The structure of the heart

The heart is a highly specialised muscular organ with the function of pumping blood through the body. As mammals have a double circulation, the heart is really **two** pumps, with each side of the heart pumping blood through two separate circulatory systems (the pulmonary and the systemic systems). The two sides of the heart are separated by a thick muscular wall (the **septum**) that runs through the centre of the heart. Each 'pump' has an upper chamber, the atrium, and a lower chamber, the ventricle. Atria and ventricles are adapted to reflect their respective roles in the pumping of blood.

- **Atria** – are relatively thin walled, as they receive blood from the lungs (**left atrium**) or the body (**right atrium**) and pump the blood into the ventricles that lie directly below them.

- **Ventricles** – have much thicker walls as they pump blood to the lungs (**right ventricle**) or around the body (**left ventricle**). As the lungs are only a few centimetres from the heart, the right ventricle does not have to pump with the force that the left ventricle has to in order to pump blood around the body. In fact, the right ventricle cannot pump with the same force or the delicate pulmonary capillaries could get damaged. Also the slower movement of blood through the lung capillaries maximises diffusion of respiratory gases. Consequently, the muscular wall of the left ventricle is considerably thicker than the wall of the right ventricle.

Note: the atria walls have similar thicknesses as they contract with equal force, forcing blood into the adjacent ventricle.

The blood leaves the heart in 'pulses' that coincide with each heartbeat and it functions as a one-way pump. Consequently, it is important that blood does not travel back into the atria when the ventricles contract to pump blood out of the heart. Similarly, it is important that the blood does not return from the arteries back into the heart when the pressure falls between pulses.

Valves prevent this backflow of blood and there are two types:

- **The atrioventricular (tricuspid** and **bicuspid)** valves – lie between the atria and the ventricles, and prevent the backflow of blood into the atria when the ventricles contract.

- **The semilunar (arterial)** valves – lie at the base of the aorta and the pulmonary artery, and prevent the backflow of blood from the arteries into the ventricles.

The **atrioventricular valves** are anchored by the **papillary muscles** that are embedded in the ventricle wall. **Chordae tendinae** (valve tendons) link the muscle and the valves. The chordae tendinae are sometimes referred to as 'heart strings', as they resemble short lengths of thread or string and therefore can function without impeding the flow of blood through the ventricle. They are extremely tough and flexible but not elastic, ensuring that when the ventricles contract (with the resulting increased pressure in the ventricles forcing the atrioventricular valves shut) they prevent the valves turning 'inside out', which would allow blood to flow back into the atria.

The **semilunar valves** are **pocket valves** on the artery walls that only close when the blood pressure in the arteries exceeds the pressure in the ventricles. When blood is being pumped out of the ventricles they are pushed flat against the artery walls and do not impede flow.

There are **four** major blood vessels that enter or leave the heart. They are:

- **The aorta** – is the major **artery** that carries **oxygenated** blood out of the **left ventricle**. Arterial branches leading from the aorta carry blood to all the major organs of the body except the lungs.

- **The pulmonary artery** – carries **deoxygenated** blood from the **right ventricle** to the lungs.

- **The vena cava** – brings **deoxygenated** blood back from the body, returning blood into the **right atrium**.

- **The pulmonary vein** – transports oxygenated blood from the lungs to the **left atrium**.

The heart itself has a very **high metabolic rate**, as it continually contracts throughout the life of the individual concerned and consequently has high respiratory demands. The coronary arteries branch off the aorta shortly after it leaves the heart and travel over the heart muscle, continually supplying it with its metabolic needs.

Note: the pulmonary artery and pulmonary vein are unusual in that the artery carries deoxygenated blood and the vein carries oxygenated blood. They are typical in that they carry blood away from and to the heart respectively, and are histologically (structurally) similar to other arteries and veins.

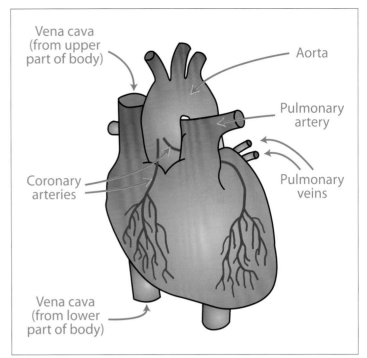

The heart in external view

Section through a mammalian heart

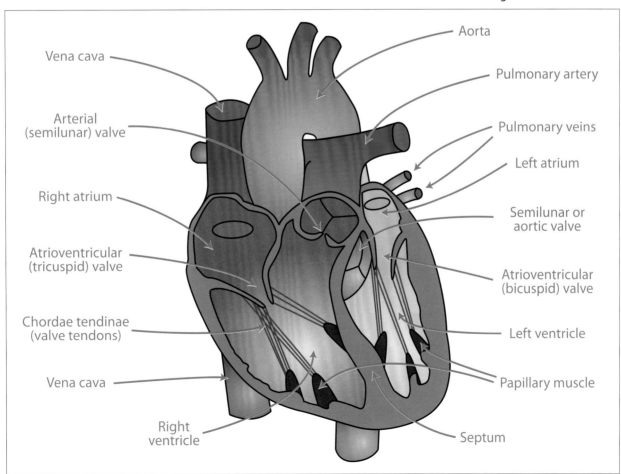

The cardiac cycle

The **cardiac cycle** describes the sequence of events that occur during one heartbeat. This sequence takes place about 70 times each minute in a human heart. Within the cardiac cycle, **diastole** describes a phase when the heart muscle is relaxed and **systole** indicates a contraction phase. The cardiac cycle is further subdivided into three stages as indicated in the table below.

Stage	Atria	Ventricles
Diastole	Atrial walls relaxed. Blood enters the atria from the venae cavae and the pulmonary vein.	Ventricle walls also relaxed and semilunar valves closed, as arterial pressure > ventricular pressure preventing reflux of blood back into the ventricles. As atrioventricular valves are open, blood enters the ventricles from the atria.
Atrial systole	Walls of the atria contract forcing more blood into the ventricles. AV valves remain open as the pressure in the atria still exceeds the pressure in the ventricles. Blood continues to enter the atria from the venae cavae and the pulmonary vein.	Walls of ventricle remain relaxed. Ventricle volume continues to increase as they fill with blood. Semilunar valves remain closed.
Ventricular systole	Walls of atria relax.	Walls of ventricles contract. AV valves close as the pressure in the ventricles now exceed the pressure in the atria. The chordae tendinae prevent the AV valves 'blowing inside out'. As ventricle pressure reaches its peak, semilunar valves are forced open, forcing blood into the arteries. By the end of ventricular systole, the ventricles will be at their smallest volume.

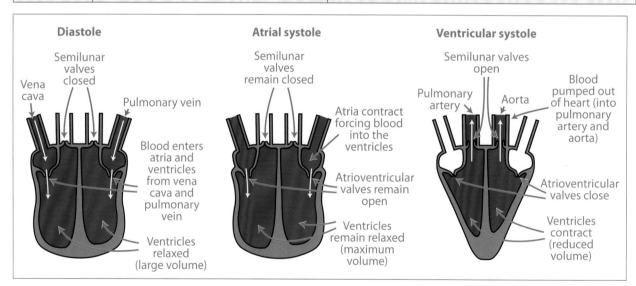

The diagram on page 155 shows the pressure changes during the cardiac cycle. Stages A–F are summarised below.

The cardiac cycle

A atrial walls contract, increasing atrial pressure. AV valves are open (as atrial pressure > ventricular pressure) and semilunar valves remain closed (as aortic pressure > ventricular pressure)

B atrial contraction complete (atria are empty of blood) and ventricles begin to contract – ventricle pressure > atrial pressure – AV valves close (**first heart sound**)

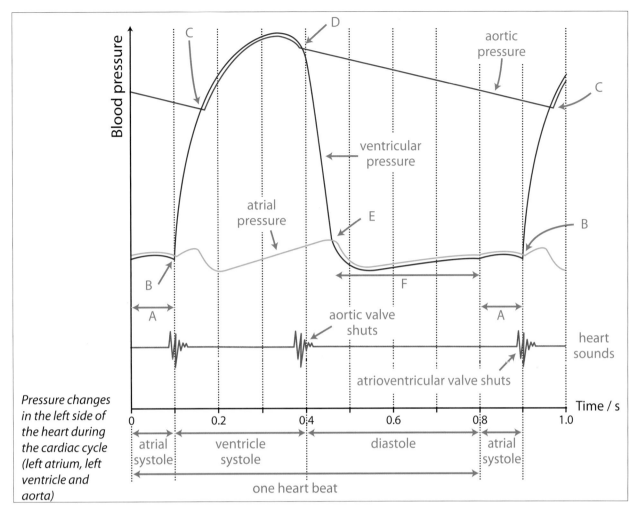

Pressure changes in the left side of the heart during the cardiac cycle (left atrium, left ventricle and aorta)

C continued contraction of ventricles – ventricle pressure > arterial pressure – semilunar valves open

D arterial pressure > ventricular pressure – semilunar valves close due to loss of blood from ventricles (**second heart sound**)

E ventricular pressure falls as little blood present and walls begin to relax – atrial pressure > ventricular pressure – AV valves open

F atrial pressure > ventricle pressure as blood flowing into atria – AV valves remain open – blood passively flows into the ventricles from the atria

The changes in atrial pressure between B and E are caused by:

- the increased pressure of the contracting ventricle causing back pressure of the contracting ventricle on the atria (B–C).
- the subsequent fall in pressure is caused by the relaxation (and increase in volume) of the atria.
- the increase in pressure between 0.2 seconds and E is caused by the atria filling with blood.

When the heart valves close, the flaps of tissue bang together to make a sound. This occurs twice in each cycle (at B and D in the diagram). The sounds can be shown in a **phonocardiogram** (see heart sounds trace in the diagram). An **electrocardiogram** (**ECG**) shows the electrical activity of the heart.

Note 1: both sides of the heart contract at the same time, with the same part of the cycle occurring simultaneously in each.

Note 2: the valves do not control the cardiac cycle, they open and close (passively) due to pressure changes within the heart.

Note 3: in general, when heart chambers relax they have a larger volume than when they are contracting.

Coordination of the cardiac cycle

The sequences within the cardiac cycle are stimulated by a coordinated wave of electrical excitation through the heart. Cardiac muscle, unlike other muscle, is **myogenic**, which means the heart can beat on its own and does not require external stimulation. The heartbeat starts with an electrical signal, originating from an area of muscle in the wall of the right atrium, the **sinoatrial node (SAN)** or **pacemaker**.

- The **SAN** sends out a wave of electrical activity over the atria, causing contraction (atrial systole). This wave of electrical activity travels rapidly, causing the atria to contract simultaneously.

- Between the atria and the ventricles is a layer of non-conductive tissue that prevents the wave of excitation passing directly through to the ventricles. The only way the electrical activity can pass through to the ventricles is via the **atrioventricular (AV) node** that conducts very slowly. As a result the contraction in the ventricles (ventricular systole) is delayed relative to the atria. This ensures that when ventricular systole begins, atrial systole is complete and the ventricles are filled with blood.

- The electrical activity passes down the **septum** of the ventricles in special tissue called the **Bundle of His** to the bottom of the ventricles. The stimulation then spreads up through the walls of the ventricles in special tissue called **Purkinje fibres**, causing contraction of the ventricle walls and forcing blood up through the arteries (ventricular systole).

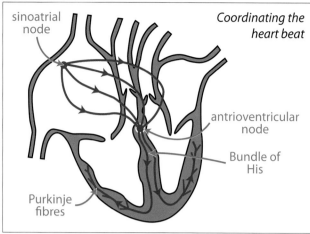

Coordinating the heart beat

Note 1: although the heart is myogenic and can beat without nervous stimulation, the sinoatrial node is under nervous system control. The rate of heartbeat can be increased (or decreased) in time of need through external nervous control. For example, during periods of exercise the rate of heartbeat is increased to ensure that the muscles receive increased glucose and oxygen for their increased respiratory needs.

Note 2: in an examination make sure you understand whether you are being asked to answer on the cardiac cycle (pressure changes and associated opening and closing of valves) or the electrical stimulation of the heart. Many candidates confuse these two areas to their cost!

The composition and function of mammalian body fluids

Blood

Blood is the term used to describe a suspension of cells (red and white blood cells) in a pale yellow liquid (plasma).

The components of blood and their functions are summarised in the flow chart on page 157.

The blood has many roles including defence, as described in the flow chart. However, a primary role is transport. The next section discusses how the materials being transported in the blood reach the cells in the tissues that the blood supplies.

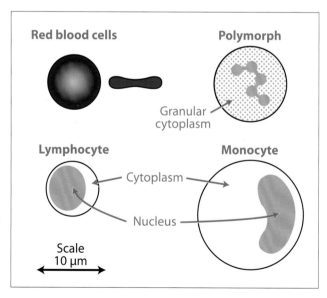

The components of blood and their functions

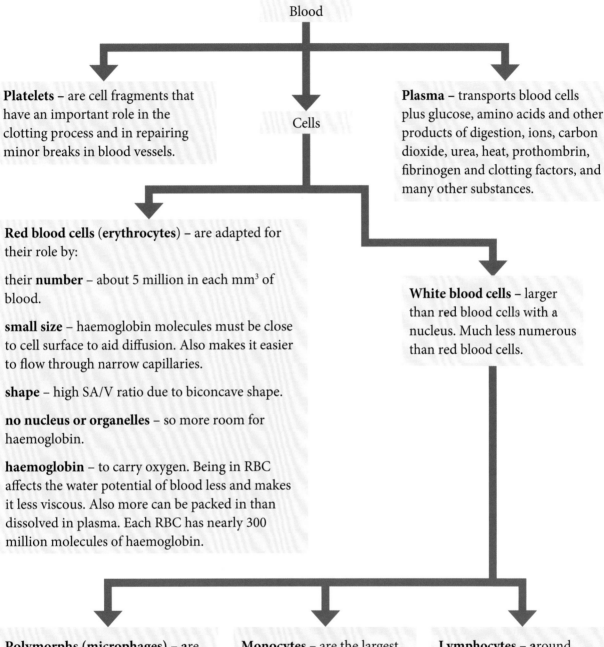

Blood

Cells

Platelets – are cell fragments that have an important role in the clotting process and in repairing minor breaks in blood vessels.

Plasma – transports blood cells plus glucose, amino acids and other products of digestion, ions, carbon dioxide, urea, heat, prothombrin, fibrinogen and clotting factors, and many other substances.

Red blood cells (**erythrocytes**) – are adapted for their role by:

their **number** – about 5 million in each mm³ of blood.

small size – haemoglobin molecules must be close to cell surface to aid diffusion. Also makes it easier to flow through narrow capillaries.

shape – high SA/V ratio due to biconcave shape.

no nucleus or organelles – so more room for haemoglobin.

haemoglobin – to carry oxygen. Being in RBC affects the water potential of blood less and makes it less viscous. Also more can be packed in than dissolved in plasma. Each RBC has nearly 300 million molecules of haemoglobin.

White blood cells – larger than red blood cells with a nucleus. Much less numerous than red blood cells.

Polymorphs (microphages) – are the most common white blood cell (**70%** of all white blood cells). They have a distinctive **multi-lobed nucleus** and granular cytoplasm. They are **phagocytic** and can pass between the squamous epithelium capillary cells, and destroy bacteria and other foreign bodies by phagocytosis at the sites of infection (for example, outside the blood system).

Monocytes – are the largest but least common white blood cell (**5%**) – they have a **bean shaped nucleus**. They are phagocytic and can move out of the blood at sites of infection and develop into **phagocytic macrophage cells**, which destroy bacteria and other foreign material. They are **longer lived** than polymorphs.

Lymphocytes – around **20–25%** of white blood cells are lymphocytes. They have a **very large nucleus** leaving only a **small amount of cytoplasm**. There are two types: **B-cells** are involved in **antibody** production and **T-cells** are involved in **cell-mediated immunity** (destroying infected and foreign **cells**).

157

The formation of tissue fluid

Tissue fluid is the fluid that lies immediately outside the capillaries and surrounds the cells of the tissues. It is the immediate environment of body cells and is important in providing a stable environment for the cells. It has many functions, including the osmoregulation of the cells, but also is important in facilitating the transport of substances between the blood and the body cells.

Tissue fluid supplies oxygen, glucose, amino acids, salts and many other substances to the tissues, and enables carbon dioxide and other waste substances to diffuse from the tissues back into the blood capillaries.

As blood travels through the arteries, the arterioles and then into the arterial end of the capillary network, the narrowing of the vessels creates a pressure called **hydrostatic (blood) pressure**, which is strong enough to force liquid and small molecules out of the capillaries. Plasma proteins and blood cells are too large to be filtered through in this process of **ultrafiltration**.

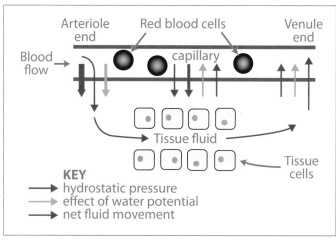

The formation of tissue fluid

Hydrostatic pressure is opposed by two other forces:

- The lower **water potential** of the blood, due to the presence of plasma proteins, that tends to pull the tissue fluid back by osmosis.
- The **hydrostatic pressure** of the tissue fluid opposes the inward flow of liquid from the capillaries.

However, at the **arterial end** of the capillary network, the hydrostatic pressure of the blood exceeds these other two forces, and liquid rich in oxygen and other materials is filtered out of the blood and into the tissue fluid that bathes the cells. Oxygen, glucose and other materials then enter the cells by diffusion.

How does the tissue fluid get back into the capillaries?

It is important that the liquid filtered out of the capillary at the arterial end is returned to the capillary after the tissues have been supplied with essential metabolites. The returning fluid transports carbon dioxide and other wastes to the capillary.

What causes it to return to the capillary? The loss of fluid from the capillary causes a reduction in hydrostatic pressure, with the result that by the time the blood reaches the venule end of the capillary, the hydrostatic pressure of the tissue fluid exceeds the hydrostatic pressure of the blood. The return of tissue fluid to the capillaries is aided by difference in water potential between the blood in the capillaries and the tissue fluid. The gradient is maintained along the length of the capillary but is much reduced at the venule end, by which time much of the filtered liquid has returned.

Blood clotting

Blood is an essential body fluid and blood clotting is a process that reduces its loss through injury. The repair and sealing of wounds also prevent the entry of pathogens.

The flow diagram below summaries the process of blood clotting, which operates on a cascading principle, with the presence of certain compounds catalysing reactions further down the chain.

The insoluble fibrin forms a mesh that traps blood cells to form a clot. As it dries, the clot forms a scab that both prevents blood loss, but in addition, prevents the entry of microbes.

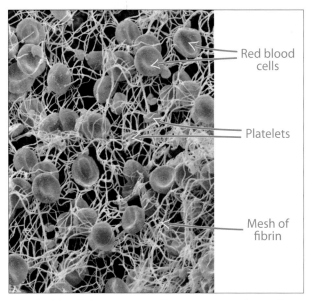

Photograph of a blood clot Susumu Nishinaga/Science Photo Library

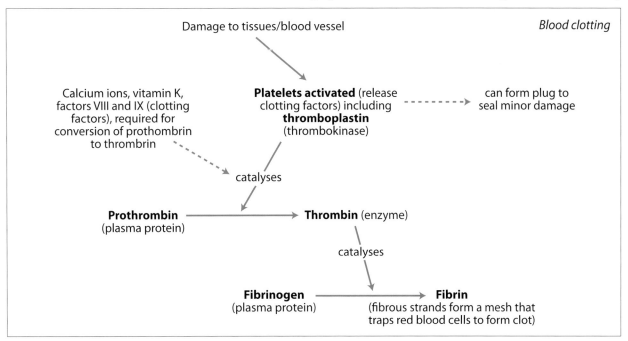

The transport of oxygen

Oxygen is transported in red blood cells through the blood system. In the capillaries it leaves the red blood cells and enters the plasma, where it is carried into the tissue fluid by the ultrafiltration of the plasma as previously described (on page 158). In the red blood cells it is the molecule **haemoglobin**, a **respiratory pigment**, that is responsible for oxygen transport.

Haemoglobin and oxygen transport

Haemoglobin consists of **four polypeptide chains** – 2 α-chains and 2 β-chains (see earlier diagram on page 15). Each polypeptide has a **haem group** (prosthetic group) attached, which contains **iron** (Fe^{2++}). Consequently, haemoglobin molecules are **conjugated** proteins. Each haem group can bind to an oxygen molecule to form

oxyhaemoglobin. The following equation shows that each molecule of haemoglobin can carry up to four molecules of oxygen.

$$Hb \; + \; 4O_2 \; \rightleftharpoons \; HbO_2$$

haemoglobin + oxygen $\rightleftharpoons$ oxyhaemoglobin

The equation also shows that the reaction is **reversible**. In conditions where oxygen levels are high, oxyhaemoglobin is formed; if oxygen levels are low the oxyhaemoglobin **dissociates** (breaks down releasing oxygen). In mammals, oxyhaemoglobin forms in the lungs where oxygen levels in the blood are high due to the rapid gaseous exchange in the lungs and dissociation takes place in the tissues where oxygen levels are low due to respiration. This physiological adaptation is essential for haemoglobin to operate as a highly adapted and efficient respiratory pigment (oxygen transport molecule).

In reality, haemoglobin normally is either deoxygenated or fully oxygenated with four oxygen molecules. It seldom transports one, two or three oxygen molecules around the body. When one oxygen molecule is taken up by a haemoglobin molecule, there is a **conformational change** (distortion) in the haemoglobin molecule, resulting in an easier (faster) uptake of the remaining three oxygen molecules (**cooperative loading**).

When one oxygen molecule binds, this distorts the shape and facilitates binding of the second oxygen molecule. Further structural alterations occur when oxygen molecules attach to the second and third haem groups, **each one** facilitating much faster uptake of oxygen than the preceding one.

If every molecule of haemoglobin in the blood is carrying four oxygen molecules, the blood is said to be 100% **saturated**. If only 50% of the haemoglobin is carrying oxygen (assuming they are all carrying four molecules), the blood is 50% saturated and so on.

The degree of saturation of haemoglobin is dependent on the amount of oxygen available in the environment in which the haemoglobin is in at that time. The oxygen concentration in the environment is referred to as its **partial pressure** (pO_2) or **oxygen tension**. The partial pressure of any gas is the proportion of total air pressure that is contributed to by that gas and is measured in **kilopascals** (kPa).

If haemoglobin molecules are exposed to a range of partial pressures of oxygen, their percentage saturation (with oxygen) can be plotted on a graph known as a **(haemoglobin) oxygen dissociation curve**.

The first graph on page 161 shows the characteristic **S-shape** (**sigmoidal**) pattern of oxygen dissociation curves. It shows that in high oxygen partial pressures, such as 14 kPa (as is found in the lungs), oxyhaemoglobin is readily formed and the haemoglobin approaches full saturation – ie every haemoglobin molecule is fully saturated with oxygen. The haemoglobin remains saturated as the partial pressure falls (as it travels through the pulmonary vein, heart, aorta, other arteries and arterioles). However, in low partial pressures, for example, 2–5 kPa (as is found in respiring tissues), dissociation takes place and the oxygen is released and diffuses into the respiring tissue cells. The sigmoidal pattern makes the process even more efficient, as over the range of partial pressures typical of respiring tissues there is **rapid dissociation**, making large quantities of oxygen available to the tissues, even though there is a relatively small fall in partial pressure.

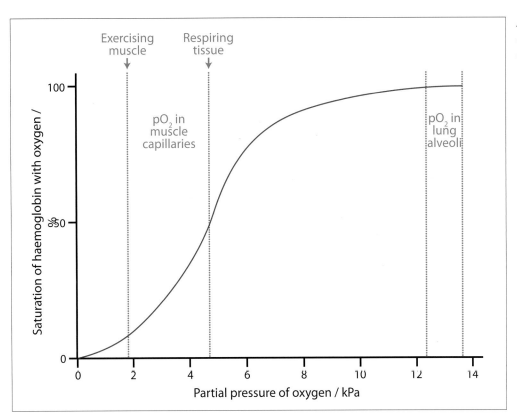

An (haemoglobin) oxygen dissociation curve

Two useful terms:

The **loading tension** – is the partial pressure at which the haemoglobin is 95% saturated with oxygen.

The **unloading tension** – of haemoglobin is a term that refers to the partial pressure of oxygen at which haemoglobin is 50% saturated.

Loading and unloading tensions are useful terms when comparing different types of haemoglobin or different respiratory pigments.

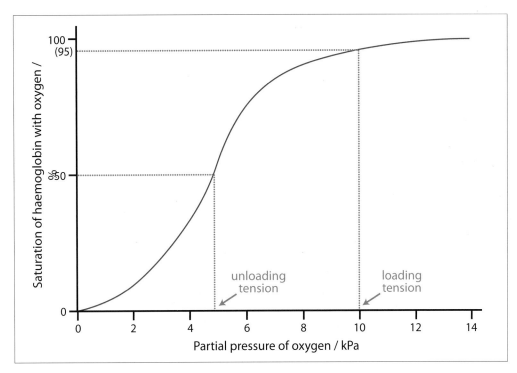

Loading and unloading tensions

The Bohr effect

The physiological ability of haemoglobin to bind with or release oxygen is primarily linked to the partial pressure of oxygen in the environment. However, the **partial pressure of carbon dioxide** (**pCO$_2$**) also affects the ability of haemoglobin to combine with oxygen. In higher concentrations of carbon dioxide, ie higher than 'normal' levels in the blood, the oxygen dissociation curve moves to the right, **the Bohr effect**, as seen in the graph below.

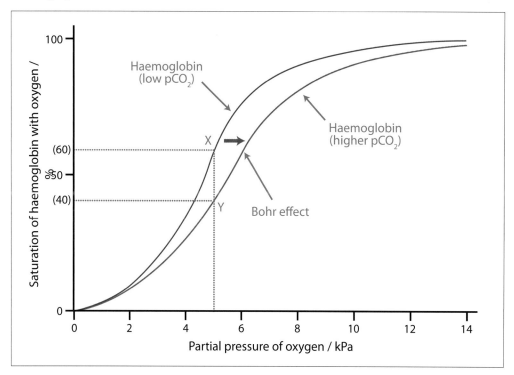

The Bohr effect

The advantage of the Bohr effect is that oxygen is released more readily from haemoglobin at a particular partial pressure of oxygen, ie the haemoglobin has **reduced affinity for oxygen**. The unloading tension shifts to the right and occurs at higher partial pressures of oxygen. Therefore there is more oxygen available for the respiring tissues.

In the above graph, under normal conditions the haemoglobin is 60% saturated when the pO$_2$ is 5 kPa (**X**), meaning that 40% of the oxygen is unloaded to the respiring tissues. With the Bohr effect, at the same partial pressure of oxygen, the haemoglobin is only 40% saturated (**Y**), meaning that 60% of the oxygen transported by the haemoglobin can be released to the tissues.

The Bohr effect occurs when **carbon dioxide levels increase**, such as when high rates of respiration are taking place, for example, during strenuous exercise. This means that increased oxygen becomes available to the tissues at times of greatest need. It is important to note that the Bohr effect is not an 'all or nothing' response. The degree of shift to the right depends on the partial pressure of CO$_2$; the curve will move further to the right if pCO$_2$ levels are very high – even more rapid oxygen dissociation occurs to match the very high respiration rate (producing the very high pCO$_2$).

The graph above also shows that the uptake of oxygen by the haemoglobin is little affected at high pO$_2$ levels, thereby ensuring that the loading of oxygen by haemoglobin in the lungs is still very efficient during the Bohr effect.

Higher blood temperature and **increased acidity** (consequences of increased respiration and increased carbon dioxide transport in the plasma respectively) also produce the Bohr effect.

Myoglobin

Myoglobin is another respiratory pigment. It does not circulate in the blood but is found in 'red' muscle. It consists of only **one polypeptide** with a single haem group. The oxygen dissociation curve for myoglobin is situated to the left of haemoglobin (see graph below).

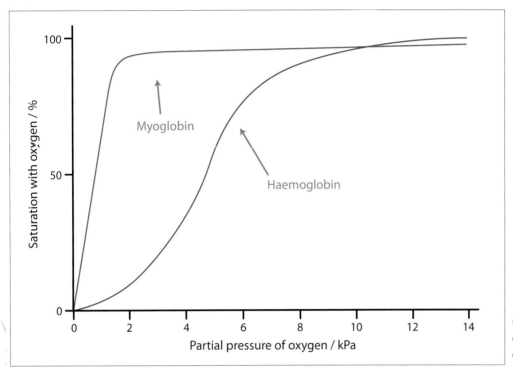

Oxygen dissociation curves of myoglobin and haemoglobin

The difference in the curves for myoglobin and haemoglobin means two things:

- the myoglobin has a **greater affinity** for oxygen than haemoglobin. This means it will remain saturated with oxygen even at relatively low partial pressures of oxygen.
- the myoglobin will only **release oxygen if the pO$_2$ becomes very low** – lower than that normally found in respiring tissues. This means that it serves as an **oxygen store** – it has no role in oxygen transport – and only releases oxygen when blood oxygen levels are very low (less than 1 kPa), such as during very strenuous exercise.

Myoglobin is ideally adapted for its role as an oxygen store. It is situated in the **skeletal muscles**, where respiratory demands are greatest during vigorous exercise and the physiological differences (as seen in the respective oxygen dissociation curves) ensures that it only begins to release oxygen when the haemoglobin reserves are depleted. The oxygen reserve held in the myoglobin allows aerobic respiration to continue for longer during strenuous exercise, thereby delaying the onset of less efficient anaerobic respiration.

But how does the myoglobin store become replenished following depletion, particularly as it is found in muscles only and does not travel in the blood to the lungs?

The answer can be explained by myoglobin's greater affinity for oxygen than haemoglobin. In the period following exercise, as blood flows through the muscle, with pO_2 being in the 'normal' range of 2–5 kPa, some of the oxygen dissociates from the haemoglobin. The graph on page 163 shows that at the same range of partial pressures the myoglobin is physiologically capable of being fully saturated (with no dissociation). Therefore the oxygen freed from the haemoglobin readily combines with any unsaturated myoglobin molecules until the myoglobin store is fully replenished.

Note 1: it is the myoglobin and its stored oxygen that is responsible for the red colour of skeletal and heart muscle.

Note 2: myoglobin is particularly abundant in the muscles of diving mammals such a seals and whales.

The effect of altitude on oxygen transport by haemoglobin

As height increases above sea level, overall atmospheric pressure and **pO_2 is reduced**. The graph below shows that if the lungs have a pO_2 environment around 7 kPa, which is typical in very high altitudes, compared to around 13 kPa in more lowland altitudes, the haemoglobin cannot become fully saturated. At high elevations, for example, above 3,500 m above sea level, the reduced oxygen levels can significantly affect normal activity and sickness can result.

After a period of time (even a few days) at high altitude, **acclimatisation** can occur. Acclimatisation involves an **increase in the number of red blood cells**. This adaptation allows for the more efficient transport of the oxygen that is available in the atmosphere (compensating for the reduced saturation of haemoglobin in the lower pO_2) and increased ventilation to maximise the diffusion of oxygen into the blood. Other subtle changes to the physiology of respiration in the cells are also involved. Not surprisingly, many athletes spend time in high altitude training to increase their red

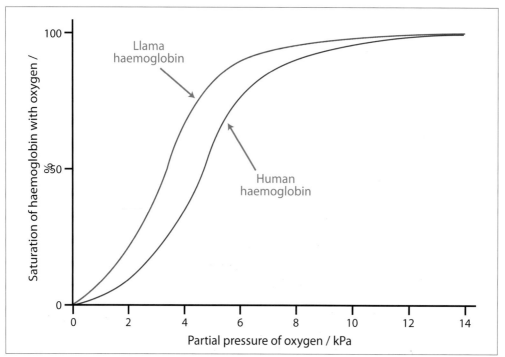

Human and llama oxygen dissociation curves

blood cell count – an adaptation that would be beneficial whether racing at low or high altitude.

Populations that have lived in high altitudes for **many generations** have evolved a type of haemoglobin that saturates at lower pO_2 levels than the more typical lower altitude populations.

Mammal species that are adapted to living at high altitudes have haemoglobin that is specialised and highly adapted for this environment. An often quoted example is the llama, a camel-like species that lives at heights of around 5,000 m in South America.

The oxygen dissociation curve for the llama is to the left of the 'normal' human oxygen dissociation curve. This could be predicted, as only a curve in this position would allow the llama haemoglobin to become fully saturated at the pO_2 values that exist high in the Andes Mountains.

Cardiovascular disease

Cardiovascular disease kills more people than any other disease in the British Isles. Coronary heart disease (CHD) is caused by damage to the coronary arteries that supply the heart with blood, carrying oxygen and glucose, for respiration.

Atheroma – is the term used to describe the build up of fatty deposits that form within the wall of an artery. The likelihood of development of atheromas in arteries can be increased by a number of risk factors including smoking, lack of exercise, too much salt in the diet, stress and high blood cholesterol levels. The development of an atheroma tends to follow the following sequence:

- The squamous endothelial cells that line the artery lumen become damaged. This damage can be caused by a number of reasons including toxins in the blood from tobacco smoke or high blood pressure that applies a greater force on the artery walls.
- Following damage to the endothelial lining, the atheroma builds up within the wall of the artery (beneath the endothelium). Macrophages (having developed from monocytes) migrate from the blood into the damaged artery wall and are involved in the accumulation of materials within the wall, particularly **cholesterol**, but including dead muscle cells, salts and fibrous tissue. In due course, the atheroma builds up into hardened **plaques**.
- As they increase in size, and toughness, the atheromas (plaques) bulge into the lumen of the artery, causing a narrowing that restricts blood flow. The fibrous material causes the artery to become less elastic and less able to regulate blood flow through vasodilation or vasoconstriction.

The 'hardening (and narrowing) of the arteries' tends to raise blood pressure further, and as a consequence further atheromas and plaques are more likely to form.

Atherosclerosis – is the disease that is caused by the thickening of the artery wall through the development of atheromas and plaques. The artery wall becomes less elastic, the artery lumen gets narrower and an increase in blood pressure results.

Thrombosis – is the formation of blood clots within the blood vessels. These can happen anywhere in the circulatory system but they will be particularly problematic in narrow arteries, such as the coronary arteries, or in arteries that have been narrowed as a result of heart disease. If a thrombosis occurs in the coronary arteries, it is known as a **coronary thrombosis**. They are more likely to happen if the artery wall becomes damaged (for example, as a result of atheromas/atherosclerosis).

If a coronary thrombosis occurs, the area of the heart affected fails to receive blood, and therefore oxygen and glucose for respiration, and the cells die if the blockage is prolonged. If a large area of the heart is affected (ie the thrombosis occurs near the origin of the coronary artery rather than near the tip) a **myocardial infarction** (heart attack) results.

Practical work

You should be able to identify and describe prepared slides and photographs of the different types of blood vessels and the blood cells described in this chapter. You should also be able to identify and describe the main parts of a heart, whether in section or dissected.

Exam Questions

1 Suggest reasons for the following features of the major blood vessels.

   (a) Arteries near the heart have a lot of elastic fibres in their walls. [2]

   (b) Arteries within major organs have a lot of smooth muscle tissue. [2]

   (c) Veins possess valves. [2]

   Question taken from CCEA's Biology Assessment Unit AS2, Organisms and Biodiversity, June 2010, © CCEA 2012

2. Contraction of heart muscle causes an increase in pressure within the heart chambers.

   (a) State the term for the phase of the cardiac cycle during which heart muscle is contracted. [1]

   (b) The muscle surrounding the heart chambers is of different thicknesses. The graph below shows the maximum pressure reached in each of the heart chambers during contraction.

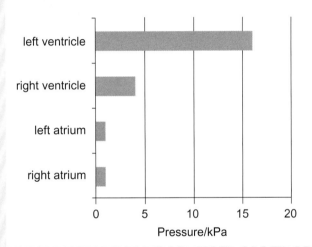

Using your understanding of the structure of the heart chambers, explain why the maximum pressure in both atria is the same, whereas the pressure in the left ventricle is much greater than the pressure in the right ventricle. [3]

   Question taken from CCEA's Biology Assessment Unit AS2, Organisms and Biodiversity, January 2011, © CCEA 2012

3. The diagrams **A** and B below show the heart at different stages during the cardiac cycle.

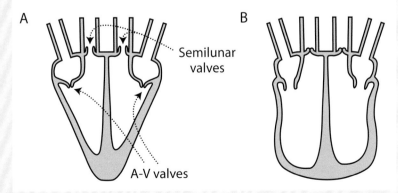

For copyright reasons this diagram has replaced the diagram from CCEA's Biology AS2, January 2010 paper.

   (a) Identify the stage of the cardiac cycle shown in diagrams **A** and **B**. [2]

The graph below shows pressure changes which take place in the left side of the heart during one complete cardiac cycle.

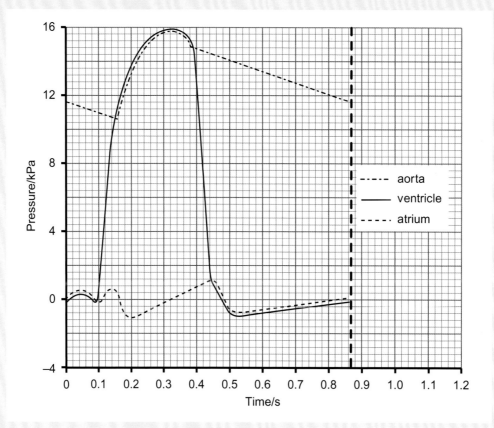

(b) Identify which of the diagrams on page 167, **A** or **B**, corresponds to the ventricular pressure rise between 0.15 and 0.3 seconds on the graph.

Explain your choice. [2]

(c) The semi-lunar valves and the A–V valves respond differently during the ventricular pressure rise between 0.1 and 0.15 seconds.

  (i) Identify the response of the A–V valves at 0.1 seconds. [1]

  (ii) Identify the response of the semi-lunar valves at 0.15 seconds. [1]

  (iii) Explain how the structure of each valve type allows for these different responses:

  • A–V valves [2]

  • semi-lunar valves [2]

(d) Explain the increase in the **atrial** pressure at each of the following points:

  • between 0 and 0.05 seconds

  • between 0.2 and 0.45 seconds [2]

Question taken from CCEA's Biology Assessment Unit AS2, Organisms and Biodiversity, January 2010, © CCEA 2012

4. (a) The flow diagram below shows the mechanism of blood clotting.

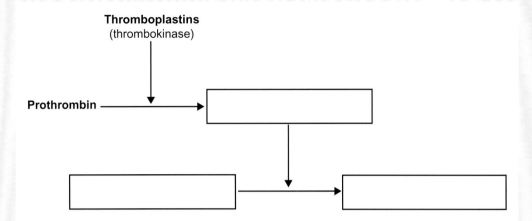

Make a copy of the diagram and complete it by entering in the boxes the names of the proteins involved in clotting. [3]

(b) Polymorphs are a type of the white blood cell. Describe the role of polymorphs at the site of a cut. [1]

Question taken from CCEA's Biology Assessment Unit AS2, Organisms and Biodiversity, June 2010, © CCEA 2012

5. The graph below shows the oxygen dissociation curves for the haemoglobin from three different mammals.

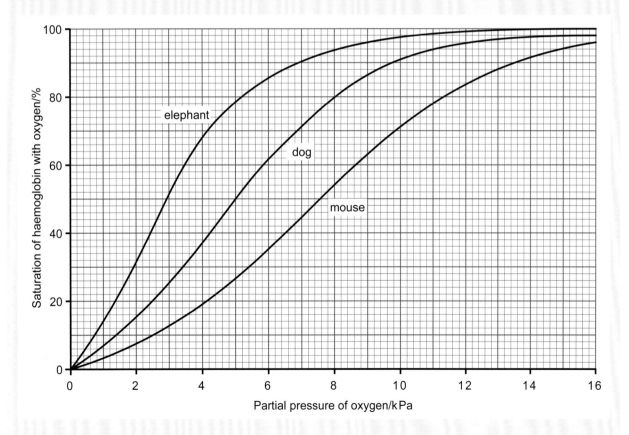

(a) The haemoglobin of which mammal has the greatest affinity for oxygen? Explain your reasoning. [2]

(b) The mouse has a higher metabolic rate than either the dog or the elephant. Explain how mouse haemoglobin is adapted for maintaining a high metabolic rate. [2]

(c) The partial pressure of carbon dioxide will influence the oxygen dissociation curve for haemoglobin.

   (i)   Make a copy of the graph on page 169 and sketch the oxygen dissociation curve you would expect for dog haemoglobin when $ppCO_2$ has increased. [1]

   (ii) Under what circumstances would the $ppCO_2$ increase in a dog? [1]

   (iii) Explain the advantage of the effect described. [2]

   Question taken from CCEA's Biology Assessment Unit AS2, Organisms and Biodiversity, June 2011, © CCEA 2012

6. The graph below shows three different oxygen dissociation curves.

   A is the dissociation curve for myoglobin.

   B and **C** are two different dissociation curves for haemoglobin at different partial pressures of carbon dioxide ($ppCO_2$).

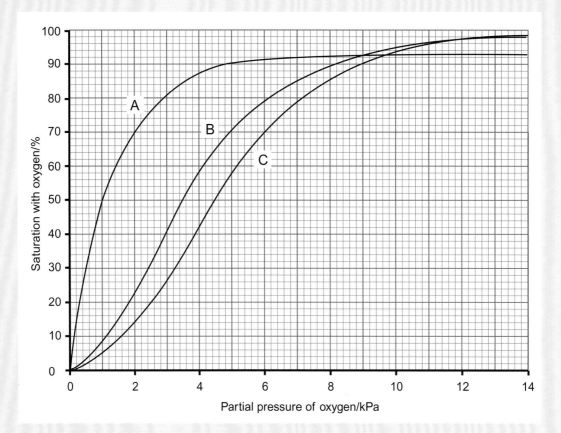

(a) (i) Myoglobin and haemoglobin are both described as conjugated proteins. Define the term "conjugated protein". [1]

(ii) Explain what is meant by the term "partial pressure of oxygen". [1]

(b) (i) State the role of myoglobin in muscle tissue. [1]

(ii) Explain the circumstances which will cause myoglobin to unload oxygen in working muscle. [2]

(c) **B** and **C** are two different dissociation curves for haemoglobin at different partial pressures of carbon dioxide ($ppCO_2$).

(i) Which of the curves, **B** or **C**, would represent the dissociation curve for haemoglobin in a muscle during exercise? Explain your choice. [3]

(ii) Use the graph on page 170 to calculate the decrease in percentage saturation of haemoglobin when, during exercise, the ppO_2 in a muscle falls from 6 kPa to 2 kPa. (Show your working.) [2]

Question taken from CCEA's Biology Assessment Unit AS2, Organisms and Biodiversity, January 2010, © CCEA 2012

7. (a) The table below includes descriptions of three types of white blood cell. Make a copy of the table and complete it by identifying each cell type and give a brief description of the function of each. [6]

Description	Identification	Function
Cells with a very large nucleus and little cytoplasm		
Cells with granular cytoplasm and a lobed nucleus		
Large cells with a kidney-shaped nucleus		

(b) The table below shows the red blood cell counts for a person living at sea level, and the same person after acclimatisation at high altitude in preparation for climbing Mount Everest.

	Red blood cell count/dm^{-3}
At sea level	5.0×10^{12}
After acclimatisation at high altitude	5.6×10^{12}

(i) Describe how the partial pressure of atmospheric oxygen varies with altitude. [1]

(ii) Explain the advantage of having a higher red blood cell count at high altitude. [2]

(iii) People such as the Quechua Indians in the Andes, who live permanently at high altitude, not only have increased red blood cell counts but possess other adaptations for life at high altitude. Describe **one** other adaptation to life at high altitude which might be expected, and explain how this adaptation aids their survival. [2]

(iv) The increased production of red blood cells is due to the release of the hormone erythropoietin (EPO) in the body. Athletes can inject EPO to artificially stimulate the red blood cell count and so boost performance. Suggest **one** possible danger to the athlete of an artificially raised blood cell count. [1]

Question taken from CCEA's Biology Assessment Unit AS2, Organisms and Biodiversity, June 2009, © CCEA 2012

8. The diagram below represents a transverse section through a blood vessel.

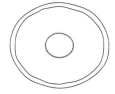

(a) Select **two** pieces of evidence visible in the diagram which suggest that this is an artery. [2]

(b) The wall of an artery contains smooth muscle tissue. Explain the role of the smooth muscle tissue in the functioning of an artery. [2]

(c) Distinguish between the terms "atheroma" and "atherosclerosis" and explain how they may lead to a coronary thrombosis (heart attack). [5]

Question taken from CCEA's Biology Assessment Unit AS2, Organisms and Biodiversity, January 2011, © CCEA 2012

9. The diagram below represents a surface view of the heart showing the coronary arteries as well as other major blood vessels.

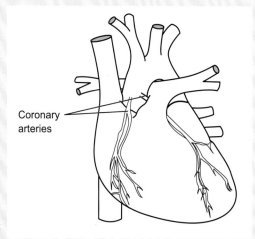

(a) (i) Make a copy of the diagram and label one of the pulmonary arteries with the letter **P**. [1]

(ii) Identify the blood vessel from which the coronary arteries arise. [1]

The development of an atheroma in the coronary arteries may lead to the formation of a clot – a coronary thrombosis – which may lead in turn to a myocardial infarction (heart attack).

(b) (i) Describe the sequence of events which leads to the development of an atheroma in the coronary arteries. [3]

(ii) Explain how a thrombosis in the coronary arteries would lead to a myocardial infarction. [2]

Patients who are considered to be susceptible to thrombosis are treated with anticoagulant drugs, such as warfarin and heparin.

(c) (i) Warfarin acts by inhibiting the production of prothrombin though this takes time, approximately 3 days. Use your understanding of blood clotting to explain why warfarin treatment prevents blood clotting. [2]

Heparin acts rapidly in preventing blood clotting. The graph below shows the effect of heparin concentration on the clotting time of blood samples.

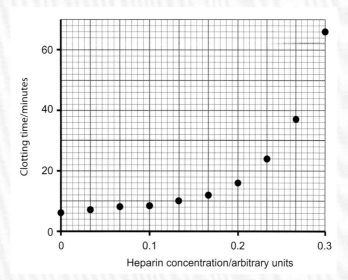

(ii) Describe the effect of adding heparin to samples of blood. What does this suggest about the concentration of heparin used to treat patients?

(iii) Warfarin is often the preferred treatment since it can be taken orally. However, medication will initially include heparin. Suggest why.

Question taken from CCEA's Biology Assessment Unit AS2, Organisms and Biodiversity, June 2011, © CCEA 2012

10. Give an account of the co-ordinated sequence of events which result in the flow of blood through the heart during one cardiac cycle. [15]

Question taken from CCEA's Biology Assessment Unit AS2, Organisms and Biodiversity, June 2009, © CCEA 2012

11. Quality of written communication is awarded a maximum of 2 marks in this section. [2]

(a) Give an account of the structure of haemoglobin and its role in absorbing oxygen in the lungs. [5]

(b) Explain how oxygen is supplied to strenuously exercising muscle. [8]

Question taken from CCEA's Biology Assessment Unit AS2, Organisms and Biodiversity, January 2011, © CCEA 2012

Chapter 11 – The Adaptation of Organisms

Students should be able to:

2.2.1 Understand that organisms are adapted to their environment.

2.2.2 Understand that ecological factors have an influence on the distribution of organisms.

2.2.3 Understand the role of selection in maintaining the adaptiveness of populations of organisms in their environment.

2.2.4 Practical work to include qualitative and quantitative techniques used to investigate the distribution and relative abundance of plants and animals in a habitat.

Adaptations in organisms

For many the image of a polar bear and her cubs epitomises life in the Arctic Circle. For many it also conjures up images of the fragility of the planet and the dangers the bears (and we) face due to global warming.

The polar bear is ideally adapted for life in polar regions, an environment which is hostile to the vast majority of species on Earth. Many of these adaptations readily spring to mind; the white colouration for camouflage, the thick fur for insulation, small ears and a short tail to further reduce heat loss, the ability to swim considerable distances between ice floes when hunting seals and their excellent sense of smell to detect their prey.

The polar bear occupies a habitat atypical for mammals (most mammals are found in more temperate or warmer areas), so has many obvious adaptations. However, **all** species are adapted in some way for the environment in which they are normally found.

The highly adapted polar bear

Living organisms tend to have a combination of behavioural, physiological and morphological adaptations that adapt them for particular environments. Returning to the polar bear, their ability to stalk seals and knowing where and when to smash through a thick layer of ice to locate their prey is a **behavioural** adaptation. The thick white fur is a **morphological** (physical) adaptation. Polar bears often have to go months without food and at this time their metabolic rate can drop to a much lower level – a **physiological** (biochemical) adaptation that conserves energy.

As part of your course, you should study organisms in their natural habitat and be aware of some of their adaptations. You should also have an understanding of the ecological factors that influence their distribution.

Ecological factors that influence the distribution of organisms

There are many factors that influence the distribution of organisms but they can be categorised into three broad groups: climatic, edaphic (soil) and biotic.

Climatic factors include:

- **Temperature range** – The distribution of many organisms is influenced by the environmental temperature. As temperatures usually vary (often considerably) many species are adapted to live within a **temperature range**. For different species the relevant range in temperature can be seasonal or even diurnal (difference between the hottest part of the day and the coldest part of the night). High temperatures will denature enzymes and in very low temperatures water will turn to ice inside cells, which can physically damage them. Most species of life on Earth live within particular latitudes, defined by the temperatures that exist there.

- **Availability of water** – Water is essential for life and very few organisms are adapted to live in environments that are effectively water free such as hot deserts. Some species of plants, such as hydrophytes, are adapted for living in water and other, such as xerophytes, are adapted for living in areas where there is little water or water retention by the soil is limited, such as marram grass on sand dunes (see earlier section on xerophytes, page 140). Mammals have a waterproof skin and a gas exchange surface that lies deep within the body, therefore they are protected from loss of water by evaporation to some extent. Consequently, they are able to exploit terrestrial habitats more successfully than many other animal groups.

- **Light intensity** – Light is necessary for photosynthesis, so all plants and ultimately most life on Earth is dependent on it. In general, the more light the faster the rate of photosynthesis and the faster the rate of growth. However, some species are highly adapted for living in low light environments. For example, many permanent cave dwelling animals have evolved an excellent sense of smell and have lost the sense of sight. Light intensity has a significant effect on the distribution of most plant species; some require high light levels and others relatively low levels. Most water plants either grow close to the shore where light can penetrate through the shallow water or float on the surface layers in deeper water.

- **Light quality** – Plants can only use certain wavelengths of light for photosynthesis, so light quality (the wavelengths it contains) is as important as intensity. This is particularly important in some species of seaweed that live in deeper water. Red light is rapidly absorbed in water so blue light tends to penetrate to the deeper depths. Species of 'red' seaweeds tend to occur in a zone around and below the low tide mark. They have a greater proportion of their light-absorbing pigments as red pigments, which absorb at the blue end of the spectrum. This adaptation allows the red seaweeds to dominate a zone inhospitable to most other seaweeds.

- **Day length** – Longer day length means more light available for photosynthesis and therefore greater growth. In many ecosystems there is a close correlation between day length and temperature. The length of the day is also crucial for those species whose activity is limited to either the day or night. For example, nocturnal feeders have only a short feeding window in Britain in mid-summer.

Some of the climatic factors noted above, such as temperature and day length, tend to have an overriding and geographically widespread influence on plant and animal distribution. However, **edaphic** (soil) factors can be very important at the local level, with small changes in soil chemistry or water content influencing species distribution and number over very short distances. Typically, edaphic factors normally have a much greater effect on plant species than animal species, but the two are often interlinked because animal distribution is frequently influenced by the distribution of the plant species they need for food or shelter.

Edaphic factors include:

- **pH values** – Soil pH affects the availability of certain ions and this availability often influences the range of plant species that can grow. The optimum pH for most plants is around neutral, with a smaller number of species adapted for acidic or alkaline conditions. Plants adapted for habitats with limestone or chalk-rich soils normally have an alkaline pH optimum. For example, many orchids, including the dark red helleborine which is limited in the British Isles to only a few areas such as the limestone pavement area of the Burren in County Clare. Heathers and other moorland plants normally have an acidic optimum pH.

- **Availability of nutrients** – **Macronutrients** such as nitrate (for amino acids) and calcium (for cell wall formation) are required by plants in relatively large amounts. **Micronutrients** are ions that are required in very small amounts, but nonetheless can be critical in plant distribution. The availability of the nutrients depends on a number of factors, including the type of parent rock from which the soil has been formed and the ecosystem.

- **Water content** – The water content of the soil has a major influence over plant distribution. Most British plant species are adapted for moist but well drained soils, with smaller numbers of highly adapted species favouring either waterlogged or very dry soils (xerophytes). Waterlogged soils have very low oxygen levels, which restricts aerobic respiration in the root cells. Waterlogged soils often have reduced nitrate levels due to denitrification (most common in waterlogged conditions) converting the nitrate to atmospheric nitrogen. The zonation of plant species on a river bank is often due to gradients of water availability.

- **Aeration of soils** – Most soils contain air in the spaces between the soil crumbs. Much of the oxygen diffuses into the cells in the plant roots and is used in respiration. Most soil microbes involved in the decomposition of organic matter also require oxygen. Peat bogs are formed from plant matter (usually rich in mosses) that has not decayed for a number of reasons, including the fact that they are waterlogged and acidic, conditions that restrict the activity of microbes.

In addition to climatic and edaphic factors, the distribution of plant and animal species is influenced by the activities of other living organisms, whether as competitors or being a predator or prey of the organism concerned. These factors can be grouped as biotic factors, examples of which are listed below.

Biotic factors include:

- **Competitors** – Organisms compete with each other for any resource that is in limited supply. The general principle of competition is that some win and others lose out. Young chicks compete for their mother's attention and the food that this will bring, with the weaker ones often losing out at the expense of the stronger ones. Only some of the young oak seedlings at the base of the parent tree survive, as they compete for light, space, water and ions. While other factors such as grazing and trampling can have an effect, it is the competition among the seedlings (and with the parent tree) that ultimately determines that the vast majority of seedlings will not survive to maturity. This type of competition, where organisms of the **same species** are competing, is **intraspecific competition**. **Interspecific competition** is where organisms of **different species** are competing for a resource, for example, a range of species of scavengers feeding off a dead carcass or different plant species competing for light on the woodland floor.

- **Predators and prey** – Numbers of predators and prey are influenced by the numbers of each other. When prey numbers are high, predator numbers are often high and the converse applies, with a fall in prey numbers often resulting in a fall in the number of predators. This is particularly true when a predator only has one main species of prey. Typically, a graph showing the numbers of prey animals in a population and the number of predators follows the pattern in the graph below.

- **Accumulation of waste** – The growth of microorganisms is often restricted by the accumulation of toxic waste, but the principle applies to any species.

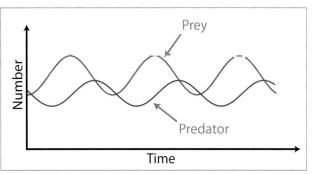

The relationship between the numbers of predator and prey

The ecological factors (climatic, edaphic and biotic) affect both the distribution of organisms and also determine the number of individuals that a particular environment can support. In reality, the individuals of many species are affected by a majority of the ecological factors listed above at any one time.

The term **ecological niche** describes an organism's role within the ecosystem. This includes its role in the food chain, its climatic and (if relevant) edaphic requirements, and its competition with other organisms.

It is unusual for more than one species to occupy the exact same ecological niche – when this does happen, interspecific competition often leads to the extinction of one of the species – **the competitive exclusion principle**.

Case Study: wild garlic

Wild garlic is a common plant occurring in deciduous woodlands (for example, oak, ash, beech) with moist soils throughout most of lowland British Isles. The species overwinters as a bulb within the soil and new leaves emerge through the soil in February/March to make use of the increasing light levels on woodland floors before the tree canopy closes. By the time the tree canopy closes (May), the wild garlic plants will be in flower. The flowers and other above ground parts of wild garlic are largely decomposed by July.

The species is particularly common in the wetter western parts of the British Isles, for example, Northern Ireland, the islands and the western coastal regions of Scotland, Cornwall and Devon. These areas give it the appropriate **temperature ranges** and **water availability**.

Wild garlic grows particularly well on nutrient-rich woodland soils with a **pH** value around neutral. It favours nitrate-rich soils (the main **macronutrient** required), which are necessary to provide the minerals required for the rapid rate of growth in late February/early March, ensuring that the plant is mature enough to benefit from the high **light intensities** and increasing **day length** at this time.

A colony of wild garlic plants

Although high rainfall levels ensure that the plants have a **moist soil**, they cannot grow in waterlogged soil. The bulbs cannot survive if the ground is waterlogged, and therefore **not aerated**, for too long a period of time. The photograph below shows the sharp demarcation on a woodland flood, at the base of a slope, between where wild garlic grows (the soil is moist, but not waterlogged) and where there is no wild garlic (the soil is frequently waterlogged).

Both of the photographs opposite emphasise that wild garlic grows in dense colonies with very few other plants present in the habitat at this stage of the year. This is because the wild garlic is able to out-compete other potential **competitors**. It grows in very high densities where conditions are favourable, through a combination of a high output of seeds per plant and extensive asexual reproduction through the production of daughter bulbs.

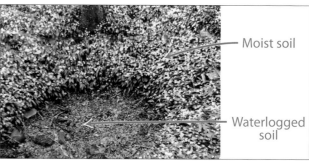

The relationship between soil moisture levels and the distribution of wild garlic

Wild garlic is virtually unique in that it can grow in **very low light intensities**, such as the light levels found at the edges and partially under rhododendron trees. The plants can do this because they are **highly adapted**, for example, they have the ability to develop very thin leaves in low light intensities. There is another very unusual (and rare) adaptation that allows the species to grow in very low light levels. The photograph below (left) shows the upper part of a wild garlic leaf growing in typical woodland (moderate) light levels. The other photograph below (right) shows the upper part of a leaf for a plant growing in very low light levels (partially under rhododendron).

Can you note the difference? The cuticle in very low light intensities is very thin (low evaporation rates in the dense shade do not require it to be any thicker) but the cuticle

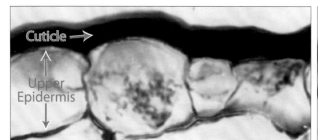

Cuticle and upper epidermis of wild garlic growing in moderate light levels (× 3000)

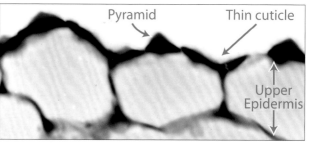

Cuticle and upper epidermis of wild garlic growing in very low light levels (× 3000)

is also thickened into microscopic 'pyramid' structures. In fact, these 'pyramids' have optical properties that allow them to concentrate and refract light onto the palisade layer below, including the light that reaches the leaf at a very low angle – light that in most leaves would be subject to reflection and be lost to the leaf. The presence of the 'pyramids' is a **morphological** adaptation and their ability to concentrate and refract light is a **physiological** adaptation. The flexibility that allows each wild garlic plant to be able to develop a cuticle appropriate to its needs may be regarded as a **'behavioural'** adaptation (although behavioural adaptations are most obvious in, and usually associated with, animals).

You do not need to know the details of wild garlic as described above, but through the 'study of organisms in their habitat' you should have a good understanding of and be able to interpret the adaptations that allow organisms to survive in a range of habitats, and the ecological factors that impact on their distribution and success.

Selection

All the individuals of any species tend to vary from each other. This variation can be **environmental** (geraniums that receive more light will grow larger than other geraniums that receive less light) but it can also be **genetic**. In Chapter 6, the role of meiosis in producing genetic variation was reviewed. Processes such as **independent assortment** of chromosomes, **crossing over** during gamete formation and the random mixing of chromosomes at **fertilisation** produce variation, as does **mutation** (spontaneous change in the DNA code).

This means that, within most species, there is considerable variation among individuals. If a population is variable, it is logical that some are better adapted than others for the particular environment within which they live.

Fitness is the term used to describe how well adapted an organism is for its environment. Due to competition or the effect of predators, the best adapted (**fittest**) are more likely to survive in nature than those less well adapted (**survival of the fittest**). This is **natural selection** (a term coined by Charles Darwin), the editing of genetically inheritable features in a population, increasing the frequency of some while decreasing the frequency of others over time.

Note: natural selection will select against (eliminate) individuals that are poorly adapted, irrespective of whether the decreased fitness is due to environmental or genetic variation. However, if it is to lead to change in a population over time, it is only the **genetic variation that is significant**, allowing the favourable traits to pass to future generations.

Natural selection at the genetic level

Genetic variation results from individuals within the population having **different alleles** for the characteristics under consideration. The best adapted individuals (with their favourable **alleles**), are more likely to **survive and pass these alleles on to the next generation**, whereas the less well adapted alleles are likely to get eliminated (together with the less well adapted individuals). This **differential reproductive success** maintains the fitness of the population, with the alleles providing the best adaptations being selected for and the alleles providing less favourable adaptations being selected against.

Over time the process of natural selection can, depending on the environmental pressures involved, maintain constancy in the genetic makeup of the population or lead to change. These respective types of natural selection (stabilising selection and directional selection) will be reviewed in the next section.

Stabilising and directional selection

In a constant environment, natural selection will tend to favour the *status quo* – **stabilising selection**. This is because as organisms evolve over time, they reach an optimum state within their environment. 'Average' individuals are best adapted, with the extremes less well adapted, therefore it is the average individuals that are more likely to survive and pass their genes on to the next generation.

A famous investigation of stabilising selection involved the analysis of births in a London hospital in the late 1930s. The data gathered showed that the babies with the best chance of survival were those of average mass. Mortality rates were higher for the smallest (usually very premature) babies and also for the largest babies (those that often developed difficulties at the birth phase due to their large size). This particular example of stabilising selection is much less pertinent now, as medical advances ensure that the vast majority of both small and large babies survive.

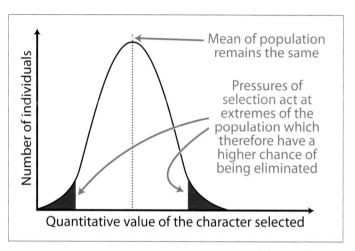

Stabilising selection

However, in nature, stabilising selection is as rigorous as it has ever been.

Directional selection is where average individuals are not the best adapted, but the best adapted individuals lie closer to one of the extremes of variation. Directional selection is most likely to happen when there is a **change in the environment**.

A good example is **pesticide resistance in insects**. Over 500 species of insects have populations that are resistant to at least one pesticide. In many species there are varying degrees of resistance (depending on the number and type of mutations).

Pesticide resistance is due to mutations that confer resistance, but the change in the insect's DNA can make it around 10% less fit than non-resistant forms in normal (pesticide free) environments. This is why the number of pesticide resistant insects in a population, not subject to pesticide application, is very low. The less well adapted pesticide resistant forms are eliminated by natural selection.

However, if the insect population is affected by the application of pesticides (pesticide use is the **selection pressure**), the resistant forms are better adapted, survive and produce offspring as the non-resistant insects without the pesticide resistant allele(s) are eliminated. Over time, in areas where pesticide spraying is common, whole insect populations have become resistant, as the normal forms have been eliminated. Consequently, there has been a directional change in allele frequency in tandem with a changing environment (from pesticide free to pesticide use). The same principle applies in the development of antibiotic resistance in bacteria.

Note: in the diagram (right) the quantitative value of the character selected could be the degree of pesticide resistance.

In general, directional selection plays a significant role in **maintaining diversity** within species and in **evolutionary change**, ensuring that populations (and species) respond to environmental change.

Some key points about natural selection:

- Natural selection is a process that acts on **populations** through its effect on **individuals**. Individuals survive or die depending on their degree of adaptation, but with directional selection the population will change over time, or evolve, as allele frequency changes.

- Fitness is **environmentally dependent**. For example, pesticide resistance is only an advantage if pesticides are used (it is a disadvantage if they are not used).

- Natural selection is effective through **differential reproductive success**. Differential reproduction is necessary to ensure that more favoured alleles get passed on to the next generation than less favoured alleles.

- Natural selection is an **ongoing process**. It is always taking place.

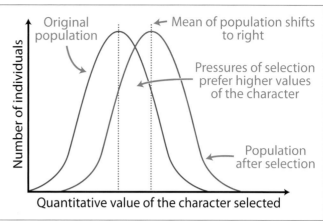

Directional selection

Case study revisited

Examples of directional selection such as pesticide resistance in insects and antibiotic resistance in bacteria are well known and used in most 'A' level Biology textbooks. However, many and probably most species exhibit directional selection in at least some of their populations.

Take, for example, our case study species, wild garlic (see page 177). Each wild garlic plant has two or three oval shaped leaves. These leaves are orientated vertically as shown in the diagram opposite.

Analysis of wild garlic populations throughout Britain has shown that there is a strong positive correlation between leaf width (do not confuse width with thickness) and soil nitrate level, although there is no correlation between leaf length and soil nitrate levels (see graphs on pages 182).

Why is there a positive correlation between leaf width and soil nitrate level but absence of correlation between leaf length and soil nitrate level?

As earlier discussed, wild garlic populations grow in very dense colonies (up to several thousand plants per square metre) and there is significant **intraspecfic** competition (the woodland floor contains very little else apart from wild garlic). In this

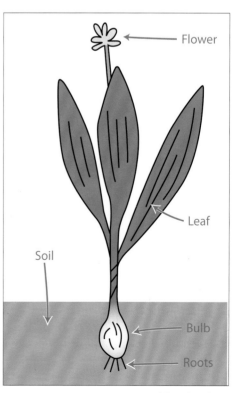

A wild garlic plant

181

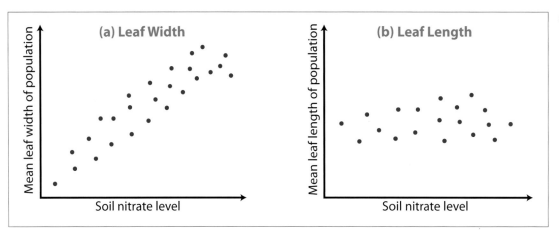

Relationship between (a) leaf width and (b) leaf length in wild garlic and soil nitrate level (graphs not to scale)

environment it is an advantage for all leaves to be of maximum length to ensure that they all absorb maximum light for photosynthesis.

In soils with high nitrate levels, the plants have leaves that are both long and reasonably wide. With no shortage of nitrate they can make a high investment in leaf area to maximise growth.

However, it is different in soils with low nitrate levels. There is not enough nitrate available to produce both long and wide leaves in the large number of plants involved. Due to the intraspecific competition for light, wild garlic plants will be at a selective advantage if they have tall narrow leaves rather than shorter but wider leaves, therefore height is the priority. The lower nitrate levels have resulted in leaf width being sacrificed in favour of leaf length, as the environment cannot support both long and wide leaves. The development of wild garlic plants with narrow leaves in nitrate poor soils is an example of **directional selection**.

Typical exam question

Using the information above, explain the development of wild garlic populations that have leaves, which on average are narrower than the leaves of other populations, as an example of directional selection. [4]

Answer

Any four from:

- leaf width is variable in the population.
- soil nitrate availability is the selection pressure.
- due to low soil nitrate levels, leaves cannot be both long and wide.
- plants with leaves that are long but narrow are more likely to compete successfully for light.
- are more likely to survive than those that have short but wide leaves.
- are more likely to produce offspring.
- alleles for narrow long leaves are more likely to be passed on to the next generation compared to alleles for wider but shorter leaves.
- over time the proportion of plants with alleles for narrower (and longer) leaves will increase in the population.

Practical work

You are expected to be familiar with a range of qualitative and quantitative techniques used to investigate the distribution and relative abundance of plants and animals in a habitat.

Sampling

It is normally not possible, or at least not efficient, to count all the individuals of one or a range of species in a habitat. Instead, the habitat is usually **sampled** to gain an accurate estimate of plant or animal species numbers, or their distribution.

When sampling, a population or a community can be **estimated** in terms of:

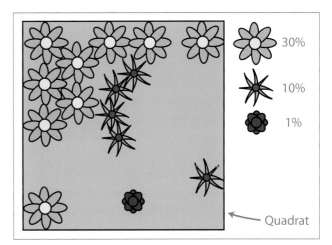

Estimating percentage cover using (frame) quadrats

- **Density** – The **number** of individuals present. Frame **quadrats** are often used in sampling to determine density. Density is a useful indicator for many **animals** but is not suitable for all plants as it is often difficult to know where one plant starts or ends.

- **Percentage cover** – Mainly used for **plants**. This gives an **estimation** of the percentage area covered by a plant species and is usually rounded up to the nearest 10%. An exception is that the value 1% is usually given to indicate the presence of a species in a quadrat, but that it has less than 5% cover (not enough to give a 10% cover rating).

- **Frequency** – For each quadrat the species may be recorded as being present or absent. Thus % frequency indicates the percentage of all quadrats that a species occurs in. Sometimes a pin or **point quadrat** (a quadrat that has a number of large pins that can be lowered onto the ground) is used to record frequency. If a pin touches a plant of a particular species, it is recorded as being present, if not, it is absent. With a pin/point quadrat a frequency of 5% indicates that 5% of pins used in the sampling process touched the species concerned.

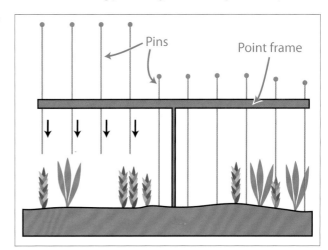

The pin or point quadrat

Mechanisms of sampling

It is important to use an appropriate number of quadrats (sample size) during sampling. Too few will not give a representative (reliable) value and too many will defeat the purpose of sampling. The graph on page 184 shows that the population size can be accurately estimated at the point where the line begins to plateau. However, it also shows that an increase in sample size (number of quadrats used) does not lead to a significant increase in accuracy.

Random sampling – If the area to be sampled is uniform or if there is absence of any clear pattern in species distribution, then **random sampling** should normally be used. Random sampling **avoids bias** and ensures that the sample is **representative**. Generally this is done by dividing the area to be sampled into a **grid** using tapes at right angles to each other and then generating **random numbers** to define the co-ordinates of the sections to be sampled.

Another variation is placing a tape along the line of the area to be sampled and placing other tapes at right angles to the original tape as shown opposite.

Sampling animals – Quadrats can be used to sample animals if they are not particularly mobile, for example, limpets on a rocky shore or snails in a sand dune system. However, more mobile (and difficult to locate) animals need to be trapped before their distribution or abundance can be measured. This can be done using **pitfall traps** (trapping woodland floor beetles), **sweep nets** (trapping insects living in the long grass in meadows) or **pooters** (trapping insects on oak leaves).

You should also have experience of measurement of some of the biotic and abiotic factors that influence the distribution of organisms, for example, soil moisture, soil pH and light intensity.

Systematic sampling – In certain conditions sampling should not be totally random but should be **systematic**. Systematic sampling should be used when there appears to be zonation/clear transition from one habitat type to another in the distribution of species, for example, up a river bank or from a woodland edge to the centre of the wood or along the sea shore. In this situation the sampling is described as being along a line or **transect**.

If sampling abundance of species from the dune slack (left of photograph) to the wooded area on the right, systematic sampling would be more appropriate.

There are a number of different types of transect used in systematic sampling:

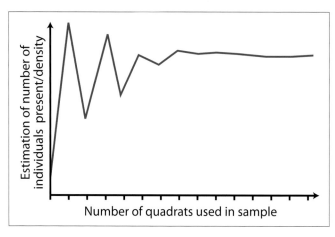

The effect of number of quadrats used in estimating abundance

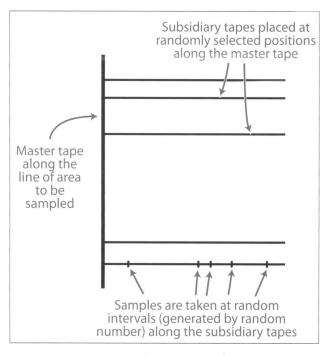

Another variation of random sampling

1. **Line transect** – Sampling either continually or at intervals (such as every 5 m) along a transect line, for example, tape. Only individuals actually touching the transect line are recorded.

2. **Belt transect** – Sampling along a transect line using **quadrats**, typically placed end to end to each other (**contiguously**) so that the transect line is continually sampled from one end to the other.

3. **Interrupted belt transects** – As for belt transect but the sampling is at intervals along the overall transect due to the large distances involved. It might be appropriate to use a belt transect up a rocky shore, from low tide mark to high tide mark. An interrupted belt transect is also likely to be appropriate when sampling a sand dune system from the sea shore to the woodland edge immediately beyond the dune system, a distance that could be a kilometre or more. In effect, interrupted belt transects are a number of belt transects nested at intervals along an overall transect.

Normally ecological data gathered in this type of investigation is presented in **kite diagrams** and/or a series of **histograms**.

Exam questions

1. The distribution of two species of marine mollusc, *Littorina littorea* (the edible periwinkle) and *Littorina saxatilis* (the rough periwinkle), was investigated on a rocky shore. A belt transect from lower shore to upper shore indicated that *L. littorea* (the edible periwinkle) was found on the lower part of the shore and *L. saxatilis* (the rough periwinkle) was limited to the upper shore.

   Both species of periwinkle graze on algae which are abundant on the rocks. Also, they have a heavy shell (with a cover over the opening) to protect them from desiccation and mechanical damage.

   However, they differ in a number of ways.

   - *L. littorea* (the edible periwinkle) produces fertile eggs which are released into the water and the larvae swim among the plankton. It has gills and can breathe for only a relatively short period out of water.

   - *L. saxatilis* (the rough periwinkle) retains the fertilised eggs inside the body where they hatch so that there is no planktonic existence. The gills are modified to absorb air and it can survive for up to a month out of water. It has a high temperature tolerance and, in extremes of desiccation and temperature, it cements itself to a rock.

   (a) The lower shore area was covered by seawater for most of the day while the sea only reached the upper shore at high tide (twice a day).

   Explain how the adaptations of the *L. saxatilis* (the rough periwinkle) equip this periwinkle for life on the upper part of the shore. [3]

   (b) Suggest an explanation why *L. littorea* (the edible periwinkle) outcompetes *L. saxatilis* (the rough periwinkle) on the lower shore. [1]

   Question taken from CCEA's Biology Unit AS2, Organisms and Biodiversity, June 2009, © CCEA 2012

2. One of the greatest environmental changes during the 19th century resulted from the increase in burning fossil fuels, especially coal. The burning coal released sulphur dioxide and black soot. Lichens on tree bark were destroyed by the sulphur dioxide and the bark was blackened by deposits of soot.

   The peppered moth, *Biston betularia*, has a speckled pattern over its wings, an effective camouflage when it is resting on lichen covered tree bark. Before 1850 a rare form of moth, which was almost black, was known. However, by 1850, in industrial cities such as Manchester, 85% of the peppered moth population in the city was the black form.

Speckled form

Black form

For copyright reasons these photographs by Olaf Leillinger have replaced drawings from CCEA's Biology AS2, June 2011 paper.

The graph below shows a period of time between 1960 and 1990 when less coal was burnt and smokeless fuel was introduced for domestic use. The graph shows the frequency of the black form of the moth over this period as well as the concentration of the two pollutants.

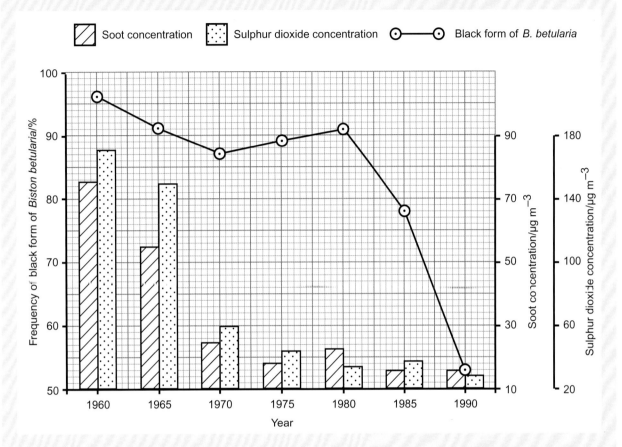

(a) Use the information in the graph and your own understanding to answer the following questions.

   (i) What is the evidence for a reduction in coal burning and the introduction of smokeless fuel? [2]

   (ii) What is the evidence for lichen regrowth on the bark of trees? [2]

(b) Suggest why the black form of the moth did not decline significantly until after 1980. [2]

(c) Explain why the changes in the frequencies of the different forms of *Biston betularia* is an example of directional selection. [2]

Question taken from CCEA's Biology Assessment Unit AS2, Organisms and Biodiversity, January 2010, © CCEA 2012

3. Bladderwrack (*Fucus vesiculosus*) is a common seaweed on most rocky shores in Northern Ireland.

  (a) In an investigation into the distribution of bladderwrack on a rocky shore, quadrats were placed at particular sites. The drawing on page 188 shows the areas in one quadrat in which bladderwrack was found. Wires were used to divide the quadrat into smaller squares.

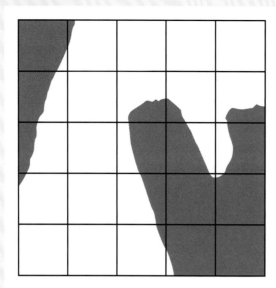

position of
bladderwrack

Determine the percentage cover of bladderwrack in the quadrat.
Explain how you arrived at your answer. [2]

(b) The rocky shore in which the investigation took place contained not only bladderwrack, but four other species of seaweed. Explain how you would investigate the distribution of the seaweeds on the rocky shore to determine whether they are adapted to specific zones of the shore. [4]

Question taken from CCEA's Biology Assessment Unit AS2, Organisms and Biodiversity, June 2011, © CCEA 2012

4. Woodlands are complex ecosystems containing plants that grow to different heights. The leaf cover of the taller trees creates shade for those below. Different tree species provide varying degrees of shading. A fallen tree reduces the shading at that point.

A student was investigating the difference in ground-level plant species at different locations in a deciduous woodland ecosystem. The procedure followed by the student is outlined below.

- A transect line was positioned from the centre of the wood to the edge.
- Six sample sites were identified at 20 m intervals along the transect line.
- One quadrat was placed at each sample site and the names of the main species present in the quadrat were recorded.

The following results were recorded by the student:

- Mosses were found mainly at site 1, but there were also some present at sites 2, 3 and 5.
- Bluebells were found in abundance at sites 2, 3 and 5 and a few were also present at site 4.
- Wood anemone was found at sites 2, 3 and 5.
- Primroses were found at sites 4 and 6.
- Lesser celandine was found mainly at sites 2 and 3, but there was also a little of this at site 1.
- Grass was present at all sites but it was densest at sites 4 and 6.

(a) Organise these results into an appropriate table to show the presence or absence of each of the species recorded by this student. The relative abundance of plants does not need to be distinguished. Your table should have a caption and suitable column headings.

The following notes on the different sample sites were also made by the student:

- Sample point 1 was in the centre of the woodland. The tree cover was very dense, so it was the darkest and wettest of the six sample sites.

- A dead tree lay near the quadrat at sample site 4, so the tree cover was less dense, and sample site 6 was at the edge of the woodland. These two sample sites were only lightly shaded and were also the driest areas of the woodland.

- Sample sites 2, 3 and 5 appeared to have similar levels of light and moisture. They were drier and lighter than site 1, but darker and moister than sites 4 and 6.

(b) Using the information from your table and the notes made by the student on the different sites, describe the conditions favoured by each of the following plants.

- Mosses
- Bluebells
- Primroses [3]

(c) Explain why the student chose to place a transect line through the woodland, rather than selecting six random sites. [1]

(d) This student simply recorded the presence of certain species at each site, although he did comment on the relative amount of some of the species. He also made general observations on the relative light and moisture conditions at each site.

Explain how this student could have obtained more meaningful and reliable results at each sample site. [3]

Question taken from CCEA's Biology Assessment Unit AS2, Organisms and Biodiversity, January 2012, © CCEA 2012

Chapter 12 – The Variety of Life

Students should be able to:

2.3.1	Understand that the biochemical basis of life is similar for all organisms.
2.3.2	Understand that biodiversity involves variation among living organisms at all levels of biological organisation.
2.3.3	Measure species diversity and appreciate that genetic diversity can be measured.
2.3.4	Understand the principle of taxonomy.
2.3.5	Understand the concept of the species.
2.3.6	Understand the other taxa within which species can be grouped.
2.3.7	Understand phylogenetic taxonomy as a means of classifying sets of species according to ancestral relationships.
2.3.8	Appreciate the five kingdom system of classification.
2.3.9	Describe the features of Prokaryotae.
2.3.10	Describe the features of Protoctista.
2.3.11	Describe the features of Fungi.
2.3.12	Describe the features of Plantae.
2.3.13	Describe the features of Animalia.

Measuring species biodiversity

Sampling is often used to provide information concerning **biodiversity** in a habitat. Biodiversity gives an indication of **both** the **range of species** in a habitat and also how evenly balanced the **numbers of individuals** are across the different species.

Biodiversity is not the same as **species-richness**. A particular habitat can be species-rich but not show much biodiversity, for example, a habitat may be species-rich but has very small numbers of most species, with only one or two species dominating the community.

Simpson's index (D) is a measure of biodiversity that takes into account both the number of species and the number of individuals of each species.

The formula for calculating D is shown below.

$$D = \frac{\sum n_i(n_i - 1)}{N(N-1)}$$

where n_i = total number of organisms of each individual species
N = total number of organisms of all species

The value of D ranges from 1 to 0. A value of 0 represents infinite biodiversity and 1 represents no biodiversity. The **lower the value of D** (ie the closer to 0), the **greater the diversity**.

To calculate Simpson's index, it is necessary to identify the number of different species present and then measure the abundance of each species. Realistically, it will probably be necessary to sample the habitat using one of the techniques described in the last chapter. When calculating Simpson's index any of the indicators discussed in Chapter 11 can be used (density, frequency or percentage cover). However, density (number) is typically used for animals and percentage cover used for plant species (due to the difficulty in identifying individual plants).

Example

Comparing the biodiversity in two habitats using Simpson's index.

Species	Average density (number) of individuals/m²	
	Habitat A	Habitat B
A	5	3
B	7	17
C	3	0
D	9	7
E	6	19
F	4	0
Number of species	6	4
Total number of individuals (N)	34	46

Habitat A

$$D = \frac{\sum n_i(n_i - 1)}{N(N-1)}$$

$$= \frac{5(4) + 7(6) + 3(2) + 9(8) + 6(5) + 4(3)}{34(33)}$$

$$= \frac{182}{1122}$$

$$D = 0.16$$

Habitat B

$$D = \frac{\sum n_i(n_i - 1)}{N(N-1)}$$

$$= \frac{3(2) + 17(16) + 7(6) + 19(18)}{46(45)}$$

$$= \frac{662}{2070}$$

$$D = 0.32$$

Note that habitat A has the greater diversity (Simpson's index value of 0.16 compared to 0.32 in habitat B) even though it has, on average, many fewer individuals per square metre. However, habitat B has fewer species in comparison and is dominated by two species (B and E).

Types of diversity

Simpson's index typically calculates species diversity, but there are other types of diversity including ecosystem diversity and genetic diversity.

Ecosystem diversity – This represents the diversity of **ecosystems** within the biosphere (the part of the Earth and its atmosphere that is inhabited by living organisms). At this stage it is worthwhile to revisit and clarify some of the ecological terms we have used since the beginning of Chapter 11:

- **Habitat** – This term refers to the places where organisms live, for example, a pond or rocky shore. Habitats can be relatively small scale, for example, an individual leaf on a tree. These very small habitats are referred to as microhabitats.

- **Environment** – The environment describes the conditions that affect organisms in a habitat. The environment determines the type of habitat that can develop and also the species that can live there. The environment can be separated into the physical and non-living (**abiotic**) and the living (**biotic**). Examples of the abiotic environment include light intensity, temperature, soil conditions and wave action. The biotic environment includes food supply or potential predators and also organisms that can compete for resources. Sometimes there is overlap, for example, a tree can affect the light that is available to a seedling.

- **Ecosystem** – An ecosystem is a community of organisms, interacting with one another and the associated environment. An ecosystem forms a balanced self-sufficient ecological unit, with its own characteristic pattern of energy flow and nutrient cycling. An ecosystem can be of any size. Examples include forests, ponds, lakes and oceans.

- **Population** – A population is made up of all the members of the same species that occur in a particular area at a particular time. Examples include the world human population and the population of bluebells in a wood.

- **Community** – A community is a group of species which occur in the same place at the same time. A woodland community includes all the living organisms within the wood.

Some ecological terms, most usually habitat and ecosystem, are often used in an interchangeable way. People can refer to the woodland ecosystem or a woodland habitat.

On a worldwide scale, many major ecosystems are at risk due to the action of man. The north and south polar regions, and their communities, are at risk due to the melting of ice due to global warming. The Amazon rainforest ecosystem is significantly affected by land clearance. Relatively few major ecosystems escape the harmful effects of the activity of man.

Woodland

Ecosystem diversity is also an important issue on a more local scale, for example, in Northern Ireland. Much of our former ecosystem diversity has been lost due to the intensification of agricultural practices and for other reasons. Most of our damp meadows and much of our hedgerow and woodland has been removed to increase the land available for agriculture. Intensively managed agricultural land does not really provide a diversity of ecosystems. The human impact on biodiversity will be covered in more detail in Chapter 13.

Genetic diversity – This refers to the **genetic variability** of the species. There are many factors that influence genetic variability, including how long a particular species has been in existence since it has evolved. Another factor is the degree of directional selection that has taken place in different populations. Genetic variability tends to be greater in species that have become adapted to a wide range of environments. Species that are subject to higher rates of mutation to their DNA than other species will be more genetically variable.

It is desirable that species are genetically diverse. Genetically diverse species are more subject to directional selection and therefore are more likely to remain adapted if the environment changes.

Classification

It is thought there are over ten million species of living organisms on Earth today, although less that two million have been identified and classified. **Classification** involves placing living organisms into **groups**. The classification of organisms into groups is not a random process. Most classification systems take account of the ancestral relationships among living organisms.

The basic unit of biological classification is the species, but what exactly is a species?

The concept of the species

The definition of a species has changed through time. Many decades ago, organisms were categorised as being a particular species almost entirely on their physical features. Now, a much greater range of information is available including anatomy, biochemistry, physiology, immunology, genetic, ancestral development and ecology. These and other features are now taken into account when determining the defining characteristics of a particular species.

A **species** can be defined as:

"a group of individuals of common ancestry that closely resemble each other, and are normally capable of interbreeding to produce fertile offspring".

This seems straightforward but it is often very difficult to determine if a particular organism belongs to a particular species. For example, a number of large cat species have been able to interbreed in captivity (such as male tiger and lioness) and a number of the hybrid offspring (tiglon) have proved to be fertile. However, tigers and lions are still classified as separate species as the hybrids tend not to occur in natural conditions.

The dog is a single species with many different breeds or types (over 300) but it is still classified as a single species as theoretically any male dog can breed with any female dog. However, what are the chances of a Great Dane breeding with a Chihuahua?

Carl Linnaeus (1707–1778), a Swedish naturalist, was the first person to make a serious attempt at classification. He devised the **binomial system** for the naming of species. Linnaeus was all too aware that the names given to particular species could vary in different countries and even regionally within the one country (think of gorse, whin, furze and so on), each with a local name referring to the same species.

The binomial system gives each species two names. The first name is the **generic** name, which indicates the **genus** (plural **genera**) to which the species belongs. In human terms this can be regarded as being equivalent to our surname. The second name is the **specific** or **species name**, which identifies the species to which the organism belongs. This is analogous to the first name of humans. There can be a number of closely related

Gorse, whin or furze? *Does the road sign near Glenavy in County Antrim suggest that furze is the common local name?*

organisms that have the same genus name but only one species has the specific name.

There are a number of conventions concerning binomial names. The system is used worldwide and the names are usually derived from Latin or Greek. They are always printed in italics with the genus name, but not the specific name, starting with a capital. When used more than once in a sequence, the generic name can be shortened to the first letter, followed by a full stop. For example, our (human) binomial name is written as *Homo sapiens* or *H. sapiens*.

An example of closely related species – Many bears belong to the *Ursus* genus as they are very closely related. However, as shown in the table below they have different specific names.

Common Name	Generic name	Specific name
Polar bear	*Ursus*	*maritimus*
Brown bear	*Ursus*	*arctos*
Asian black bear	*Ursus*	*thibetanus*

The giant panda *Ailuropoda melanoleuca* is also a bear, but is slightly more distantly related and belongs to a different genus.

Taxonomy

The arrangement of organisms into groups is known as **classification** but the science or study of classification is called **taxonomy**. There are many systems of classification but they all involve the organisation of species into hierarchical groups of increasing size. Each group is called a **taxon** (plural **taxa**). The groups (in increasing size) are **species, genus, family, order, class, phylum** and **kingdom**. Consequently, the number of species in each classification group increases as the sub-sets become larger. For example, the kingdom is the largest grouping with the animal kingdom containing all 'animal' species.

The taxonomic system can be sub-divided into sub-categories. Many species have sub-species where, although all the members of the species fit the species definition described earlier in this chapter, two or more populations may be distinct enough to form distinct groupings or sub-species. For example, the 'grizzly' bear is a sub-species of the brown bear and is named *Ursus arctos horribilis* (the sub-species name is usually added to the end of the species name).

This taxonomic hierarchy can be summarised in the following table.

Taxon	Definition of taxon
Genus	A group of similar and closely related species.
Family	A group of related genera.
Order	A group of related families.
Class	A group of related orders.
Phylum	A group of related classes.
Kingdom	A group of related phyla.

Revisiting the bears – The following table shows the classification of the polar bear.

Kingdom	Animalia
Phylum	Chordata
Class	Mammalia
Order	Carnivora
Family	Ursidae
Genus	*Ursus*
Species	*maritimus*

All the other bear species discussed in the earlier section belong to the family Ursidae (and consequently the same order, class, phylum and kingdom).

Taxonomy involves both **nomenclature** (the scientific naming of organisms using the binomial system) and **systematics** (the placing of organisms into groups based on their similarities and differences). Recent taxonomic systems attempt to classify species and the larger groupings based on their ancestral relationship, rather than just a superficial accumulation of similarities.

Phylogenetic taxonomy (phylogeny)

Phylogenetic taxonomy is the process of the classification of species and larger groups according to their ancestral relationships. In effect, the different species in a genus do not just have a large number of similarities, they also share common ancestry, ie they have evolved from a common ancestor. Groups of species that have shared a common ancestor more recently than other species will consequently be more closely related.

Phylogenetic taxonomy is now a much more scientific process due to a greater understanding of the evolutionary development of life on Earth. Additionally, there is exponential progress in the techniques available to elucidate relationships among organisms at the microscopic and biochemical level, as well as the more obvious physical and behavioural characteristics of organisms (which was all that Linnaeus had available to him as he attempted to develop a phylogenetic taxonomy over 200 years ago).

What are the techniques that are used to establish phylogeny? They include morphology and anatomy (external and internal features), cell structure and biochemistry.

Morphology and anatomy – **Morphology** refers to the **external** features of an organism (for example, the presence of four limbs) and **anatomy** the **internal** features (for example, the presence of a backbone). Historically, these have been very important in the early classification systems. They are still important and can often be readily and easily used to classify organisms and show relationships. A good example is the vertebrate 'pentadactyl' limb.

The pentadactyl limb is the basic unit upon which the many forms of vertebrate limb have evolved, including legs, arms, wings and flippers. This similarity shows that all vertebrates are related and have common ancestry, even though the limbs have evolved into a wide range of structures that look very different and have very different functions.

Nonetheless, the presence of a modified form of 'pentadactyl' limb clearly identifies the different species as a member of the Phylum Chordata (vertebrates).

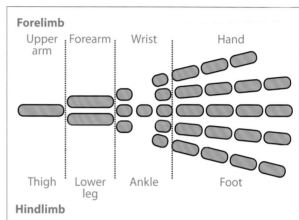

The pentadactyl limb

However, appearances can be misleading. Bats and birds have wings that can look very similar in some species. While the two groups belong to the Phylum Chordata (they have the characteristic features of the vertebrates, including the pentadactyl limb), they are not as closely related as their morphology suggests. Birds have wings with feathers whereas the bat wing is an extension of the skin. They have superficially similar morphologies but very different ancestries, as birds belong to the Class Aves and bats to the Class Mammalia.

Cell structure – The key difference in cell structure is whether the organism in question is **prokaryotic** or **eukaryotic**. The first cells were prokaryotic and for many millions of years life on Earth was entirely prokaryotic. Eventually, eukaryotic cells evolved and four out of five kingdoms in the most common classification system used today are eukaryotic. With the split between prokaryotic and eukaryotic organisms taking place very early in the development of life on Earth, this means that the organisms in the four eukaryotic kingdoms (Protoctista, Plantae, Fungi and Animalia) are more closely related to each other than they are to the organisms in the kingdom Prokaryotae.

Cell structure is also important in classifying other groups. Cell structural differences are important in classifying organisms as plants, fungi or animals.

Biochemistry – In recent years, biochemistry has become increasingly important in classification. In the last decade or so, it has been possible to analyse the genomes (complete DNA map) of species. Almost always, genome analysis and other biochemical techniques have confirmed the phylogenetic relationships already established by more traditional methods, but occasionally they have resulted in species taking up a new position in classification systems.

The biochemical basis of life is similar in all organisms. They all contain carbohydrates, lipids, nucleic acids and proteins. The more closely related species are, the more similar their DNA will be. As DNA codes for the amino acid sequence in a protein through the medium of mRNA, it follows that the more closely related species are, the more similar their RNA and protein sequences will be.

Once two or more species (or groups) evolve from an ancestral species, certain **mutations** will spontaneously take place in the DNA of one of the species but not necessarily in the other(s). Over time the species will increasingly differ in their DNA (and RNA and amino acid sequences in proteins). The relationships among species and the length of time since they shared a common ancestor, can be evaluated through analysing similarities in DNA, RNA or protein, using the degree of change at gene or biochemical level as a type of **molecular clock**.

The table below shows the degree of similarity in the amino acid sequences of a particular protein in five species. Using the degree of similarity in protein structure, the phylogenetic sequence and the relationship among the species can be worked out to give a possible phylogenetic history as seen in the figure on the right.

Using DNA and biochemical data to work out phylogeny

Species	Degree of similarity in amino acid sequence / %
A–B	93
A–C	94
A–D	81
A–E	70
B–C	98
B–D	78
B–E	67
C–D	80
C–E	69
D–E	73

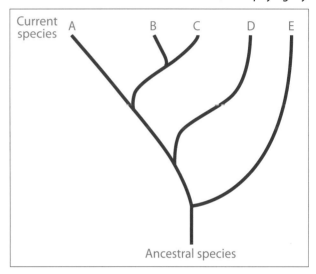

The five kingdom classification

The **five kingdom** classification system, as noted earlier in this chapter, is the system currently recognised by many scientists. However, classification systems are subject to review as new information and techniques evolve. 40 years ago 'A' level textbooks referred to there being two kingdoms, within which all living forms were placed – plants and animals!

The current model recognises the five kingdoms **Prokaryotae, Protoctista, Fungi, Plantae** and **Animalia**.

The five kingdom system suggests that there are three overarching levels of organisation as shown in the diagram to the right.

The three levels of organisation are:

- **Prokaryotic** – prokaryotic cells, kingdom Prokaryotae

- **Eukaryotic unicellular** (some multicellular, if multicellular have only limited differentiation) – kingdom Protoctista

- **Eukaryotic multicellular** – kingdoms Fungi, Plantae and Animalia

The five kingdom system

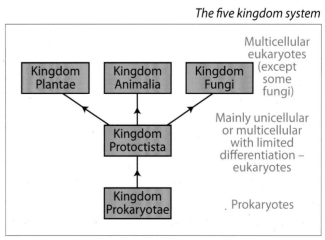

Kingdom Prokaryotae

Prokaryotae occur as single cells or clusters or 'strings' of cells stuck together.

Organisms in the kingdom Prokaryotae have **prokaryotic cells**, ie they possess the features associated with prokaryotic cells and reviewed in Chapter 3 (Cells).

Prokaryotic cells are **without a nucleus or membrane-bound organelles. DNA lies free in the cytoplasm** and is not organised into chromosomes. **Ribsosomes are smaller than in eukaryotic cells (20 nm (70S)). Cell walls** are **present** but are made of **peptidoglycans.** There are **no microtubules** and **cell division is by fission** (splitting into two without mitosis).

Examples include bacteria and blue-green algae. Prokaryotes have existed on Earth for over 3.5 billion years and in that time the eukaryotic kingdoms have evolved from these relatively simple forms.

Kingdom Protoctista

Protoctistans are **eukaryotic unicellular or multicellular. If multicellular, they have limited differentiation into different tissues**.

This is a very diverse group and to some extent it operates as a 'bin' including those organisms that do not fit into the other kingdoms.

Many species are unicellular but many others are organised into filaments with cells joined end to end in a long thread like structure (for example, some green seaweeds) or are multicellular. If multicellular, they have limited differentiation (for example brown seaweeds).

Some are autotrophic and photosynthesise, such as Phylum Chlorophyta (green algae). Protoctistans in this phylum have typical 'plant' cells with cellulose cell walls and chlorophyll but are not classified in the kingdom Plantae as they are often unicellular (or filamentous/or cell aggregates) and not true multicellular forms. Examples include *Pleurococcus* species, unicellular protoctistans that are often found on damp tree trunks, creating the characteristic green slimy covering that many trunks possess. *Spirogyra* species form a genus of filamentous algae whereas *Ulva lactuca* (sea lettuce) forms sheet-like structures from aggregates of cells.

Fucus vesiculosus (bladderwrack), a brown seaweed

Phylum Protozoa consists of unicellular protoctistans that are heterotrophic, ingesting and digesting their food. They are not classified as animals as they are unicellular.

Kingdom Fungi

Fungi are **eukaryotic** but can be unicellular (for example, yeast) or multicellular (most fungi). Although multicellular, fungi are often organised as **hyphae** (long filaments which together form the mycelium, the hyphal network). The elongated hyphal strands, characteristic of fungi, are frequently **multinucleate** and not clearly divided into separate cells.

They have a **cell wall** made of **chitin** (not cellulose as in plants).

Fungi have a **lysotrophic** or **saprophytic mode of nutrition**. They feed by decomposing organic matter.

They **secrete hydrolytic enzymes** into the soil by **exocytosis** and after the enzymes have digested the organic material in the soil (for example, dead roots), they **absorb** the products of digestion. As their enzymes work outside the cell this is called (**extracellular digestion**). Fungi store carbohydrates as glycogen.

Fungi are important **decomposers**, crucial in the breakdown and recycling of organic matter. They are very common in woodland where they are particularly important in decomposing plant material, including wood.

Examples include moulds (such as blue mould), mushrooms and toadstools.

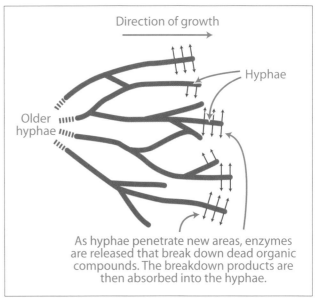

Extracellular digestion in fungi

Note: The toadstool and the mushroom are specialised fungal reproductive structures. These structures are raised above ground to facilitate the release and dispersal of spores.

Some types of fungi

Bracket fungus helping decompose a dead tree stump.

This fruiting body is all that is visible of this fungus. The fungal hyphae are underground feeding lysotrophically on organic material.

Mould growing on an orange.

Kingdom Plantae

Plants are **multicellular eukaryotes** that exhibit **autotrophic nutrition** (photosynthesise and make complex organic materials from simple inorganic raw materials). They possess **chlorophyll in chloroplasts** and have a **cellulose cell wall**.

They store carbohydrates as starch and lipids as oils.

Examples include mosses, ferns, conifers and flowering plants.

Fern growing at the base of a tree.

Moss on a wall.

Variegated holly.

Conifers

Kingdom Animalia

Animals are **multicellular eukaryotes** that feed **heterotrophically** (by consuming organic food). A key difference between animals and fungi is that an animal takes in its food then digests it, whereas fungi digest their food before taking it in.

Animal cells do not possess a cell wall. Animals store carbohydrates as glycogen and lipids as fats. **Most are capable of locomotion**.

Examples include flatworms, insects and chordates (fish, amphibians, reptiles, birds and mammals).

Swans on the Broadwater, County Antrim

Exam questions

1. The holm oak (*Quercus ilex*) is a tree of Mediterranean origin which was introduced into Ireland during the sixteenth century.

(a) The leaf of the holm oak possesses a thick waxy cuticle. What does this suggest about its adaptation to a Mediterranean climate? Explain your reasoning. [2]

Only two species of insect feed on the leaves of holm oak and both of these are moth larvae. The table below shows data for the abundance of these moth larvae in a group of holm oaks.

Insect feeding on holm oak	Number of individuals
Holm oak leaf-mining moth (*Phyllonorycter messaniella*) larvae	526
Lacky moth (*Malacosoma neustrium*) larvae	371

(b) Calculate the value for Simpson's Diversity Index (D) for holm oak.
The formula for calculating D is presented as:

$$D = \frac{\sum_i n_i(n_i - 1)}{N(N - 1)}$$

where n_i = the total number of organisms of each individual species.
N = the total number of organisms of all species

(Show your working.) [2]

The lacky moth larvae graze the edges of the leaves. However, the leaf-mining moth larvae feed internally on the mesophyll (following the placing of an egg into the interior of the leaf) and are thus said to "mine" the leaf.

(c) Suggest how placing the egg inside the leaf is an advantage for the survival of the leaf-mining moth larvae. [2]

The number of insect species associated with certain deciduous and coniferous trees in Ireland is given in the table below. Two of the deciduous trees are native to Ireland while two have been introduced by man.

Tree	Type	Number of insect species
Sessile oak (*Quercus petraea*)	native deciduous	284
Birch (*Betula pendula*)	native deciduous	229
Beech (*Fagus sylvatica*)	introduced deciduous	64
Sycamore (*Acer pseudoplatanus*)	introduced deciduous	15
Pine (*Pinus sylvestris*)	coniferous	91
Yew (*Taxus baccata*)	coniferous	4

(d) Which tree would you expect to have the highest value for Simpson's Index (D)? Explain your reasoning. [1]

(e) Suggest which tree species should be planted in new woodlands with a view to increasing biodiversity. Explain your reasoning. [2]

Question taken from CCEA's Biology Assessment Unit AS2, Organisms and Biodiversity, June 2011, © CCEA 2012

2. The list below represents the taxonomic hierarchy of the stoat (*Mustela erminea*).

    • Animalia
    • Chordata
    • Mammalia
    • Carnivora
    • Mustelidae
    • *Mustela*
    • *erminea*

    (a) Name the class to which a stoat belongs. [1]

    (b) What is the species name of the stoat? [1]

    (c) Define the term "species". [2]

    Question taken from CCEA's Biology Assessment Unit AS2, Organisms and Biodiversity, January 2010, © CCEA 2012

3. Fungi are described as lysotrophs and feed by extracellular digestion.

    (a) Explain why fungi are described as lysotrophs. [1]

    (b) Describe the process of extracellular digestion. [2]

    Question taken from CCEA's Biology Assessment Unit AS2, Organisms and Biodiversity, January 2011, © CCEA 2012

4. Kingdom Fungi includes edible mushrooms such as *Agaricus bisporus* (common mushroom) and *Agaricus campestris* (field mushroom) as well as a variety of moulds such as *Mucor mucedo* and *Penicillium* species.

    Their cells are described as eukaryotic.

    Bacteria belong to the kingdom Prokaryotae whose cells are described as prokaryotic.

    (a) State two differences between prokaryotic and eukaryotic cells. [2]

    (b) Identify the species name of the field mushroom. [1]

    Members of both kingdoms are involved in the decomposition of dead organisms with the resultant recycling of nutrients.

    (c) Describe how the fungi carry out decomposition of dead or waste organic materials. [3]

    Early classification systems, such as that used by Carl Linnaeus, divided all organisms into two kingdoms, Plantae and Animalia. Bacteria, fungi, protozoans and algae were all included in the Plantae.

    Since the middle of the twentieth century various scientists have suggested more appropriate divisions of organisms, such as the 'five kingdom' system: Prokaryotae, Protoctista, Fungi, Plantae and Animalia.

    (d) Suggest **two** reasons why it is inappropriate to classify fungi in the Plantae. [2]

Seaweeds are algae which are autotrophic. They contain eukaryotic cells, with cellulose cell walls, which are aggregated into tissues showing limited differentiation.

(e) Algae are now classified as the Protoctista instead of the Plantae, but not all scientists agree with this.

(i) Suggest **one** reason why some scientists might think it is more appropriate to include the algae in the Plantae. [1]

(ii) Suggest **one** reason why many scientists think it is not appropriate to include algae in the Plantae. [1]

Question taken from CCEA's Biology Assessment Unit AS2, Organisms and Biodiversity, January 2012, © CCEA 2012

5. Use the dichotomous key below to help you identify the five kingdoms labelled A to E. [5]

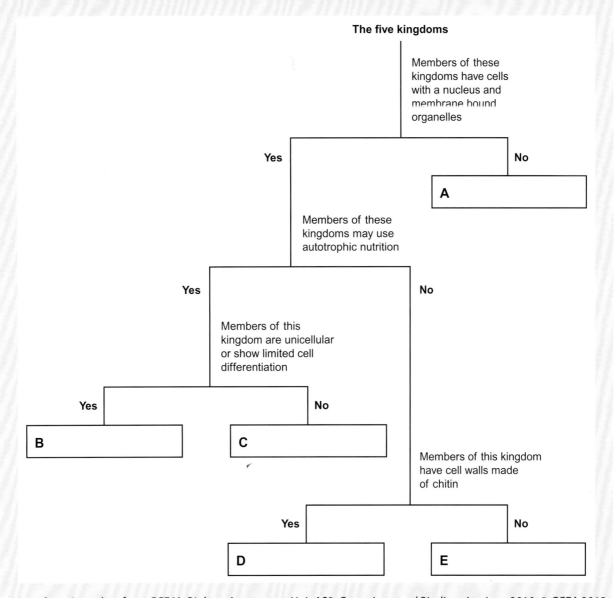

Question taken from CCEA's Biology Assessment Unit AS2, Organisms and Biodiversity, June 2010, © CCEA 2012

6. The medium ground finch, *Geospiza fortis*, is found on the island of Daphne Major in the Galapagos Islands, off the coast of Ecuador. The species was one of many noted by Charles Darwin, when he visited the islands in 1835.

Since 1973, other scientists have been studying this finch in relation to natural selection. One characteristic they have studied is the depth of the finches' beaks.

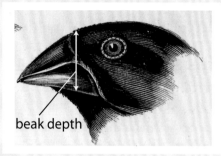

Paul D Stewart/Science Photo Library

In 1975, the mean beak depth in the *G. fortis* population on Daphne Major was 9.42 mm. In 1978, when a new generation of birds had reached maturity, it was 9.84 mm.

(a) Calculate the percentage increase in beak depth between 1975 and 1978. (Show your working.) [2]

Some scientists have suggested an explanation for the increase in beak depth.

They knew that a severe drought in 1976 affected Daphne Major, significantly limiting plant growth on the island. As a result, the availability of seeds became very low. Those birds with a greater beak depth were able to crack open and eat larger seeds than those with smaller beaks. These scientists argued that the larger beak size was selected for, since it represented increased fitness.

(b) Explain what is meant by the term 'fitness'. [1]

(c) Suggest how the mean beak depth in the population might have increased between 1975 and 1978. [4]

(d) State the type of selection shown by the increase in beak depth in *G. fortis*. [1]

Some information about the classification of *Geospiza fortis* and three other finch species, *Vidua macroura*, *Geospiza fuliginosa* and *Certhidea olivacea* is given below.

• The small ground finch, *Geospiza fuliginosa*, is also found on the Galapagos Islands.

• *G. fortis* is a member of the order Passeriformes, as are finches of the genus Vidua (family Viduidae).

• Both *G. fortis* and the warbler finch, *Certhidea olivacea*, are members of the family Thraupidae.

(e) State **two** distinct types of evidence which may be used to classify species. [2]

(f) (i) Which of the three species is most closely related to *G. fortis*? [1]

(ii) Which species is most distantly related to *G. fortis*? [1]

Question taken from CCEA's Biology Assessment Unit AS2, Organisms and Biodiversity, January 2012, © CCEA 2012

Chapter 13 – Human Impact on Biodiversity

Students should be able to:

2.3.14   Appreciate factors that have an adverse impact on biodiversity.

2.3.15   Appreciate neglect/lack of management resulting in hedgerows changing into rows of trees with gaps.

2.3.16   Appreciate the need for strategies to encourage biodiversity.

2.3.17   Appreciate initiatives for the protection of habitats.

Biodiversity is a reflection of both the number of species in an area and how evenly distributed the numbers of living organisms are spread across the range of species present. This chapter deals with the factors that affect biodiversity in Northern Ireland rather than at a global level, where global warming has become a very significant factor. In Northern Ireland (and in general) biodiversity has been significantly reduced by the activities of man. Agricultural practices that have seen the local extinction, or significant reduction in number, of many once-common species have been a major contributor to the reduction of biodiversity in our local ecosystems.

Factors that reduce biodiversity

The loss of woodland and hedgerow

In recent decades there has been a significant reduction in woodland and hedgerows for both **agricultural** and **developmental** (for example, building) purposes. The need for more housing and the associated infrastructure, such as roads and shopping complexes, and the requirement for greater agricultural productivity to feed a growing population have resulted in a continual reduction in biodiversity as woodland and hedgerows are removed.

Northern Ireland is now the least wooded part of Europe (6–7% compared to the European average of over 30%). Much of the native woodland in Northern Ireland is in areas unsuitable for agriculture, for example, steeply sloping ground (such as in the photograph below).

This figure of 6% woodland cover is even worse than it seems, as most of the woodland in Northern Ireland is introduced conifer plantation rather than native mixed species (for example, oak and ash) broadleaf native woodland. Conifer plantations have much less biodiversity compared with native broadleaf woodland. They have a low biodiversity for a number of reasons, including their 'evergreen' canopy providing little light penetration to the ground below at any stage of the year. Additionally, fallen needles on the woodland floor are very slow to

Native broadleaved woodland in Northern Ireland – this woodland forms a narrow strip on sloping ground along a lake edge

decompose (taking up to 10 years), and their presence and decomposition leads to the development of acidic soils – all conditions that are not conducive to the establishment of a ground flora and associated fauna on the woodland floor.

This loss of woodland/hedgerow and its increasing fragmentation leads to loss of biodiversity through the loss of habitat and food for many woodland and hedgerow species. This in turn impacts adversely on other species, for example, those higher up the food chain.

Typical hedgerow

Image courtesy of
Dr Terence Henry

Note that the hedgerow in the photograph to the right forms a barrier that restricts the movement of farm animals, which is largely why hedgerows were developed. As well as the hedgerow itself providing a habitat for many species, for example, birds and insects, their uncultivated margins can also provide species-rich habitats. Hedgerows also act as wildlife '**corridors**' linking areas of woodland or other species-rich habitats. These 'corridors' facilitate the movement and dispersal of many species, including small mammals, birds, amphibians and insects, such as butterflies.

Hedgerows are often cleared for many reasons, including increasing the land available for agricultural purposes. Their removal also facilitates easier and more efficient cultivation with large modern machinery. This loss of hedgerow through clearing does more than reduce biodiversity directly. It also leads to **increased soil erosion** due to the land being more exposed to **wind** and **rain**, and the reduction in the soil binding role of plant roots.

Loss of biodiversity can also arise through **poor hedgerow management** or from **damage to hedgerows**.

This can occur due to:

- hedgerows being cut too frequently or at the wrong time of the year.
- loss of hedgerow trees through senescence (death) or being cut without being re-planted.
- damage to hedgerows due to over-grazing. For example, this can be caused by sheep if stocking rates (number of sheep per field) are too high.

Neglect or over-grazing can result in the hedgerow developing gaps and with time can become little more than rows of trees with intervening gaps.

*This farmland shows
the almost total loss
of hedgerow*

Agricultural intensification

Intensive agricultural practice is also linked with the reduction in local biodiversity. Over 50 species have become locally extinct in the last century, mainly due to changes in agricultural practice. Agricultural intensification has involved the loss of woodland and hedgerow but its effects extend beyond that. The main features of intensive agricultural practices that cause a reduction in biodiversity (largely through habitat change or habitat loss) include:

- Increased use of **monoculture** – Whole areas of farming land are often given over to **one species** of crop (for example, wheat) or even perennial rye grass that provide rich swards for silage or for grazing by cattle or sheep. As well as reducing biodiversity there are other problems with monoculture. These include the build up of pests specific to the crop being grown.

- Increased use of **pesticides** – The pesticides are used to maximise crop production through eliminating pests that reduce production. There are many types of pesticides, including insecticides, that have been commonly used in agriculture. Pesticides significantly reduce biodiversity through killing other organisms (as well as the intended target). They remove many of the **soil organisms** that are involved in decomposition and improving soil structure. In addition, the pesticide can eliminate natural **predators** of the main pest and can cause **pest resurgence**, allowing the pest to return in even greater numbers.

- Increased use of **herbicides** – (a particular type of pesticide used to eliminate weeds/competitor plant species) both reduces plant biodiversity (as it eliminates **non-crop species**) and reduces the variety of **food** available to a variety of animal species, thereby reducing animal species diversity.

- **Nutrient enrichment of soils** – Agricultural productivity is increased by nutrient (nitrate and phosphate) enrichment of the soil. This is particularly important in intensive agricultural practices when maximum productivity is the goal. Soils are enriched both to maximise crop yield and also to maintain high stocking rates in livestock farming. The use of **artificial fertiliser**, with high levels of nitrate, to encourage the fast growth of crops is particularly harmful to biodiversity, as it allows the **target crop to outcompete** and eliminate many other slower growing plant species. It also leads to loss of soil crumb structure, which can result in increased **soil erosion**. Nutrient enrichment has caused the loss of much of Northern Ireland's **species-rich grassland** for this reason. The use of artificial fertiliser has also contributed significantly to the eutrophication of many of Northern Ireland's waterways (this will be covered in more detail at A2).

- **Drainage schemes** – These have been used to increase the area of land available for agricultural purposes. Typically the land is drained and then ploughed, followed by re-seeding. While increasing agricultural productivity, drainage schemes dramatically reduce biodiversity through a reduction in wetland and semi-wetland habitats, for example, marsh and damp meadow habitats.

Improved, unimproved and species-rich grassland habitats

Most agricultural land is described as 'improved grassland' or 'arable land'. The photographs at the top of page 208 show examples of improved agricultural land; land

Sheep farming on species-poor, nutrient-enriched grassland

Winter cereal crops emerging in December

that has been 'improved' through the use of one or more of fertiliser, pesticide, herbicide application, drainage, monoculture or hedgerow removal.

Unimproved grassland or pasture is land that has not been subjected to intensive agricultural practices such as drainage or the extensive use of fertiliser. However, it may not be particularly species-rich or have high biodiversity.

Species-rich grassland tends to have high biodiversity, although remember that species-richness and biodiversity are not exactly the same thing. Species-rich land is invariably land that has not been significantly improved for agricultural purposes (will have low soil nitrate levels) and/or is a habitat or range of habitats that have specific ecological characteristics. Examples of species-rich grassland type habitats include damp meadows and calcareous grassland (grassland found on chalk or limestone, where the soil is often too shallow to enable the land to be used for intensive agriculture).

Unimproved land
Image courtesy of Dr Terence Henry

Species-rich grassland
Image courtesy of Dr Terence Henry

Strategies that encourage biodiversity

Reducing or reversing the impact of many of the factors just discussed will encourage biodiversity or at the very least slow its ongoing reduction.

Woodland management and hedgerow restoration and maintenance

Woodland – The conservation of existing native woodland and the increased planting of native broadleaved trees (for example, oak and ash) will maintain and increase the very low percentage of tree cover in Northern Ireland. Native woodland provides many habitat types and supports numerous species of animals, plants and fungi – many that are only found in woodland habitats. Any increase in the area of native woodland will have a very significant impact on increasing biodiversity locally.

There are many strategies deployed to conserve and increase woodland cover. Grants are available to encourage tree planting and farmers are encouraged to plant native tree species on their land, in hedgerows or in less productive land or field margins. Conservation Volunteers and similar groups help support woodland through removing litter and invasive species such as rhododendron. The development of new plantations of woodland is a long-term but potentially important strategy in increasing biodiversity.

Native woodland
Image courtesy of
Dr Terence Henry

Hedgerows – The planting of new hedgerows and the restoration and maintenance of existing ones helps support biodiversity. Hedgerows most likely to encourage biodiversity are those that contain a range of shrub and tree species, which in turn provide a range of different habitats and food sources for birds and other animals.

Biodiversity-friendly **hedgerow trimming** will further increase biodiversity through:

- allowing hedgerow trees to grow to maturity at intervals in the hedge.

- only trimming on a 2–3 year rotation. This allows shrubs to flower and produce berries, providing food for birds over the winter months.

- trimming during the winter (January–February) to avoid the destruction of bird nests during the spring and summer and allowing berries to develop in the autumn, again providing food for birds.

- maintaining a range of hedge heights and widths by staggering trimming regimes. This maintains a wide range of habitats. For example, different bird species have different preferences for hedgerow heights and width – thrushes and chaffinches prefer taller hedges and robins and yellowhammers shorter hedges. Hedges cut in an 'A' shape, as opposed to box shape, can be particularly diverse as this allows more light to penetrate to ground level.

Mature hedgerow with trees. Image courtesy of Dr Terence Henry

Protecting a new hedge. Image courtesy of Dr Terence Henry

When establishing a new hedgerow, or carrying out substantial repairs to an existing one, it is important to protect the young hedgerow trees/shrubs from grazing. This can be done by planting the hedge between a double fence, which both protects the young hedge and forms an effective boundary in the interim. In due course the fence can be removed. It is also important to plant a mixture of woody species in a new hedge with associated biodiversity benefits, ie avoid a monoculture of hawthorn.

Other sustainable agricultural practices

Farmers through education or legislation are encouraged to adopt more sustainable agricultural practices. These include:

- **Polyculture** – This is the growing of a **range of different crops** at the one time or sequentially in the one place. There are many advantages with polyculture, including the provision of a wider range of food sources and habitats for wildlife. **Crop rotation** is a particular type of polyculture. It is the planting of different crops in the same field over a period of years. Crop rotation helps conserve soil fertility as the different crops (for example, wheat and turnip) make different demands on soil nutrients. Crop rotation can be particularly effective in improving soil fertility when nitrogen-fixing crops, such as peas, beans and clover, are part of the cycle. Crop rotation also reduces the likelihood of a build up of pests specific to one crop in an area.

- **Increased use of organic fertiliser** – The use of organic fertiliser (farmyard manure) and the consequent decrease in the use of artificial (bagged) fertiliser also helps promote soil fertility. This helps preserve soil crumb structure as the humus in the farmyard manure holds the crumb structure together. Farmyard manure also releases nutrients at a slower rate with less mineral loss due to leaching, as the plants can make use of a greater proportion of the more slowly released nutrients. Organic fertiliser is more difficult to store and spread than artificial fertiliser and its nutrient content is more variable. Artificial fertiliser still has its role but there is now a greater awareness of the need to match the mineral content of the fertiliser used to the specific nutrient needs of the land being fertilised.

Note: organic fertiliser as **farmyard manure** is more beneficial than the use of **slurry**, which is also an organic fertiliser, as the slurry is more harmful to soil organisms, in particular earthworms.

A predator strip

Image courtesy of
Dr Terence Henry

- **Implementation of integrated pest management schemes – Broad-spectrum pesticides** have been widely used in the past and these have proved to be detrimental to biodiversity. They may kill many of the target pests but also eliminate the natural predators of the pest and kill soil organisms important in decomposition of organic matter and the maintenance of soil fertility. More integrated pest management approaches are now being encouraged, which include the use of **narrow-spectrum pesticides** that only affect the target pest species. Additionally,

strategies such as crop rotation help prevent the build up of large pest populations, as the absence of a specific crop for a few years may prevent the pest being able to complete its life cycle. The development of **predator strips** (small areas of rough grass left undisturbed at field hedges) will encourage the increase in numbers of many crop pests' natural predators on the farmland. Carabid beetles and ladybirds can thrive in relatively species-rich predator strips (undisturbed through the absence of fertiliser or pesticides) and feed on the harmful aphids that damage the crop.

- **Set-aside land** – predator strips and other areas of land left undisturbed (set-aside) encourage the development of new habitats that help support biodiversity by encouraging the establishment of a wider range of species. Set-aside land is often situated at field margins or in other land less likely to be agriculturally productive due to size, poor drainage or poor fertility. Set-aside land can be left for a few years or even longer to allow more mature (for example, woodland) habitats to develop.

There are many other environmentally friendly farming practices that can be used in specific situations. For example, the stubble left after a crop (for example, wheat) is harvested is often ploughed into the ground soon after harvesting. Ploughing will kill many non-crop species and will even bury crop seeds that were lying on the ground. By not ploughing until much later in the winter/early spring, the stubble and crop seeds (the spilt grain that remains after the harvesting) will provide an important food source for birds, small mammals and other species.

Government initiatives to encourage biodiversity

There are a number of government initiatives to encourage biodiversity including:

- The Northern Ireland Biodiversity Strategy
- Biodiversity Action Plans (NI District Councils)
- Habitat Action Plan for species-rich hedgerows
- DARD agri-environment schemes, for example, the Countryside Management Scheme where farmers receive grant aid to plant new hedges, leave stubble and grow wild bird cover, all aimed at encouraging biodiversity.

In general, the above initiatives identify conservation priorities and outline the strategies necessary.

The protection and conservation of specific ecosystems and habitats are supported through:

- **Areas of Special Scientific Interest (ASSI)** – Ecologically important areas with high conservation value that are managed in cooperation with the landowners. In Northern Ireland there are over 200 ASSIs, ranging in size from large expanses of water and their shores, such as Lough Neagh, to small areas of woodland or grassland.

- **Special Areas of Conservation (SACs)** – These areas are given special protective status under the EU Habitats Directive to conserve threatened species and habitats. There are over 50 SACs in Northern Ireland, which are protected to conserve threatened habitats and/or the species they contain. For example, Rathlin Island has SAC status in an attempt to conserve the reefs, vegetated sea cliffs and the sea caves around its coast, and the rare or endangered species they contain.

- **Nature Reserves** – These are often managed at a local level and are important in conserving specific (usually uncommon or rare) habitats and/or species.
- **Special Protection Areas (SPAs)** are areas given protection at a European legislative level for the protection of bird species.

Case Study: The corncrake

The corncrake (*Crex crex*) as recently as a few decades ago used to be common over much of Northern Ireland. It is now at best very rare in Northern Ireland, with only the occasional report of its presence. Even a few decades ago it could be heard in Fermanagh and other less intensively farmed areas of Northern Ireland.

Corncrakes are summer migrants, arriving in Ireland and other European countries from Southern and Eastern Africa. They breed in Ireland and other northern countries, arriving from early April and returning south around August or September.

In Ireland, corncrakes have traditionally nested in hay meadows and other similar vegetation, where the tall vegetation provides cover for the birds. Ideally the vegetation cover will be 20–50 cm in height. There are two broods of chicks, with the first hatching by early June and the second by late July. They remain in the meadows throughout the summer months, a habitat that provides both food and shelter. Corncrakes feed mainly on insects and other small animals but also on plant seeds.

By 2005 the numbers of corncrakes in Ireland had fallen to less than 200 and their distribution is largely restricted to three areas: north Donegal, County Mayo and the Shannon Callows.

What has caused the decline? The loss of its typical habitat has been the major cause (this has been the main reason for the extinction of many species worldwide over the last century). Hay as a food for cattle has been replaced by silage in most areas. Typically the harvesting of tall grass for hay took place much later in the summer, providing the corncrakes with food and shelter throughout much of the summer. Silage is cut more frequently, with the first cut being too early in the season to allow the grass to reach a sufficient height for the parents to become established and set up a nest. If breeding does take place, many of the chicks are killed by the mechanised harvesting.

How can the species be conserved in Ireland? The conservation of species-rich, unimproved or semi-improved meadow and a return to traditional hay cutting, as opposed to silage, can play a part. Other measures include cutting the hay from the centre of the field outwards, as opposed to cutting from the outside of the field in, which gives the young chicks a chance to escape into surrounding vegetation. Additionally, further cover surrounding the crop (for example, field margins), with vegetation that could provide protection after the hay is cut, also reduces mortality during the harvesting season. Managed grassland, where the grass (hay) has a loose structure rather than unmanaged vegetation which can be more dense, is conducive to corncrakes and aids their movement and camouflage.

Exam questions

1. In an investigation of hedgerow biodiversity, two hedges were systematically sampled (ie sampled at regular intervals) along their length. The two hedges differed in the degree to which they were managed and one had become 'gappy' through lack of management. The hedges were arbitrarily called **A** and **B**.

   (a) Describe another location where the use of systematic sampling along a transect is appropriate. Explain why this technique is most suitable in this situation. [2]

   The table below shows the results of sampling the plant species within hedge **A**.

Species found	Number of each species (n_i)	$n_i(n_i - 1)$
Bramble, *Rubus spp.*	26	650
Ivy, *Hedera helix*	13	156
Stinging nettle, *Urtica dioica*	8	**X** _____
Cleavers, *Galium aparine*	6	30
Cow parsley, *Anthriscus sylvestris*	5	20
Gorse, *Ulex europaeus*	4	12
Herb Robert, *Geranium robertianum*	3	6
Hawthorn, *Crataegus monogyna*	4	12
Hazel, *Corylus avellana*	2	2
Sycamore, *Acer pseudoplatanus*	2	2
Wild cherry, *Prunus avium*	2	2
Total	**N = 75**	$\Sigma n_i(n_i - 1)$ _____

   (b) (i) Complete the table by calculating the missing values **X** and $\Sigma n_i(n_i - 1)$. [2]

       (ii) Using values from the table and the formula below calculate a Simpson's index value for hedge **A**. (Show your calculations.) [2]

   The formula for the Simpson's index is $D = \dfrac{\Sigma n_i(n_i - 1)}{N(N - 1)}$

       (iii) Hedge **B** had a Simpson's index of 0.4. State which hedge was managed to encourage biodiversity. Explain your choice. [2]

   (c) Describe **two** strategies which are recommended to maintain a good hedge. [2]

   Question taken from CCEA's Biology Assessment Unit AS2, Organisms and Biodiversity, January 2011, © CCEA 2012

2. In Northern Ireland farmers have been encouraged to be more environmentally friendly in their farming practice. One example is the planting of double row hawthorn hedges to replace single wire fences on many farms.

   (a) (i) Explain how the planting of the hedges encourages biodiversity. [2]

   (ii) Describe **one** other strategy which is used to encourage biodiversity. [1]

An ecological survey was carried out in and around a small Northern Ireland woodland to investigate the distribution of two plant species, wood sorrel (*Oxalis acetosella*) and meadow buttercup (*Ranunculus acris*). A transect line was placed from the edge of the woodland to its centre and the percentage cover of the two species of plant was measured using a quadrat placed at five metre intervals along the transect line.

   (b) (i) Explain why a transect was used in this ecological survey. [1]

   (ii) Explain why the investigators measured the percentage cover of the two species of plant and not just the number of individual plants. [1]

Question taken from CCEA's Biology Assessment Unit AS2, Organisms and Biodiversity, January 2010, © CCEA 2012

3. Farmland birds are an important measure of the biodiversity of the countryside. Population numbers and ranges of many familiar birds have halved since 1970.

Changes in farm practice have been the major causes for the decline of many species such as the skylark, *Alauda arvensis*. The skylark is an insect-feeding bird and nests on the ground producing two broods during the year. An early brood is produced in April/May while a late brood is produced in July/August. Skylarks frequently nest in wheat fields and their decline is associated with a change towards planting wheat seed in the previous autumn rather than in the spring. This change has meant that the ground is covered in wheat earlier in the year – wheat sown in autumn is in full leaf at the beginning of June, forming a dense 60 cm high 'closed canopy'. This is good for the farmers in that they can harvest their crop earlier in the year, but poor for the skylarks which need an open area in which to nest successfully.

In 2002, trials of two alternative sowing strategies designed to improve the nesting success of skylarks were carried out. These and the control are described below.

   • Normal autumn sowing with early closure of the canopy in June (control).

   • Autumn sowing, but seeds more widely spaced, causing later closure of the canopy.

   • Autumn sowing, but with areas within the field which were left unsown and kept open throughout the year.

The graph below shows the success of rearing chicks in each of the two broods (early and late) and in each of the different trials.

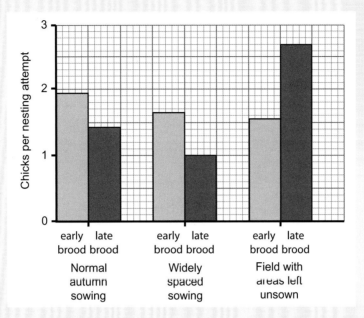

(a) (i) Which of the strategies would be recommended for improving the breeding success of skylarks? Explain your answer. [2]

(ii) Describe **two other** trends evident in the graph. [2]

(b) The table below shows the average numbers of ground insects caught in pit-fall traps in the fields used in these trials. Suggest how these results may be related to the success of rearing chicks. [2]

	Normal autumn Sowing	Widely spaced sowing	Field with areas left unsown
Mean number of insects per pit-fall trap	4.6	6.0	9.3

(c) Another strategy to improve conditions for farmland birds was to leave field margins unplanted. The success of this strategy was then tested alongside the strategy of leaving unsown areas within the field. The total number of birds of different species, in fields which had either unplanted margins or unsown areas or had both strategies or had neither strategy, were counted. The results are shown in the graph at the top of page 216.

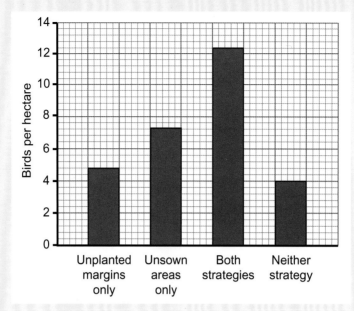

(i) Calculate the percentage increase in the total number of farmland birds in fields with both strategies used in comparison to fields with neither strategy used. (Show your working.) [3]

(ii) Describe the data that you would need from this research to calculate a biodiversity index for farmland birds such as Simpson's Index. [2]

(iii) The formula for the Simpson's Index is $D = \dfrac{\Sigma n_i(n_i - 1)}{N(N - 1)}$

Suggest how values for Simpson's Index for farmland birds might have changed since changes in farm practice were introduced. [2]

Question taken from CCEA's Biology Assessment Unit AS2, Organisms and Biodiversity, June 2010, © CCEA 2012

4. Read the passage below and then use the information in the passage, and your own understanding, to answer the questions which follow.

Ireland is one of the least wooded countries in Europe, even though forestry plantations have increased tree cover from less than 1% of land cover to about 10% in the last century. A new plan aims to increase this to 17% by 2030, mainly by planting new commercial forests at approximately 20,000 hectares per year. This increase represents a huge change in land use across Ireland, and has far-reaching economic, social and ecological consequences.

The most widely planted species in these commercial forests is sitka spruce (*Picea sitchensis*). This is a non-native conifer, which maintains a canopy of needle-like leaves throughout the year. A policy change in the late 1990s promoted the use of broadleaf trees in plantations. The planting of ash (*Fraxinus excelsior*), which is a deciduous tree with a full canopy only during the summer months, has increased significantly and broadleaf trees now constitute 20% of new plantings.

In a project investigating the diversity of plant species growing within these different woodland types, the plants were categorised as either bryophytes or as vascular plants. Bryophytes, mostly mosses, form a ground layer close to the soil surface as they require dampness. They are shade-tolerant plants.

The vascular plants, ferns and flowering plants, form a herbage layer. These plants may be either shade-tolerant, mostly the ferns, or grow rapidly in early spring before the tree canopy closes out the light during the summer season.

(a) State **two** features of the kingdom Plantae. [2]

(b) (i) Explain why ferns may be relatively abundant in both sitka spruce and ash woodlands. [1]

(ii) Identify the niche occupied by most species of flowering plants in the ash woodland.

(c) The number of different species (species richness) of vascular plants and bryophytes was determined for each woodland type. The results are shown in the graph below.

Describe the trends evident in the graph. [3]

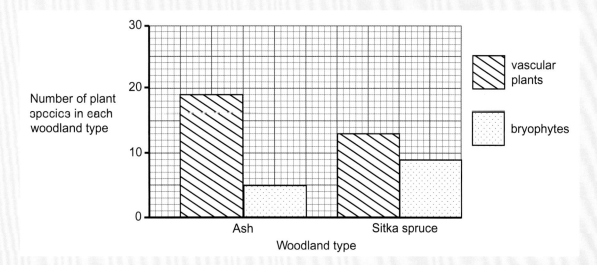

(d) (i) Explain how the diversity of animal species may be increased by greater plant species diversity. [1]

(ii) Suggest how the introduction of a non-native conifer as the main forest plant has decreased animal diversity. [1]

(e) Suggest **one** economic consequence of increased commercial forests in Ireland. [1]

(f) Briefly describe **one** strategy which encourages biodiversity and explain how this strategy conserves or improves biodiversity. [2]

Question taken from CCEA's Biology Assessment Unit AS2, Organisms and Biodiversity, June 2009, © CCEA 2012

5. Read the passage below and then use the information in the passage, and your own understanding, to answer the questions which follow.

The barn owl, *Tyto alba*, is an instantly recognisable white owl and is characteristic of lowland mixed farmland where it feeds on small mammals found in rough grassland along field margins, roadways, riverbanks, woodland edges and around farm buildings. In Northern Ireland, its diet consists mainly of mice, shrews and young rats. It nests inside buildings, mature hollow trees and rock crevices. It will also use nest boxes.

The barn owl has been in serious decline across Britain and Ireland since the 1930s. It is thought that, in Northern Ireland, there has been a decline of 69% between 1932 and 1985.

Today the Northern Ireland population is estimated to be between 45–65 pairs.

The population remains fragile and fragmented.

Factors which have caused the decline are fairly well understood: a reduction in the area of rough grassland, loss of hedgerows, more frequent periods of heavy or continuous rain and flooding, loss of suitable nest and roost sites, and widespread use of rodenticides. Other hazards include road deaths and drowning in farmland water troughs. In the latter case, the birds bathe to remove parasites but, if they fall in, their soft plumage waterlogs very quickly.

(a) The table below shows the classification of *Tyto alba*. Make a copy of the table and complete it by inserting the names of the three missing taxonomic groups.

Kingdom	Animalia
	Chordata
Class	Aves
	Strigiformes
Family	Tytonidae
	Tyto
Species	*alba*

(b) Explain why rodenticides, which are used to kill rats and mice, would prove lethal to barn owls. [2]

(c) Barn owls have difficulty hunting in periods of sustained wet weather.
    Suggest **two** reasons for this. [2]

(d) A number of schemes have been designed to develop favourable conditions for the improvement in barn owl numbers. Suggest three strategies which would be beneficial to barn owls. [3]

(e) With a small and fragmented population of barn owls in Northern Ireland, there is a danger of inbreeding which would result in a loss of genetic diversity. Explain why genetic diversity (variability) is important to populations. [2]

Question taken from CCEA's Biology Assessment Unit AS2, Organisms and Biodiversity, June 2011, © CCEA 2012

Copyright

Acknowledgements

Questions from CCEA AS1 Biology Papers – 2009-12 and CCEA AS2 Biology Papers – 2009-12 are included with the permission of the Northern Ireland Council for the Curriculum, Examinations and Assessment, © CCEA 2012.

For copyright reasons the following photographs, diagrams, graphs and tables have replaced those from CCEA AS1 Biology Papers – 2009-12 and CCEA AS1 Biology Papers – 2009-12. The numbers denote page numbers.

54 (bottom), 110, 129 (top), 130, 144, 147 (top), 167 (bottom), 186 (both)

Credits

The following photographs, diagrams, graphs and tables are all included with the kind permission of the copyright holders. The numbers denote page numbers:

Biodisc, Visuals Unlimited/Science Photo Library: 135 (right)
Biophoto Associates/Science Photo Library: 104 (bottom)
CCEA: 29, 20 (both), 32, 33, 34, 35, 36 (all), 37 (all), 53 (all), 54 (top), 67 (both), 68 (both), 69, 70 (both), 71, 72, 83 (both), 84 (both), 85, 86 (both), 87 (both), 89, 100, 101 (top), 102, 128 (bottom), 129 (both), 145 (both), 147 (bottom), 167 (top), 168, 169 (both), 170, 171 (both), 172 (both), 173, 187, 188, 201 (all), 203, 213, 215, 216, 217, 218
Dr Gerard Brennan, School of Biological Sciences, Queen's University, Belfast: 40, 51
Pr G Gimenez-Martin/Science Photo Library: 101 (bottom four)
iStockPhoto: 175